A NEW HOME

A NEW HOME

OR

LIFE IN THE CLEARINGS

Mrs. Caroline Matilda Kirkland

EDITED AND WITH AN INTRODUCTION

BY JOHN NERBER

G. P. PUTNAM'S SONS
NEW YORK

TO SALLY

TABLE OF CONTENTS

[A section of illustrations will
be found following page 152.]

A NEW HOME

INTRODUCTION

Mrs. Kirkland's *A New Home—Who'll Follow?* was first published pseudonymously in 1839. Its success was immediate: overnight it became an "undoubted sensation," as Poe later recorded, and the thirty-eight-year-old pioneer wife, who with belated caution had signed the fictitious name of "Mrs. Mary Clavers" to her demure portrait of frontier society, was suddenly a literary figure of international proportions. She had, at one stroke, "opened up a new vein in our national literature," as one reviewer prophetically wrote, and the book was recognized, both here and in England, as a classic expression of a new and indigenous American literature.

The name of Caroline M. Kirkland is now nearly forgotten; her literary reputation hardly survived her death in 1864, and then only as long as her sophisticated and appreciative contemporaries lived. She has been eclipsed by that paradoxical obscurity which often overtakes the most distinguished writers, and which is caused purely by natural circumstance.

A woman of formidable intelligence and character, she was both an original and an *outré* writer, a journalist, in our modern sense, dealing truthfully and uncompromisingly with the western frontier of 1840, a period in our history which later generations, squeamishly aware of the conventions of European nobility and culture, were only too glad to ignore, or, if reminded, preferred either to deprecate or to view as incorrigibly romantic. How could a late Victorian read with pleasure a woman who could, and did, describe Queen Victoria as a dumpy, plain and blotchy-complexioned woman obviously devoid of taste?

Her reputation did not, as a matter of fact, last the century, for by 1900 the literary historians had linked her name with that of Herman Melville as representative of those mid-century writers whose promise lacked achievement, whose work in the end came to nothing. Time has, of course, reversed this appraisal of Melville, and only recently has Poe's critical estimate of Mrs. Kirkland been seriously re-examined. "Unquestionably," he wrote, in his *Literati of New York,* "she is one of our best writers. . . ."

A New Home, in essence, is a highly realistic and straightforward account of what life on the western frontier, the Michigan border of the Jacksonian expansion, was like from the point of view of the actual settlers. It is comprised of a series of related sketches, vignettes in chapter form, which together trace the development of a typical western settlement—in reality, the present-day town of Pinckney, Michigan (approximately sixty miles northwest of Detroit, and about twenty miles from the university town of Ann Arbor), which Mrs. Kirkland herself named. It is, of course, the "Montacute" of the narrative—from the felling of the trees on its forest site, the construction of the vital grist mill and "temperance" tavern, the cluster of log huts straggling along a road no more than a cowpath, to the emergence of the settled village with its locus and distinctive domestic manners, its insular prejudices and snobberies, and its inevitable political alignments.

But beyond the thoroughly knowledgeable and accurate description of the backwoodsmen's effort in bringing the wilderness to heel, are the invaluable appraisals and insights into the character of the backwoodsman himself as he reacted to the primitive conditions under which he lived. Mrs. Kirkland was plain-spoken in this respect. She called a spade a spade only if it were not a manure fork. She neither romanticized the hardships of his lot—after all, she shared them—nor sentimentalized him as a rustic imbued with a native

4

shrewdness and intelligence, a sharpness that exceeded the mother-wit of his eastern cousins. In no sense was it a portrayal in dialect—the invariable method of frontier writers —treating the frontiersman as a humorous figure. She did not find herself fundamentally "funny."

Instead, here for the first time in American fiction was a consistently serious realistic treatment of a way of life whose aspects were transient, soon to disappear. Cooper had treated the backwoods romantically, Charles Fenno Hoffman and the Halls had reported it. Mrs. Kirkland caught it objectively in much of its entirety.

One of the surprises for us is Mrs. Kirkland's revelation that the frontier was already an anachronism in her day in everything except fact. Civilization had caught up with it; it was no longer a question of a foothold but of expansion. Within fifty years, two-thirds of an enormous continent was to be captured. In the late thirties the wealthy and leisured classes were building villas cheek by jowl with the homesteading pioneers. In 1836 the steamboats were bringing a thousand immigrants a day into the port of Detroit, a town of about five thousand people, from Buffalo and the Erie Canal. No one knows how many immigrants were pouring in from the overland trails to the south. And a couple of hundred miles away in Ohio, at least one historical society had been formed and was publishing a professional magazine devoted nostalgically to the departed days of the pioneer.

Consequently, *A New Home* is what we would now call a documentary book. It is one of the few sources to which we can go—apart from the historical novels, which are at best reconstructions embroidering the main business of the love story—for an authoritative and rounded view of the life of the average man on the frontier, and more particularly his wife, for Mrs. Kirkland was one of the first writers to examine the pioneer woman's daily life unromantically and in detail.

It is, or was to the pioneer, a recognizably real transcript, for all its fictional glosses, of his daily life. After its publication, the literary frontier was never the same again. How

5

real Mrs. Kirkland's transcript was can be judged by the fury with which her neighbors in Pinckney read the book when copies of it, speeded by rumor, finally trickled back into the woods. It was not a matter for congratulation they told her irately—to her hurt astonishment. Their reaction, their wounded pride, their refusal to trust her again as one of them, played a part in the Kirklands' decision to return to New York in 1843.

It is somewhat misleading to refer to Mrs. Kirkland merely as a frontier wife and mother. She was both, certainly; but she was also one of the outstanding American women of the nineteenth century. She was one of the best educated women in America when she arrived on the frontier in 1836. She both read and spoke Latin, French, and Italian, and knew enough German to read Goethe in the original. She had been trained as a scholar on the one hand and as a girl destined to a worldly and fashionable role on the other; her social accomplishments were reinforced by the scholar's midnight oil.

Hence she was in a peculiarly fortunate position, given her temperament and learning, from which to observe the preoccupations of the frontier.

She and her husband, William Kirkland, the scion of an old and distinguished New England family—a slight, scholarly, nearsighted and deaf man (he was later in New York to walk off the end of a pier and drown because he could not see his footing)—had founded the settlement in 1837, deep in the Michigan woods, and together with their four small children, had struggled as urban, professional people with the exigencies of a one-room "loggery," where a toad, attracted by the free traffic of flies through the open door, lived in a corner by the flour barrel, and rattlesnakes habitually crept under the floor for warmth.

She knew at first hand the anxieties of a new country, the evils of land speculations, a faltering and worthless currency, the bleakness of depression—the Panic of 1837 (caused essentially by overspeculation and currency manip-

6

ulations), was hard felt on the frontier where its negative effect was operative as late as 1842-1843—and there was always the immediate and practical problem of wringing sustenance out of forest land.

If there were drawbacks there were compensations too; the wilderness itself—and Mrs. Kirkland saw the primeval with an acute and sophisticated appreciation trained by an aesthetic background—the backwoods parties of one kind or another, the "bees, sociables, and raisings," as well as other seasonal gatherings. Fundamentally, there were the settlers themselves, pitted together against the wilderness, the sense of brotherhood, of participation, the very real sense of personal achievement.

Mrs. Kirkland thus wrote from an inside position: she was both a part of the scene, and yet outside. She was living, and had lived, for some time in the settlement whose homely aspects she was recording. She had only to glance out of her window to refresh her observation, a view of denuded forest land not yet subdued, whose stumps thrust up to the very dwelling doors—the settler, continually combating the forest, grew to hate the sight of a tree and automatically reached for his ax—and the utilitarian objects of a people to whom aesthetic considerations were by necessity impractical. And beyond these clearings the woods and swamps stretched in every direction. Such a view, day in and out, tended to keep a woman's feet sensibly on the ground.

No one can doubt that Mrs. Kirkland's feet were well anchored. *A New Home* reveals a charming, whimsical, but strongly commonsensical and practical person. It is tempting in this respect to speculate a little upon her marriage; she was, after all, married to a scholar, and one whose handicaps accented his scholarly nature. But he was, in turn, a New Englander, and presumably could swap a horse to some advantage, despite Mr. Mazard, when the necessity arose.

Mrs. Kirkland, at any rate, saw clearly what was before her eyes. And what she saw was nothing like the Emigrant Guides or anything else on the frontier she had read. It was

7

far removed, obviously, from Chateaubriand and the other French romancers whose improbable tales of natural innocence and inherent nobility she had absorbed.

What actually led her to write *A New Home* was presumably the urging of her friends and family "back at the East," who from time to time received her rueful and witty letters recounting the mishaps of her own experience. At the same time she wanted to give those who came after her into the wilderness a reasonable notion of what to expect.

Preserved by accident, a letter written to a friend in 1842 by a Miss Emily Mason who visited the Kirklands in Pinckney, three years after the publication of *A New Home*, is illuminating:

Pinckney is itself a most miserable little village though situated in one of the most beautiful counties in the state. I am confident Mrs. K[irkland] has not at all exaggerated the character of the population with which she is surrounded. They seem to be a most miserably low sort of people—not one neighbor of her own calibre—she is very desolate for want of society and as she says she must have sympathy, so having no one beside her own family to listen to her trials and tribulations she goes to the public with her grievances. . . .

When the dazzled and highly flattered Miss Mason's testimony of her visit to the "celebrated Mrs. Clavers," as she called her, is discounted, we have an invaluable glimpse into the wellspring of *A New Home*. It is obvious that in 1842, the year her second book, *Forest Life*, was published, and the year before the Kirklands left Michigan never to return, Mrs. Kirkland was a woman still beset by her own psychological necessities, by isolation, conversational famine, and exasperation. These factors are germinal. She had nowhere to turn excepting her pen. The invaluable Miss Mason continued:

She is "noways proud" as the country people say—but invites the blacksmith's wife—the carpenter's—shoemaker's—to tea at

8

two o'clock & gives them apple *saase* & other favorite dishes. They bring their babies too—only think of the Goths!

This was the surface which Miss Mason saw. She missed the point: Mrs. Kirkland respected and valued her neighbors. She had a deep-seated affection for them. They were close to her in a way few others would ever be; they were under her skin—as her narrative shows. And, had one of them appeared on her doorstep later in New York, when she had the most distinguished *salon* in the country, there would have been no hesitancy in her cordial welcome.

Miss Mason herself was to receive it in 1845, when a stranger, and outside the *ton,* in New York. Her comments reveal Mrs. Kirkland's character and position as nothing else does:

I must tell you how a new era has dawned upon my benighted New York life through Mrs. Kirkland's kindness in introducing me to her set—she through her literary reputation—her witty conversation & cordial friendly manner has won her way to the very top of the *really good* society here—you would wonder to see her improvements—her Western coarseness gone—her mass of flesh reduced to comparative delicacy—tastefully but plainly dressed she is now in her *element* & Mr. H. G. Tuckerman [the poet] tells me her house last winter was crowded with everybody who was *anybody*—in literary reputation or in talent & cleverness—all the professional men of literary taste who are quiet people, never going to balls or parties but seeking relaxation from (their) labor in the brilliant conversation at her house. Besides these we have the professors from the colleges—the instructors of the youth who *should* be ornaments to society—the editors of the best papers—Bryant for instance. . . . Fancy what a contrast this is to my previous association in New York. . . . Mrs. K—so kind—so anxious that I should learn to like her native city spares no pains to make me feel at home and pleased.

This is indeed a contrast to Pinckney. Mrs. Kirkland for her part never underestimated the effect of her western sojourn in the development of her own character. She was to maintain for the rest of her life that, by and large, the frontier folk were the salt of the earth. And she said flatly that her own education in the humanities began on the frontier, that her judgment was refined if not formed by her "uncouth" neighbors whose innate delicacy was an indication of their essential quality.

An idealist as well as an intensely patriotic woman, Mrs. Kirkland believed firmly in the part the frontier, once tamed, was to play in the national greatness; that it was, in reality, to be the backbone of the nation. The backwoodsmen, for all their virtues, failed to realize their historic role, and she was sharply critical of the all too human contrariness of action and spirit, the procrastinations bred by an unavoidable ignorance and natural self-interest. Yet to be disinterested often meant going hungry and, as Miss Mason suggests, Mrs. Kirkland missed few meals on the frontier. Exasperation probably accounts for the wit and the precision with which she punctured the engrossed self-complacency of the frontier state of mind.

If the settlers resented this, it was only natural. Mrs. Kirkland, in turn, never quite recovered from their rejection of her portrayal. As late as 1848 she could write bitterly to a friend in Ypsilanti:

. . . For although I am told some Western people find fault with my sketches, yet there is a much greater number who confirm your judgment that my pictures are in the main true— The Western people wish to be flattered. Self glorification is the order of the day there—but I will not flatter—though I shall be equally careful not to misrepresent. I love the West, and shall be glad to do it good by telling the truth, even if I get the dislike of some. . . .

If *A New Home* is filled with the sparkle of a satiric wit at times—the settlers writhed at the dexterity with which she employed their provincial mannerisms—it is a wit animated, not by a sarcastic and snobbish disregard for their

10

situation, but by a real affection and belief in their innate destiny. She wanted them to get at it, to measure up visibly to the greatness she foresaw, in which she felt herself passionately involved. Her irony was both rueful and double-edged; she could laugh at herself as much as she could them, and it is this quality in her which enhances her wit without losing its force. If she could report the hilarious story of Mrs. Howard's sending around to borrow a baby because her own had a mouth too sore to nurse (this was the story which so provoked the settlers and which so amused the outside world), Mrs. Kirkland could also write of the death of a bee hunter with a tenderness and sympathy that transcended the event and became intensely personal.

She could, however, on occasion be sarcastic, as Poe was quick to admit from his own personal experience as a guest in her house in New York. He had his own methods of feminine conquest, and undoubtedly one of these extravagances misfired with Mrs. Kirkland, whose sense of the ridiculous was strongly developed. It is interesting to note that when Mrs. Kirkland was editing the *Union Magazine* from 1847 to 1849, Poe submitted "Ulalume" for publication, and Mrs. Kirkland rejected it on young Stoddard's advice as not making too much sense.

Consequently, when she decided to write of frontier life as it actually was, exasperation was an element that helped free her of the prevailing rhapsodic and sentimental invention, the romantic description of what the settler's life *ought* to be, not what it really was. She wrote as a journalist; her purpose was to set down the truth as she observed it. In effect, it was an exposé.

That anyone should think this a novelty, or a daring innovation, strikes us as odd. But we have only to remember the impact of *Main Street*, which is, granting the obvious differences of time and place, roughly the *New Home* of 1920. Lewis, as a matter of fact, is directly a literary descendant of Mrs. Kirkland through Hamlin Garland and her son Joseph Kirkland—who persuaded Garland to turn his talent to the field of the novel, and in line with the principles of

11

objective realism developed by Mrs. Kirkland. Joseph himself became a famous realist, the author of *Zury; The Meanest Man in Spring County,* and his disciplines were learned at his mother's knee—he was one of the four small children in the one-room log house.

Mrs. Kirkland brought into focus for the first time and unified, as no other American writer to that time, realism as a vital fictional approach to the American scene. It had been employed before—Cooper for one wrote at times realistically—but not as a sustained and encompassing literary method. It was a realism having as its first principle an accurate and pragmatic reporting of what the writer saw with his own eyes and experienced with his own senses, devoid of both romantic glosses and sentimental empathies. It was, as *Main Street* shows, to exert a profound influence in American letters.

Mrs. Kirkland became, with *A New Home,* the mother, so to speak, of a traditional and thoroughly American literary method. It has given us interpretively some of our significant insights into our own past.

Mrs. Kirkland's literary style is difficult to assess: it is too integral a part of her own personality. Nervous and flexible, its self-conscious vivacity is peculiarly American, and, allowing for the natural changes in the literary conventions between her day and ours, is curiously modern. Her very digressions (so misunderstood in the late nineteenth century) are an important and calculated part of the narrative. They interpret Mrs. Kirkland's essential point of view. Her sense of humor—which Poe saw expressed as a mixture of wit and "pure fun"—her impatience with foolishness of any sort, her use of understatement—a weapon as deadly in her hands as it was in Jane Austen's—and her knowledge of the world beyond the boundaries of Livingston County, coalesced into a lively and intensely personal literary style admirably suited to her purpose.

The result is an authoritative microcosm of the pioneering impulse at a moment when it preoccupied a nation. As an insight into the whole of the westward immigration it has not been surpassed in accuracy. It is Mrs. Kirkland's achievement that she saw the frontier both psychologically and historically, and was able to fix it in a comparable literary form.

A New Home was written under the stimulation of Mrs. Kirkland's first encounter with the strangeness of the frontier. Consequently, it has a fresh immediacy that she was never to capture again. It remains her single best volume. *Forest Life*, the continuation of *A New Home*, was liberally padded with didactic reflections, though it was meant to extend the range of the first book. It is more directly interpretive, less concerned with the sharp characterization that made *A New Home* memorable. In 1845 Mrs. Kirkland, then living in New York, published the last of her frontier books, a collection of short stories entitled *Western Clearings*, which are uneven in quality though providing further insights into frontier character.

After this, Mrs. Kirkland, except for occasional sketches which appeared in various magazines, notably her own *Union Magazine* during 1847 and 1848, was a professional writer, compiling and editing various gift and special interest books for a feminine audience. These have little interest for us now, apart from their reference to her frontier writings.

Caroline Matilda Stansbury (Kirkland) was born January 11, 1801, in New York City. The eldest of eleven children, she was the daughter of a sophisticated, socially prominent family that had been on the Loyalist side during the Revolution. Her grandfather, Joseph Stansbury, was a Loyalist poet of distinct satiric powers though his verses ran to doggerel. Doggerel or not, they gave a certain literary tradition to the Stansburys.

Caroline was educated by her aunt, Lydia Philadelphia Mott, the headmistress of several schools in succession, each, under her care, noted for the soundness of its academic training. Caroline was accounted a precocious child who habitually led her classes without sacrificing her popularity. Since the Stansburys maintained a social position, however handicapped by lack of affluence, she was well versed in music, dancing and the social deportments. It was particularly important, since she was accounted something of a beauty who was both vivacious and genuinely amusing. She attended many of the New York functions and fashionable watering places in her role of belle. Yet, at the same time, she assisted her aunt by teaching in her schools. Teaching was to be her career, and her students were later to report that she was a "natural" teacher, one who taught easily and sympathetically, yet firmly enough to implant knowledge into the most recalcitrant of youthful heads.

Socially she was widely acquainted; when she returned from Michigan in 1843, she entered at once the innermost circle of the New York literary set, and had, herself, for a time, one of the most distinguished of literary salons. Her presence went a long way in making Anne Lynch's succeeding salon effective, for she was one of Miss Lynch's intimate friends. She knew almost everyone, as Miss Mason has indicated, and the literary people with whom she was on intimate terms is a roster of the "names" of the day.

In 1822, however, after the death of her father, she persuaded her mother to move west to Clinton, New York, the seat of Hamilton College, where her fiancé, William Kirkland, was tutoring in the classics. They were married January 10, 1828.

It was a very respectable match; William Kirkland came from a distinguished New England family that not only founded Hamilton College but had a president of Harvard among its ranks. Both William and Caroline Kirkland were serious-minded people who had in common the education of the young. Shortly after they were married they moved westward to Geneva where they founded a girls' school, at which, naturally, they both taught. There their first four children were born, including Joseph who was to make his mark also in the literary world.

In 1835 the Kirklands made their trek to Michigan. Mr. Kirkland had been offered the job of principal of the newly opened Detroit Female Seminary. Caroline continued to teach, though in August she bore another child.

In the following January Mr. Kirkland began buying land in Putnam Township, Livingston County, sixty miles northwest of Detroit. By the end of the year he had bought eight hundred acres and, with his father's additional purchases, controlled over thirteen hundred acres of choice woodland and swamp. Mrs. Kirkland was to find the swampland of somewhat dubious value, though entertaining enough in its own way.

Mr. Kirkland resigned his post as principal in November, 1836, in order to lay out a settlement on his holdings. The family continued to live in Detroit while he journeyed back and forth. In March Mrs. Kirkland had her sixth child, on the same day that one of her daughters toppled from a window of the seminary to her death.

In the autumn of 1837, the Kirklands moved to Pinckney, as Mrs. Kirkland named the new settlement, where they were to live until 1843. There, of course, *A New Home* (1839) was written, and *Forest Life* (1842).

In 1843 the Kirklands returned to New York. There were several reasons for this move. The western adventure had not been a financial success, and the publication of *A New Home* had not been conducive to an atmosphere of communal intimacy in Pinckney on the whole. Mrs. Kirkland wanted to devote more of her time to her writing, and Mr. Kirkland had wearied of the struggle. His interest had shifted to the world of the newspaper.

Back in New York, Mrs. Kirkland opened a school for girls, while Mr. Kirkland concentrated on the newspaper field. By 1846, the year of his death, he was the editor of the *New York Evening Mirror*, as well as editor of his own paper, *The Christian Inquirer*.

The rest of Mrs. Kirkland's life was spent in literary pursuits and in teaching. She edited, for eighteen months beginning in 1847, a new literary magazine of real quality, *The Union Magazine*. She went abroad twice, first in 1848, and then in 1850. She was received abroad by both Dickens and the Brownings, who respected and admired her. And Harriet Martineau, who had possibly a more masculine mind than any other woman in England, became a fast friend, writing her bulletins on the state of Wordsworth's fluctuating health during 1850.

Mrs. Kirkland died April 6, 1864, of apoplexy. She had been much grieved by the Civil War, and had worked incessantly in the Union cause. Too, her son, Joseph, was in the Union Army, and this intensified her feeling. When the Metropolitan Fair was held in the Spring of 1864 for the benefit of the U. S. Sanitary Commission, Mrs. Kirkland took an active and leading part in its successful presentation. As head of the "Department of Arms and Trophies," she was forced to spend a great deal of time in behalf of the exhibits. At any rate, she attended the opening of the fair on Monday, April 4, and on the following Wednesday night she died in her sleep.

Bryant wrote her obituary, as an intimate friend, and her pallbearers included Willis, Bryant, and Peter Cooper.

This editing of *A New Home*, and those portions of *Forest Life* which by substance belong to the earlier narrative, is not meant in any way to be definitive. It is designed only as an introduction for the modern reader to a delightful and nearly forgotten classic of another day. Mrs. Kirkland's text and punctuation have been retained without major change.

The editor has, of necessity, consulted many people and sources, and his gratitude for their interest and response can only be noted, not repaid.

Particular acknowledgments are due to Mrs. Morrow Krum and Mrs. Boyd Hill, Mrs. Kirkland's great-granddaughters, for their invaluable and systematic help; to Mrs. Lulu Darrow, Mrs. Edla Potter, and Mr. Paul Curlett, of Pinckney, Michigan, for their long hours of devoted research.

Special thanks must go Miss Ida C. Brown, Mr. F. Clever Bald, and the staff of the Michigan Historical Collections in Ann Arbor; to Mrs. Elleine Stones, and her staff, of the Burton Historical Collections at the Detroit Public Library;

to Mr. Henry D. Brown of the Detroit Historical Collection; to Dr. Lewis Beeson of the Michigan Historical Commission in Lansing; to the staff of the Newberry Library in Chicago; and to Mr. Robert Hill, and the New York Public Library, for advice and labor beyond the demands of professional courtesy. To these, and particularly the New York Public Library, the editor is grateful for the help and permissions extended him in assembling the illustrations used in this book. To Mr. Langley Carleton Keyes, whose doctoral dissertation at Harvard, *Caroline M. Kirkland: A Pioneer in Realism* (1935), must remain the cornerstone of any future study of Mrs. Kirkland, the editor is under a special and very heavy debt.

—JOHN NERBER

July, 1953
New York

1

JOURNEY INTO THE INTERIOR—
VIA MUD-HOLES

OUR FRIENDS in the "settlements" have expressed so much interest in such of our letters to them, as happened to convey any account of the peculiar features of western life, and have asked so many questions, touching particulars which we have not thought worthy of mention, that I have been for some time past contemplating the possibility of something like a detailed account of our experiences. And I have determined to give them to the world, in a form not very different from that in which they were originally recorded for our private delectation; nothing doubting, that a veracious history of actual occurrences, an unvarnished transcript of real characters, and an impartial record of every-day forms of speech (taken down in many cases from the lips of the speaker) will be pronounced "graphic," by at least a fair proportion of the journalists of the day.

'Tis true there are but meagre materials for anything which might be called a story. I have never seen a cougar— nor been bitten by a rattlesnake. The reader who has patience to go with me to the close of my desultory sketches, must expect nothing beyond a meandering recital of common-place occurrences—mere gossip about every-day people, little enhanced in value by any fancy or ingenuity of the writer; in short, a very ordinary pen-drawing; which, deriving no interest from coloring, can be valuable only for its truth.

A home on the outskirts of civilization may certainly be expected to furnish some curious particulars for the consideration of those whose daily course reverses primitive arrangements, who "call night day and day night," and who are apt occasionally to forget that a particular class, that "those creatures" the servants, are partakers with themselves of a common nature.

I can only wish, like other modest chroniclers, my respected prototypes, that so fertile a theme had fallen into worthier hands. If Miss Mitford, who has given us such charming glimpses of Aberleigh, Hilton Cross, and the Loddon, had by some happy chance been translated to Michigan, what would she not have made of such materials as Tinkerville, Montacute, and the Turnip?

When my husband purchased two hundred acres of wild land on the banks of this to-be-celebrated stream, and drew with a piece of chalk on the bar-room table at Danforth's the plan of a village, I little thought I was destined to make myself famous by handing down to posterity a faithful record of the advancing fortunes of that favored spot.

"The madness of the people" in those days of golden dreams took more commonly the form of city-building; but there were a few who contented themselves with planning villages, on the banks of streams which certainly never could be expected to bear navies, but which might yet be turned to account in the more homely way of grinding or sawing—operations which must necessarily be performed somewhere for the well-being of those very cities. It is of one of these humble attempts that it is my lot to speak, and I make my confession at the outset, warning any fashionable reader who may have taken up my book, that I intend to be "decidedly low."

Whether the purchaser of *our* village would have been moderate under all possible circumstances, I am not prepared to say, since, never having enjoyed a situation under

19

government, his resources have not been unlimited;—and for this reason any remark which may be hazarded in the course of these my lucubrations touching the more magnificent plans of wealthier aspirants, must be received with some grains of allowance. "Il est plus aisé d'etre sage pour les autres, que de l'être pour soi-même."

When I made my first visit to these remote and lonely regions, the scattered woods through which we rode for many miles were gay in their first gosling-green suit of half-opened leaves, and the forest odors which exhaled with the dews of morning and evening, were beyond measure delicious to one "long in populous cities pent." I desired much to be a little sentimental at the time, and feel tempted to indulge to some small extent even here—but I forbear; and shall adhere closely to matters more in keeping with my subject.

I think, to be precise, the time was the last, the very last of April, and I recollect well that even at that early season, by availing myself with sedulous application, of those times when I was fain to quit the vehicle through fear of the perilous mud-holes, or still more perilous half-bridged marshes, I picked upwards of twenty varieties of wild flowers—some of them of rare and delicate beauty;—and sure I am, that if I had succeeded in inspiring my companion with one spark of my own floral enthusiasm, one hundred miles of travel would have occupied a week's time.

The wild flowers of Michigan deserve a poet of their own. Shelley, who sang so quaintly of "the pied wind flowers and the tulip tall," would have found many a fanciful comparison and deep-drawn meaning for the thousand gems of the road-side. Charles Lamb could have written charming volumes about the humblest among them. Bulwer would find means to associate the common three-leaved white lily so closely with the Past, the Present, and the Future—the wind, the stars, and the tripod of Delphos, that all future botanists, and eke all future philosophers, might fail to unravel the "linked sweetness." We must have a poet of our own.

20

Since I have casually alluded to a Michigan mud-hole, I may as well enter into a detailed memoir on the subject, for the benefit of future travellers, who, flying over the soil on rail-roads, may look slightingly back upon the achievements of their predecessors. In the "settlements," a mud-hole is considered as apt to occasion an unpleasant jolt—a breaking of the thread of one's reverie—or in extreme cases, a temporary stand-still or even an overturn of the rash or the unwary. Here, on approaching one of these characteristic features of the "west"—(How much does that expression mean to include? I never have been able to discover its limits)—the driver stops—alights—walks up to the dark gulf—and around it if he can get round it. He then seeks a long pole and sounds it, measures it across to ascertain how its width compares with the length of his waggon —tries whether its sides are perpendicular, as is usually the case if the road is much used. If he finds it not more than three feet deep, he remounts cheerily, encourages his team, and in they go, with a plunge and a shock rather apt to damp the courage of the inexperienced. If the hole be narrow the hinder wheels will be quite lifted off the ground by the depression of their precedents, and so remain until by unwearied chirruping and some judicious touches of "the string" the horses are induced to struggle as for their lives; and if the fates are propitious they generally emerge on the opposite side, dragging the vehicle, or at least the fore wheels after them. When I first "penetrated the interior" (to use an indigenous phrase) all I knew of the wilds was from Hoffman's tour or Captain Hall's "graphic" delineations: I had some floating idea of "driving a barouche-and-four anywhere through the oak-openings"—and seeing "the murdered Banquos of the forest" haunting the scenes of their departed strength and beauty. But I confess, these pictures, touched by the glowing pencil of fancy, gave me but incorrect notions of a real journey through Michigan.

Our vehicle was not perhaps very judiciously chosen;— at least we have since thought so. It was a light high-hung carriage—of the description commonly known as a buggy or shandrydan—names of which I would be glad to learn the etymology. I seriously advise any of my friends who are about flitting to Wisconsin or Oregon, to prefer a heavy lumber-waggon, even for the use of the ladies of the family; very little aid or consolation being derived from making a "genteel" appearance in such cases.

At the first encounter of such a mud-hole as I have attempted to describe, we stopped in utter despair. My companion indeed would fain have persuaded me that the many wheel tracks which passed through the formidable gulf were proof positive that it might be forded. I insisted with all a woman's obstinacy that I could not and would not make the attempt, and alighted accordingly, and tried to find a path on one side or the other. But in vain, even putting out of the question my paper-soled shoes—sensible things for the woods. The ditch on each side was filled with water and quite too wide to jump over; and we were actually contemplating a return, when a man in an immense bearskin cap and a suit of deer's hide, sprang from behind a stump just within the edge of the forest. He "poled" himself over the ditch in a moment, and stood beside us, rifle in hand, as wild and rough a specimen of humanity as one would wish to encounter in a strange and lonely road, just at the shadowy dusk of the evening. I did *not* scream, though I own I was prodigiously frightened. But our stranger said immediately, in a gentle tone and with a French accent, "Me watch deer—you want to cross?" On receiving an answer in the affirmative, he ran in search of a rail which he threw over the terrific mud-hole—aided me to walk across by the help of his pole—showed my husband where to plunge—waited till he had gone safely through and "slow circles dimpled o'er the quaking mud"—then took himself off by the way he came, declining any compensation with a most polite "rien, rien!" This instance of true and genuine politeness I record for the benefit of all bearskin caps, leathern jerkins and cowhide boots, which ladies from the eastward world may hereafter encounter in Michigan.

22

Our journey was marked by no incident more alarming than the one I have related, though one night passed in a wretched inn, deep in the "timber land"—as all woods are called in Michigan—was not without its terrors, owing to the horrible drunkenness of the master of the house, whose wife and children were in constant fear of their lives, from his insane fury. I can never forget the countenance of that desolate woman, sitting trembling and with white, compressed lips in the midst of her children. The father raving all night, and coming through our sleeping apartment with the earliest ray of morning, in search of more of the poison already boiling in his veins. The poor wife could not forbear telling me her story—her change of lot—from a well-stored and comfortable home in Connecticut to this wretched den in the wilderness—herself and children worn almost to shadows with the ague, and her husband such as I have described him. I may mention here that not very long after I heard of this man in prison in Detroit, for stabbing a neighbor in a drunken brawl, and ere the year was out he died of delirium tremens, leaving his family destitute. So much for turning our fields of golden grain into "firewater"—a branch of business in which Michigan is fast improving.

Our ride being a deliberate one, I felt, after the third day, a little wearied, and began to complain of the sameness of the oak-openings and to wish we were fairly at our journey's end. We were crossing a broad expanse of what seemed at a little distance a smooth shaven lawn of the most brilliant green, but which proved on trial a little better than a quaking bog—embracing within its ridgy circumference all possible varieties of "muirs, and mosses, slaps and styles"—I had just indulged in something like a yawn, and wished that I could see our hotel. At the word, my companion's face assumed rather a comical expression, and I was preparing to inquire somewhat testily what there was so laughable—I was getting tired and cross, reader—when down came our good horse to the very chin in a bog-hole, green as Erin on the top, but giving way on a touch, and seeming deep enough to have engulphed us entirely if its width had been proportionate. Down came the horse—and this was not all—down came the driver; and I could not do less than follow, though at a little distance—our good steed kicking and floundering—covering us with hieroglyphics, which would be readily deciphered by any Wolverine we should meet, though perchance strange to the eyes of our friends at home. This mishap was amended. Tufts of long marsh grass served to assoilize our habiliments a little, and a clear stream which rippled through the marsh aided in removing the eclipse from our faces. We journeyed on cheerily, watching the splendid changes in the west, but keeping a bright look-out for bog-holes.

2

DANFORTH'S TAVERN

THE SUN had just set when we stopped at the tavern, and I then read the cause of my companion's quizzical look. My hotel was a log-house of diminutive size, with corresponding appurtenances; and from the moment we entered its door I was in a fidget to know where we could possibly sleep. I was then new in Michigan. Our good hostess rose at once with a nod of welcome.

"Well! is this Miss Clavers?" (my husband had been there before,) "well! I want to know! why do tell if you've been upsot in the mash? why, I want to know!—and didn't ye hurt ye none? Come, gals! fly around, and let's git some supper."

"But you'll not be able to lodge us, Mrs. Danforth," said I, glancing at three young men and some boys, who appeared to have come in from their work, and who were lounging on one side of the immense open chimney.

"Why, bless your heart! yes I shall; don't you fret yourself: I'll give you as good a bed as anybody need want."

I cast an exploring look, and now discovered a door opposite the fire.

"Jist step in here," said Mrs. Danforth, opening this door, "jist come in, and take off your things, and lop down, if you've a mind to, while we're a getting supper."

I followed her into the room, if room it might be called, a strip partitioned off, just six feet wide, so that a bed was

25

accurately fitted in at each end, and a square space re-mained vacant between the two.

"We've been a getting this room made lately, and I tell you it's real nice, so private, like!" said our hostess, with a complacent air. "Here," she continued, "in this bed the gals sleeps, and that's my bed and the old man's; and then here's a trundle-bed for Sally and Jane," and suiting the action to the word, she drew out the trundle-bed as far as our standing place would allow, to show me how convenient it was.

Here was my grand problem still unsolved! If "me and the old man," and the girls, and Sally and Jane, slept in this strip, there actually could be no room for more, and I thought with dismay of the low-browed roof, which had seemed to me to rest on the tops of the window-frames. And, to make a long story short, though manifold were the runnings up and down, and close the whisperings before all was ready, I was at length ushered up a steep and narrow stick-ladder, into the sleeping apartment. Here, sur-rounded by beds of all sizes spread on the floor, was a bed-stead, placed under the peak of the roof, in order to gain space for its height, and round this state-bed, for such it evidently was, although not supplied with pillows at each end, all the men and boys I had seen below stairs, were to repose. Sundry old quilts were fastened by forks to the rafters in such a way as to serve as a partial screen, and with this I was obliged to be content. Excessive fatigue is not fastidious. I called to mind some canal-boat experi-ences, and resigned myself to the "honey-heavy dew of slumber."

I awoke with a sense of suffocation—started up—all was dark as the Hall of Eblis. I called—no answer came; I shrieked! and up ran one of the "gals."

"What on airth's the matter?"

"Where am I? What ails me?" said I, beginning to feel a little awkward when I heard the damsel's voice.

"Why, I guess you was scairt, wa'n't ye?"

"Why am I in the dark? Is it morning?"

26

"Morning? why, the boys have been gone away this hour, and, you see, there ain't no winder up here, but I'll take down this here quilt, and then I guess you'll be able to see some."

She did so, and I began to discern "a faint shadow of uncertain light," which, after my eyes had become somewhat accustomed to it, served very well to dress by.

Upon descending the ladder, I found our breakfast prepared on a very neat-looking table, and Mrs. Danforth with her clean apron on, ready to do the honors.

Seeing me looking around with inquiring eye, she said, "Oh! you'm lookin' for a wash-dish, a'n't ye!" and forthwith put some water into a little iron skillet, and carried it out to a bench which stood under the eaves, where I performed my very limited ablutions *al fresco,* not at all pleased with this part of country habits.

I bethought me of a story I had heard before we crossed the line, of a gentleman travelling in Michigan, who instead of a "wash-dish" was directed to the spring, and when he requested a towel received for answer: "Why, I should think you had a hankercher!"

After breakfast, I expressed a wish to accompany Mr. Clavers to the village tract; but he thought a very bad marsh would make the ride unpleasant.

"Lord bless ye!" said Mr. Danforth, "that *mash* has got a real handsome bridge over it since you was here last."

So we set out in the buggy and rode several miles through an alternation of open glades with fine walnut trees scattered over them, and "bosky dells" fragrant as "Araby the blest" at that delicious hour, when the dews filled the air with the scent of the bursting leaves.

Bye and bye, we came to the "beautiful bridge," a newly-laid causeway of large round logs, with a slough of despond to be crossed in order to reach it. I would not consent to turn back, however, and in we went, the buggy standing it most commendably. When we reached the first log our poor Rosinante stopped in utter despair, and some persuasion was necessary to induce him to rear high enough to place his fore feet upon the bridge, and when he accomplished this feat, and after a rest essayed to make the buggy rear too, it was neck or nothing. Yet up we went, and then came the severe part of the achievement, a "beautiful bridge" half a mile long!

Half a rod was enough for me, I cried for quarter, and was permitted to pick my way over its slippery eminences, to the utter annihilation of a pair of Lane's shoes.

3

MR. MAZARD, THE LAND-SHARK

THE MORNING passed in viewing and reviewing the village site and the "Mill privilege," under the condescending guidance of a regular land speculator, into whose clutches —but I anticipate.

The public square, the water lots, the value *per foot* of this undulating surface, clothed as it then was with burr-oaks, and haunted by the red deer; these were almost too much for my gravity. I gave my views, however, as to the location of the grand esplanade, and particularly requested that the fine oaks which now graced it might be spared when the clearing process commenced.

"Oh, certainly, mem!" said our Dousterswivel, "a place that's designed for a public promenade must not be divested of shade trees!" Yet I believe these very trees were the first "Banquos" at Montacute. The water lots, which were too valuable to sell save by the foot, are still in the market, and will probably remain there for the present.

This factotum, this Mr. Mazard, was an odd-looking creature, with "diverse ocular foci," and a form gaunt enough to personify Grahamism. His words sometimes flowed in measured softness, and sometimes tumbled over each other, in his anxiety to convince, to persuade, to inspire. His air of earnest conviction, of sincere anxiety for your interest, and, above all, of entire forgetfulness of his own, was irresistible. People who did not know him always

29

believed every word he said; at least so I have since been informed.

This gentleman had kindly undertaken to lay out our village, to build a mill, a tavern, a store, a blacksmith's shop; houses for cooper, miller, &c. &c., to purchase the large tracts which would be required for the mill-pond, a part of which land was already improved; and all this, although sure to cost Mr. Clavers an immense sum, *he,* from his experience of the country, his large dealings with saw-mills, &c., would be able to accomplish at a very moderate cost. The mill, for instance, was to be a story and a half high, and to cost perhaps twenty-five hundred dollars at the utmost. The tavern, a cheap building of moderate size, built on the most popular plan, and connected with a store, just large enough for the infant needs of the village, reserving our strength for a splendid one, (I quote Mr. Mazard) to be built out of the profits in about three years. All these points being thus satisfactorily arranged, Mr. Mazard received *carte blanche* for the purchase of the lands which were to be flowed, which he had ascertained might be had for a mere trifle.

The principal care now was to find a name—a title at once simple and dignified—striking and euphonious—recherché and yet unpretending. Mr. Mazard was for naming it after the proprietor. It was a proper opportunity, he thought, of immortalizing one's-self. But he failed in convincing the proprietor, who relished not this form of fame, and who referred the matter entirely to me. Here was a responsibility! I begged for time, but the matter must be decided at once. The village plot was to be drawn instanter —lithographed and circulated through the United States, and, to cap the climax, printed in gold, splendidly framed, and hung up in Detroit, in the place "where merchants most do congregate."

I tried for an aboriginal designation, as most characteristic and unworn. I recollected a young lady speaking with enthusiastic admiration of our Indian names, and quoting *Ypsilanti* as a specimen. But I was not fortunate in my

30

choice; for to each of the few which I could recollect, Mr. Mazard found some insuperable objection. One was too long, another signified *Slippery Eel,* another *Big Bubble;* and these would be so inappropriate! I began to be very tired. I tried romantic names; but these again did not suit any of us. At length I decided by lot, writing ten of the most sounding names I could muster from my novel reading stores, on slips of paper, which were mingled in a *shako,* and out came—Montacute. How many matters of greater importance are thus decided.

4

TWO FRONTIER LADIES AT HOME

MUCH WAS YET to be done this morning, and I was too much fatigued to wander about the hills any longer; so I sought shelter in a log-house at no great distance, to await the conclusion of the survey. I was received with a civil nod by the tall mistress of the mansion, and with a curiously grave and somewhat sweeping curtsey by her auburn-tressed daughter, whose hair was in curl papers, and her hands covered with dough. The room was occupied at one end by two large beds not partitioned off "private like," but curtained in with cotton sheets pinned to the unhewn rafters. Between them stood a chest, and over the chest hung the Sunday wardrobe of the family; the go-to-meeting hats and bonnets, frocks and pantaloons of a goodly number of all sizes.

The great open hearth was at the opposite end of the house, flanked on one side by an open cupboard, and on the other by a stick-ladder.

Large broadside sheets, caravan show bills were pasted on the logs in different places, garnished with mammoth elephants, and hippopotamuses, over which "predominated" Mr. Van Amburgh, with his head in the lion's mouth. A strip of dingy listing was nailed in such a way as to afford support for a few iron spoons, a small comb, and sundry other articles grouped with the like good taste; but I must return to my fair hostesses.

They seemed to be on the point of concluding their morning duties. The hearth was newly swept, a tin reflector was before the fire, apparently full of bread, or something equally important. The young lady was placing some cups and plates in a pyramidal pile on the cupboard shelf, when the mother, after taking my bonnet with grave courtesy, said something, of which I could only distinguish the words "slick up."

She soon after disappeared behind one of the white screens I have mentioned, and in an incredibly short time emerged in a different dress. Then taking down the comb I have hinted at, as exalted to a juxtaposition with the spoons, she seated herself opposite to me, unbound her very abundant brown tresses, and proceeded to comb them with great deliberateness; occasionally speering a question at me, or bidding Miss Irene (pronounced Irenee) "mind the bread." When she had finished, Miss Irene took the comb and went through the same exercise, and both scattered the loose hairs on the floor with a coolness that made me shudder when I thought of my dinner, which had become, by means of the morning's ramble, a subject of peculiar interest. A little iron "wash-dish," such as I had seen in the morning, was now produced; the young lady vanished —reappeared in a scarlet circassian dress, and more combs in her hair than would dress a belle for the court of St. James; and forthwith both mother and daughter proceeded to set the table for dinner.

The hot bread was cut into huge slices, several bowls of milk were disposed about the board, a pint bowl of yellow pickles, another of apple sauce, and a third containing mashed potatoes took their appropriate stations, and a dish of cold fried pork was brought out from some recess, heated and re-dished, when Miss Irene proceeded to blow the horn.

The sound seemed almost as magical in its effects as the whistle of Roderick Dhu; for, solitary as the whole neighborhood had appeared to me in the morning, not many moments elapsed before in came men and boys enough to fill the table completely. I had made sundry resolutions not to

33

touch a mouthful; but I confess I felt somewhat mortified when I found there was no opportunity to refuse.

After the "wash-dish" had been used in turn, and various handkerchiefs had performed, not for that occasion only, the part of towels, the lords of creation seated themselves at the table, and fairly demolished in grave silence every eatable thing on it. Then, as each one finished, he arose and walked off, till no one remained of this goodly company, but the red-faced heavy-eyed master of the house. This personage used his privilege by asking me five hundred questions, as to my birth, parentage, and education; my opinion of Michigan, my husband's plans and prospects, business and resources; and then said, "he guessed he must be off."

Meanwhile his lady and daughter had been clearing the table, and were now preparing to wash the dishes in an iron pot of very equivocal-looking soapsuds, which stood in a corner of the chimney place, rinsing each piece in a pan of clean water, and then setting it to *"dreen"* on a chair. I watched the process with no increasing admiration of Michigan economics—thought wofully of dinner, and found that Mrs. Danforth's breakfast-table, which had appeared in the morning frugal and homely enough, was filling my mind's eye as the very acme of comfort. Everything is relative.

But now, prospects began to brighten; the tea-kettle was put on; the table was laid again with the tea equipage and a goodly pile of still warm bread, redolent of milk-yeast—the unfailing bowls of apple-sauce and pickles, a plate of small cakes, and a saucer of something green cut up in vinegar. I found we had only been waiting for a more lady-like meal, and having learned wisdom by former disappointment, I looked forward with no small satisfaction to something like refreshment.

The tea was made and the first cup poured, when in came my husband and Mr. Mazard. What was my dismay when I heard that I must mount and away on the instant! The buggy at the door—the sun setting, and the log causeway and the black slough yet to be encountered. I could not obtain a moment's respite, and I will not pretend to describe my vexation, when I saw on looking back our projector already seated at my predestined cup of tea, and busily engaged with my slice of bread and butter!

I walked over the logs in no very pleasant mood and when we reached the slough it looked blacker than ever. I could not possibly screw up my fainting courage to pass it in the carriage, and after some difficulty, a slender pole was found, by means of which I managed to get across, thinking all the while of the bridge by which good Mussulmans skate into Paradise, and wishing for no houri but good Mrs. Danforth.

We reached the inn after a ride which would have been delicious under other circumstances. The softest and stillest of spring atmospheres, the crimson rays yet prevailing, and giving an opal changefulness of hue to the half-opened leaves;—"the grass beneath them dimly green"—could scarcely pass quite unfelt by one whose delight is in their beauty: but, alas! who can be sentimental and hungry?

I alighted with gloomy forebodings. The house was dark —could it be that the family had already stowed themselves away in their crowded nests? The fire was buried in ashes, the tea-kettle was cold—I sat down in the corner and cried.

I was awakened from a sort of doleful trance by the voice of our cheery hostess.

"Why, do tell if you've had no supper! Well, I want to know! I went off to meetin' over to Joe Bunner's and never left nothing ready."

But in a space of time which did not seem long even to me, my cup of tea was on the table, and the plate of snow-white rolls had no reason to complain of our neglect or indifference.

5

A WALK THROUGH THE WOODS

THE NEXT DAY I was to spend in the society of my hostess; and I felt in no haste to quit my eyrie, although it was terribly close, but waited a call from one of the little maidens before I attempted my twilight toilet. When I descended the ladder, nobody was visible but the womankind.

After breakfast Mrs. Danforth mentioned that she was going about a mile into the woods to visit a neighbor whose son had been bitten by a Massisanga (I spell the word by ear) and was not expected to live.

I inquired of course—"Why, law! it's a rattlesnake; the Indians call them Massisangas and so *folks* calls 'em so too."

"Are they often seen here?"

"Why, no, not very; as far from the *mash*. I han't seen but two this spring, and them was here in the garden, and I killed 'em both."

"*You* killed them!"

"Why, law, yes!—Betsey come in one night after tea and told me on 'em, and we went out, and she held the candle while I killed them. But I tell you we had a real chase after them!"

My desire for a long walk through the woods, was somewhat cooled by this conversation; nevertheless upon the good dame's reiterated assurance that there was no danger, and that she would "as lief meet forty on 'em as not," I consented to accompany her, and our path through the dim forest was as enchanting as one of poor Shelley's

36

gemmed and leafy dreams. The distance seemed nothing and I scarcely remembered the rattlesnakes.

We found the poor boy in not quite so sad a case as had been expected. A physician had arrived from ——, about fourteen miles off, and had brought with him a quantity of spirits of Hartshorn, with which the poisoned limb had now been constantly bathed for some hours, while frequent small doses of the same specific had been administered. This course had produced a change, and the pale and weary mother had begun to hope.

The boy had been fishing in the stream which was to make the fortune of Montacute, and in kneeling to search for bait, had roused the snake which bit him just before the knee. The entire limb was frightfully swollen and covered with large livid spots "exactly like the snake," as the woman stated with an air of mysterious meaning.

When I saw the body of the snake, which the father had found without difficulty, and killed very near the scene of the accident, so slow are these creatures generally—I found it difficult to trace the resemblance between its brilliant colors, and the purplish brown blotches on the poor boy's leg. But the superstition once received, imagination supplies all deficiencies. A firm belief in some inscrutable connexion between the spots on the snake and the spots on the wounded person is universal in this region, as I have since frequently heard.

During our walk homeward, sauntering as we did to prolong the enjoyment, my hostess gave me a little sketch of her own early history, and she interested me so strongly by her unaffected kindliness, and withal a certain dash of espièglerie, that I listened to the homely recital with a good deal of pleasure.

"I was always pretty lucky" she began—and as I looked at her benevolent countenance with its broad expansive brow and gentle eyes, I thought such people are apt to be "lucky" even in this world of disappointments.

"My mother didn't live to bring me up," she continued, "but a man by the name of Spangler that had no children

37

took me and did for me as if I had been his own; sent me to school and all. His wife was a real mother to me. She was a weakly woman, hardly ever able to sit up all day. I don't believe she ever spun a hank of yarn in her life; but she was a proper nice woman, and Spangler loved her just as well as if she had been ever so smart."

Mrs. Danforth seemed to dwell on this point in her friend's character with peculiar respect,—that he should love a wife who could not do her own work. I could not help telling her she reminded me of a man weeping for the loss of his partner—his neighbors trying to comfort him, by urging the usual topics; he cut them short, looking up at the same time with an inconsolable air—"Ah! but she was such a dreadful good creature to work!"

Mrs. Danforth said gravely, "Well, I suppose the poor feller had a family of children to do for;" and after a reflective pause continued—"Well, *Miss* Spangler had a little one after all, when I was quite a big girl, and you never see folks so pleased as they! Mr. Spangler seemed as if he could not find folks enough to be good to, that winter. He had the prayers of the poor, I tell ye. There wasn't a baby born anywheres in our neighborhood, that whole blessed winter, but what he found out whether the mother had what would make her comfortable, and sent whatever was wanted.

"He little thought that baby that he thought so much on was going to cost him so dear. His wife was never well again! She only lived through the summer and died when the frost came, just like the flowers; and he never held up his head afterwards. He had been a professor for a good many years, but he didn't seem then to have neither faith nor hope. He wouldn't hear reason from nobody. I always thought that was the reason the baby died. It only lived about a year. Well, I had the baby to bring up by hand, and so I was living there yet when Mr. Spangler took sick. He seemed always like a broken-hearted man, but still he took comfort with the baby, and bye and bye the little dear took the croup, and died all in a minute like. It began to be bad after tea and it was dead before sun-rise. Then I saw plain enough nothing could be done for the father. He wasted away just like an April snow. I took as good care on him as I could, and when it came towards the last he wouldn't have anybody else give him even so much as a cup of tea. He set his house in order if ever any man did. He settled up his business and gave receipts to many poor folks that owed him small debts, besides giving away a great many things, and paying all those that had helped take care of him. I think he knew what kind of a feller his nephew was, that was to have all when he was gone.

"Well, all this is neither here nor there. George Danforth and I had been keeping company then a good while, and Mr. Spangler knew we'd been only waiting till I could be spared, so he sent for George one day and told him that he had long intended to give me a small house and lot jist back of where he lived, but, seein things stood jist as they did, he advised George to buy a farm of his that was for sale on the edge of the village, and he would credit him for as much as the house and lot would have been worth, and he could pay the rest by his labor in the course of two or three years. Sure enough, he gave him a deed and took a mortgage, and it was so worded, that he could not be hurried to pay, and everybody said it was the greatest bargain that ever was. And Mr. Spangler gave me a nice settin out besides.—But if there isn't the boys comin in to dinner, and I bet there's nothin ready for 'em!" So saying, the good woman quickened her pace, and for the next hour her whole attention was absorbed by the "savory cates," fried pork and parsnips.

6

MRS. DANFORTH'S STORY

WHEN WE WERE quietly seated after dinner, I requested some further insight into Mrs. Danforth's early history, the prosy flow of which was just in keeping with the long dreamy course of the afternoon, unbroken as it was by any sound more wakening than the ceaseless click of knitting-needles, or an occasional yawn from the town lady who found the *farniente* rather burdensome.

She smiled complacently and took up the broken thread at the right place, evidently quite pleased to find she had excited so much interest.

"When Mr. Spangler's nephew came after he was dead and gone, he was very close in asking all about the business, and seein' after the mortgages and such like. Now, George had never got his deed recorded. He felt as if it wasn't worth while to lose a day's work, as he could send it any time by one of his neighbors. But when we found what sort of a man Mr. Wilkens was, we tho't it was high time to set about it. He had talked a good deal about the place and said the old man must have been crazy to let us have it so cheap, and once went so far as to offer my husband a hundred dollars for his bargain. So John Green, a good neighbor of ours, sent us word one morning that he was going, and would call and get the deed, as he knew we wanted to send it up, and I got it ready on the stand and put the big bible on it to keep it safe. But he did not come, something happened that he could not go that day: and I had jist took up the

40

deed to put it back in the chest, when in came Wilkins. He had an eye like a hawk; and I was afraid he would see it was a deed, and ask to look at it, and then I couldn't refuse to hand it to him, you know, so I jist slipped it back under the bible before I turned to ask him what was his will.

" 'Didn't John Saunderson leave my bridle here?' says he. So I stepped into the other room and got it, and he took it and walked off without speaking a word; and when I went to put away the deed, it was gone!

"My husband came in while I sat crying fit to break my heart; but all I could do I could not make him believe that Wilkins had got it. He said I had put it somewhere else without thinking, that people often felt as sure as I did, and found themselves mistaken after all. But I knew better, and though I hunted high and low to please him, I knew well enough where it was. When he found we must give it up he never gave me a word of blame, but charged me not to say anything about the loss, for, wherever the deed was, Wilkins was just the man to take advantage if he knew we had lost it.

"Well, things went on in this way for a while, and I had many a good cryin' spell, I tell ye! And one evening when George was away, in comes Wilkins, I was sittin' alone at my knittin', heavy hearted enough, and the schoolmaster was in the little room; for that was his week to board with us.

" 'Is your man at home?' says he; I said—No; but I expected him soon, so he sat down and began the old story about the place, and at last he says,

" 'I'd like to look at that deed if you've no objection, Mrs. Danforth.' I was so mad, I forgot what George had told me, and spoke right out.

"I should think, says I, you've had it long enough to know it all by heart.

" 'What does the woman mean?' says he.

"You know well enough what I mean, says I, you know you took it from off this table, and from under this blessed book, the very last time you was in this house.

41

"If I had not known it before, I should have been certain then, for his face was as white as the wall and he trembled when he spoke in spite of his impudence. But I could have bit off my own tongue when I tho't how imprudent I had been, and what my husband would say. He talked very angry as you may think.

" 'Only say that where anybody else can hear you,' says he, 'and I'll make it cost your husband all he is worth in the world.'

"He spoke so loud that Mr. Peeler, the master, came out of the room to see what was the matter, and Wilkins bullied away and told Peeler what I had said, and dared me to say it over again. The master looked as if he knew something about it but did not speak. Just then the door opened, and in came George Danforth led between two men as pale as death, and dripping wet from head to foot. You may think how I felt! Well, they wouldn't give no answer about what was the matter till they got George into bed—only one of 'em said he had been in the canal. Wilkins pretended to be too angry to notice my husband, but kept talking away to himself—and was jist a beginning at me again, when one of the men said, 'Squire, I guess Henry'll want some looking after; for Mr. Danforth has just got him out of the water.'

"If I live to be a hundred years old I shall never forget how Wilkins looked. There was everything in his face at once. He seemed as if he would pitch head-foremost out of the door when he started to go home—for Henry was his only child.

"When he was gone, and my husband had got warm and recovered himself a little, he told us, that he had seen Henry fall into the lock, and soused right in after him, and they had come very near drowning together, and so stayed in so long that they were about senseless when they got into the air again. Then I told him all that had happened—and then Peeler, he up, and told that he saw Wilkins take a paper off the stand the time I opened the bed-room door, to get the bridle, for he was at our house then.

"I was very glad to hear it to be sure; but the very next

morning came a new deed and the mortgage with a few lines from Mr. Wilkins, saying how thankful he was, and that he hoped George would oblige him by accepting some compensation. George sent back the mortgage, saying he would rather not take it, but thanked him kindly for the deed. So then I was glad Peeler hadn't spoke, 'cause it would have set Wilkins against him. After that we thought it was best to sell out and come away, for such feelings, you know, a'n't pleasant among neighbors, and we had talked some of coming to Michigan afore.

"We had most awful hard times at first. Many's the day I've worked from sunrise til dark in the fields gathering brush heaps and burning stumps. But that's all over now; and we're got four times as much land as we ever should have owned in York-State."

I have since had occasion to observe that this forms a prominent and frequent theme of self-congratulation among the settlers in Michigan. The possession of a large number of acres is esteemed a great good, though it makes but little difference in the owner's mode of living. Comforts do not seem to abound in proportion to land increase, but often on the contrary, are really diminished for the sake of it: and the habit of selling out so frequently makes that *home*-feeling, which is so large an ingredient in happiness elsewhere, almost a nonentity in Michigan. The man who holds himself ready to accept the first advantageous offer, will not be very solicitous to provide those minor accommodations, which, though essential to domestic comfort, will not add to the moneyed value of his farm, which he considers merely an article of trade, and which he knows his successor will look upon in the same light. I have sometimes thought that our neighbors forget that "the days of man's life are three score years and ten," since they spend all their lives in getting ready to begin.

7

A SEAT IN THE MUD

OUR RETURN to Detroit was accomplished without any serious accident, although we were once overturned in consequence of my enthusiastic admiration of a tuft of splendid flowers in a marsh which we were crossing by the usual bridge of poles, or *corduroy* as it is here termed.

While my eyes were fixed upon it, and I was secretly determining not to go on without it, our sober steed, seeing a small stream at a little distance on one side, quietly walked towards it, and our attention was withdrawn from the contemplation of the object of my wishes by finding ourselves *spilt* into the marsh, and the buggy reposing on its side, while the innocent cause of the mischief was fairly planted, fetlock deep, in the tenacious black-mud: I say the innocent cause, for who ever expected any proofs of education from a livery-stable beast?—and such was our brown friend.

'T were vain to tell how I sat on the high bog, (the large tufted masses in a marsh are so called in Michigan,) which fortunately received me in falling, and laughed till I cried to see my companion hunting for his spectacles, and D'Orsay (whom I ought sooner to have introduced to my reader) looking on with a face of most evident wonder. D'Orsay, my beautiful grey-hound, was our *compagnon de voyage,* and had caused us much annoyance by his erratic propensities, so that we were obliged to tie him in the

44

back part of the buggy, and then watch very closely that he did not free himself of his bonds.

Just at this moment a pedestrian traveller, a hard-featured, yellow-haired son of New England, came up, with a tin trunk in his hand, and a small pack or knap-sack strapped on his shoulders.

"Well! I swan!" said he with a grim smile, "I never see anything slicker than that! Why, you went over jist as *easy!* You was goin' to try if the mash wouldn't be softer ridin', I s'pose."

Mr. Clavers disclaimed any intention of quitting the causeway, and pointed to my unfortunate pyramid of pale pink blossoms as the cause of our disaster.

"What! them posies? Why, now, to my thinking, a good big double mary gold is as far before them pink lilies as can be: but I'll see if I can't get 'em for you if you want 'em."

By this time, the carriage was again in travelling trim, and D'Orsay tolerably resigned to his imprisoned state. The flowers were procured, and most delicately beautiful and fragrant they were.

Mr. Clavers offered guerdon-remuneration, but our oriental friend seemed shy of accepting anything of the sort.

"If you've a mind to trade, I've got a lot o' notions I'd like to sell you," said he.

So my travelling basket was crammed with essences, pins, brass thimbles, and balls of cotton; while Mr. Clavers possessed himself of a valuable outfit of pocket-combs, suspenders, and cotton handkerchiefs—an assortment which made us very popular on that road for some time after.

We reached the city in due time, and found our hotel crowded to suffocation. The western fever was then at its height, and each day brought its thousands to detroit. Every tavern of every calibre was as well filled as ours, and happy he who could find a bed anywhere. Fifty cents was the price of six feet by two of the bar-room floor, and these choice lodgings were sometimes disposed of by the first served at "thirty per cent, advance." The country inns were thronged in proportion; and your horse's hay cost you nowhere less than a dollar *per diem;* while, throughout the whole territory west of Detroit, the only masticable articles set before the thousands of hungry travellers were salt ham and bread, for which you had the satisfaction of paying like a prince.

8

DETROIT: A TOUR TO BUY
A TOWN OR TWO

OUR BREAKFAST-TABLE at —— House was surrounded by as motley a crew as Mirth ever owned. The standing ornament of the upper end was a very large light-blue crape turban, which turban surmounted the prolonged face of a lady, somewhere (it is not polite to be exact in these matters) between forty and fifty, and also partly concealed a pair of ears from which depended ear-rings whose pendants rested not far from the Apalachian collar-bones of the dignified wearer. This lady, turban and ear-rings, were always in their places before the eggs came, and remained long after the last one had disappeared—at least, I judge so; for I, who always take my chance (rash enough in this case) for a breakfast, never saw her seat vacant. Indeed, as I never met her anywhere else, I might have supposed her a fixture, the production of some American Maelzel, but that the rolling of her very light grey eyes was quite different from that of the dark Persian orbs of the chess-player; while an occasional word came to my ear with a sharp sound, even more startling than the "Echec" of that celebrated personage.

Another very conspicuous member of our usual party was a lady in mourning, whom I afterwards discovered to be a great beauty. I had indeed observed that she wore a great many curls, and that these curls were carefully arranged and bound with a ribbon, so as to make the most of a pair of

47

dark eyes; that nothing that could be called throat was ever enviously shaded, even at breakfast; and that a pair of delicately white hands, loaded with rings of all hues, despite the morning garments, were never out of sight. But I did not learn that she was a beauty till I met her long after at a brilliant evening party in rouge and blonde, and with difficulty recognized my neighbor of the breakfast-table.

But if I should attempt to set down half my recollections of that *piquant* and changeful scene, I should never get on with my story: so, begging pardon, I will pass over the young ladies, who never were hungry, and their papas, who could never be satisfied, and their brothers, who could not get anything fit to eat; the crimson-faced *célibataire*, who always ate exactly three eggs, and three slices of bread and butter, and drank three cups of tea, and then left the table, performing the whole in perfect silence; the lady, who played good mamma, and would ever have her two babies at the table with her, and feed them on sausage and strong coffee, without a mouthful of bread; and the shoals of speculators, fat and lean, rich and poor, young and old, dashing and shabby, who always looked very hungry, but could not take time to eat. I saw them only at breakfast, for the rest of the day we usually spent elsewhere.

While we were awaiting the arrival of our chattels from the east, Mr. Clavers accepted an invitation to accompany a party of these breakfast-table companions last mentioned, men of substance literally and figuratively, who were going to make a tour with a view to the purchase of one or two cities. Ponies, knapsacks, brandy-bottles, pocket-compasses, blankets, lucifers, great India rubber boots, coats of the same, and caps with immense umbrella capes to them: these things are but a beginning of the outfit necessary for such an expedition. It was intended to "camp out" as often as might be desirable, to think nothing of fasting for a day or so, and to defy the ague and all its works by the aid of the potent exorcisor contained in the bottle above mentioned. One of the company, an idler from ——, was almost as keen in his pursuit of game as of money, and he carried a double-barrelled fowling-piece, with all things thereunto appertaining, in addition to his other equipments, giving a finishing touch to the grotesque cortége. My only parting charge to my quota of the expedition was to keep out of the water, and to take care of his spectacles. I should have cautioned him against buying a city, but that he was never very ambitious, and already owned Montacute. He went merely *pour se désennuyer;* and I remained at the very focus of this strange excitement an unconcerned spectator, weary enough of the unvarying theme which appeared to fill the whole soul of the community.

The party was absent just four days; and a more dismal sight than they presented on their return cannot well be imagined. Tired and dirty, cross and hungry, were they all. No word of adventures, no boasting of achievements, not even a breath of the talismanic word "land," more interesting to the speculator of 1835-6 than it ever was to the ship-wrecked mariner. They seemed as if they would, Esau-like, have sold their city lots for a good supper, though I doubt whether the offer of a "trade" would not have aroused all their energies, and so prevented the bargain.

After tea, however, things brightened a little: I speak for one of the party only. The bath, the razor, the much needed change of those "lendings" on which so much of the comfort of life depends, produced their usual humanizing effect; and by questions skilfully timed and cautiously worded, I drew from my toil-worn spouse a tolerably circumstantial account of the journey.

The first day had been entirely consumed in reaching Shark River, or rather its junction with another considerable stream. Twilight had already shaded the woody path, when the surveyor, who was acquainted with the whole region, informed them that they had yet some miles of travel before they could hope to reach any kind of shelter. They had been for some hours following an Indian trail, and some of the city gentlemen recollecting, as the day declined, that they were a little rheumatic, began to give vent to their opinion that the evening was going to be particularly damp. One went so far as to hint that it would have been as well if Mr. —— (the sportsman) had not taken quite so long to ascertain whether that white moving thing he had seen in the woods was a deer's tail or not.

To this the city Nimrod had replied, that as to its being a deer's tail, there was no possibility of question; that if the other gentlemen had been a little more patient, they might have had venison for supper; and this little discussion, growing more and more animated as it proceeded, at length occupied the attention of the whole party so completely, that they lost the trail and found themselves at the end of what had seemed to them an open path. There was nothing for it, but to turn the horses' heads right about, and retrace the last mile or more, while the faint gleam of daylight was disappearing.

The good humor of the party was, to say the least, not increased by this little *contretemps,* and the following of a trail by star-light is an exercise of skill and patience not likely to be long agreeable to gentlemen who have been for many years accustomed to pavements and gas-lamps. Not a word was said of "camping out," so manfully planned in the morning. The loads of preparations for a bivouac seemed entirely forgotten by every body—at least, no one thought proper to mention them; and after some few attempts of the younger members to be funny, the whole caravan yielded to fate, and plodded on in gloomy and determined silence.

The glimmer of a distant light had an electrical effect. The unlucky sportsman was fortunately in the van, and so had an opportunity of covering up his offences by being the announcer of joyous tidings.

He sang out cheerily, "So shines a good deed in this naughty world!" and pricked on his tired Canadian into something akin to a trot, while the soberer part of the cavalcade followed as fast as they could, or as they dared. Ere long they reached the much desired shelter, and found that their provident care in regard to the various items requisite for food and lodging had not been in vain.

The log cabin which received the weary way-farers was like many others which have served for the first homes of settlers in Michigan. It was logs and nothing else, the fire made on the ground, or on a few loose stones, and a hole in the roof for the escape of the smoke. A family of tolerably decent appearance inhabited this forlorn dwelling, a man and his wife and two young children. They seemed little moved at the arrival of so large a company, but rendered what assistance they could in providing for the ponies and preparing the meal from such materials as were afforded by the well-stored hampers of the baggage pony.

After the conclusion of the meal, the blankets were spread on the ground, and happy he who could get a bag for a pillow. But the night's rest was well earned, and Nature is no niggard paymaster.

9

A CITY BENEATH THE SWAMP

THE MORNING SUN showed the river and its adjunct bright and beautiful, though a *leetle* marshy at the sides. The dead silence, the utter loneliness, the impenetrable shade, which covered the site of the future city, might well call to mind the desolation which has settled on Tadmor and Palmyra; the anticipation of future life and splendor contrasting no less forcibly with the actual scene than would the retrospect of departed grandeur. The guide, who had been much employed in these matters, showed in the course of the day six different points, each of which, the owners were fully satisfied, would one day echo the busy tread of thousands, and see reflected in the now glassy wave the towers and masts of a great commercial town. If already this infatuation seems incredible, how shall we make our children believe its reality?

The day was to be spent in exploring, and as it was desirable to see as much as could be seen of the river so important to the future fortunes of the company, it was concluded to follow the bank as closely as the marshes would allow, and pass the night at the house of a French trader near the outlet of the stream.

The spirits of the party were not very high during the ride. There was something a little cooling in the aspect of the marshes, and, although nobody liked to say so, the ground seemed *rather* wet for city building. However, the trader's dwelling looked very comfortable after the ac-

52

commodations of the preceding night, and a few Indian huts at no great distance gave some relief to the extreme solitariness of the scene, which had contributed not a little to the temporary depression of the party.

The Frenchman was luckily at home, and with his Indian wife treated the travellers with much civility: the lady, however, declining conversation, or indeed notice of any sort unless when called on to perform the part of interpreter between the gentlemen and some wretched looking Indians who were hanging about the house. Several children with bright, gazelle-like eyes, were visible at intervals, but exhibited nothing of the staring curiosity which is seen peeping from among the sun-bleached locks of the whiter broods of the same class of settlers.

The Indians to whom I have alluded, had come to procure whiskey of the trader, and after they had received the baleful luxury which performs among their fated race the work of fire, famine and pestilence, they departed with rapid steps. They had scarcely quitted the house when another was seen approaching the door with that long easy *trot* which is habitual with the savage when on a journey. He was well dressed, in his way; his hat boasted a broad band of silver lace; his tunic, leggins and moccasins were whole and somewhat ornamented; his blanket glorying in a bright red border; and on his shoulders, slung by a broad thong, was a pack of furs of considerable value. He seemed an old acquaintance of the family, and was received with some animation even by the grave and dignified mistress of the mansion. The trader examined and counted the skins, spoke to the Indian in his own tongue, and invited him to eat, which however he declined, with a significant gesture towards the huts before alluded to.

This evening's supper was made quite luxurious by the preserved cranberries and maple syrup furnished by the settlers; and our friends retired to rest in much more comfortable style than on the preceding night.

The first nap was in all its sweetness, when the whole party was aroused by a hideous yelling, which to city ears could be no less than an Indian war-whoop. Every one was on foot in an instant; and the confusion which ensued in the attempt to dress in the dark was most perplexing and would have been amusing enough but for certain unpleasant doubts. The noise continued to increase as it approached the house, and terror had reached its acmé,—everyone catching at something which could be used as a weapon; when a violent knocking at the door aroused the trader, who slept in an inner room or closet, and who had not been disturbed by the bustle within doors of the yelling without. He seemed much surprised at the confusion which reigned among his guests—assured them it was "noting at all" but the Indians coming for more whiskey; and then admitted one of them, and coolly shutting the door in the face of the rest, spoke to the desperate looking savage very sharply, evidently reprobating in no gentle terms the uproar which had disturbed the sleepers.

The Indian made scarce any reply, but pointed with an impatient gesture to the keg, repeating "Whiskey! whiskey!" till the trader re-filled it; he then departed leaving our party once more to repose.

The next morning, much was said of the disturbance of the night. The Frenchman seemed to look upon it as a thing of course, and unblushingly vindicated his own agency in the matter. He said that they would get whiskey from some-one—that an Indian could not live without it, and that they would pay honestly for what they got, although they would steal anything they could lay their hands on, from the farmers who lived within reach of their settlements. Bitter complaints he said were often made of corn, potatoes, or cucumbers being spirited away in the night, and the Indians got the blame at least, but from him they took nothing. His lady listened with no pleased aspect to this discussion of the foibles of her countrymen, and seemed quite willing to expedite the departure of the guests.

The way to the "Grand Junction" seemed shortened as they went. The day was fine and the ponies in excellent spirits. The sportsman came very near shooting a fat buck, and this miss kept him in talk for all day. The old gentlemen were much pleased with certain statistical accounts furnished them by the trader, whom they decided on the whole to be a very sensible fellow: and when they reached once more the chosen spot, they saw at a glance how easily the marshes could be drained, the channel of the Shark deepened, and the whole converted into one broad area on which to found a second New-York.

They passed another night at the log-hut which had first received them, and leaving with the poor couple who inhabited it, what cheered their lonely dwelling for many a day, they returned to Detroit.

Our friends considered the offers which had been made them so very advantageous that the bargain for the site at the "Grand Junction" was concluded the very next day. "Only one hundred shares at three hundred dollars each!" the money might be quadrupled in a month. And some of the knowing ones, who took shares "merely to oblige," did realize the golden vision, while the more careful, who held on to get the top of the market—but why should I tell secrets?

Nobody happened to mention to these eastern buyers that the whole had been purchased for four hundred dollars, just a week before they reached Detroit.

These things certainly cost a good deal of trouble after all. They ought to have paid well, unquestionably. When lots were to be sold, the whole fair dream was splendidly emblazoned on a sheet of super-royal size; things which only floated before the mind's eye of the most sanguine, were portrayed with bewitching minuteness for the delectation of the ordinary observer. Majestic steamers plied their paddles to and fro upon the river; ladies crowding their decks and streamers floating on the wind. Sloops dotted the harbors, while noble ships were seen in the offing. Mills, factories, and light-houses—canals, rail-roads and bridges, all took their appropriate positions. Then came the advertisements, choicely worded and carefully vague, never setting forth anything which might not come true at sometime or

55

other; yet leaving the buyer without excuse if he chose to be taken in.

An auctioneer was now to be procured (for lots usually went rather heavily at a private sale,) and this auctioneer must not be such a one as any Executive can make, but a man of genius, or ready invention, of fluent speech; one who had seen something of the world, and above all, one who must be so thoroughly acquainted with the property, and so entirely convinced of its value, that he could vouch on his own personal *respectability,* for the truth of every statement. He must be able to exhibit certificates from—no matter whom—Tom-a-Nokes perhaps—but "residing on the spot"—and he must find men of straw to lead the first bids. And when all this had been attended to, it must have required some nerve to carry the matter through; to stand by, while the poor artizan, the journeyman mechanic, the stranger who had brought his little all to buy government land to bring up his young family upon, staked their poor means on strips of land which were at that moment a foot under water. I think many of these gentlemen earned their money.

It is not to be supposed that the preliminaries I have enumerated, preceded every successful land-sale. Many thousand acres were transferred from hand to hand with a rapidity which reminded one irresistibly of the old French game of "le petit bon homme" (anglicised into "Robin's alive")—while all gained save him in whose hand Robin died.

I have known a piece of property bought at five hundred dollars, sold at once for twenty thousand; five thousand counted down, and the remainder secured by bond and mortgage. Whether these after payments were ever made, is another question, and one which I am unable to answer. I mention the transaction as one which was perfomed in all truth and fairness savoring nothing of the "tricksy spirit" on which I have been somewhat diffuse.

I must not omit to record the friendly offer of one of the gentlemen whose adventures I have recapitulated, to take "two Montacute lots at five hundred dollars each." As this was rather beyond the price which the owner had thought fit to affix to his ordinary lots, he felt exceedingly obliged, and somewhat at a loss to account for the proposition, till his friend whispered, "and you shall have in payment a lot at New-New-York at a thousand; and we have not sold one at that I can assure you."

The obliged party chanced to meet the agent for New-New-York about a year after and inquired the fortunes of the future emporium—the member of inhabitants, &c.

"There's nobody there," said he "but those we hire to come."

10

MOVING DAY ON THE WILDERNESS ROAD

AT LENGTH came the joyful news that our moveables had arrived in port; and provision was at once made for their transportation to the banks of the Turnip. But many and dire were the vexatious delays, thrust by the cruel Fates between us and the accomplishment of our plan; and it was not till after the lapse of several days that the most needful articles were selected and bestowed in a large waggon which was to pioneer the grand body. In this waggon had been reserved a seat for myself, since I had far too great an affection for my chairs and tables, to omit being present at their debarcation at Montacute, in order to ensure their undisturbed possession of the usual complement of legs. And there were the children to be packed this time,—little roley-poley things, whom it would have been in vain to have marked—"this side up," like the rest of the baggage.

A convenient space must be contrived for my plants among which were two or three tall geraniums and an enormous Calla Ethiopica. Then D'Orsay must be accommodated, of course; and, to crown all, a large basket of live fowls; for we had been told that there was none to be purchased in the vicinity of Montacute. Besides these, there were all our travelling trunks; and an enormous square box crammed with articles which we then in our greenness considered indispensable. We have since learned better.

After this enumeration, which yet is only partial, it will

not seem strange that the guide and director of our omnibus was to ride "on horseback after we." He acted as a sort of adjutant—galloping forward to spy out the way, or provide accommodations for the troop—pacing close to the wheels to modify our arrangements, to console one of the imps who had bumped its pate, or to give D'Orsay a gentle hint with the riding-whip when he made demonstrations of mutiny— and occasionally falling behind to pick up a stray handkerchief or parasol.

The roads near Detroit were inexpressibly bad. Many were the chances against our toppling load's preserving its equilibrium. To our inexperience the risks seemed nothing less than tremendous—but the driver so often reiterated, "that a'n't nothin'," in reply to our despairing exclamations, and what was better, so constantly proved his words by passing the most frightful inequalities (Michiganicé "sidlings") in safety, that we soon became more confident, and ventured to think of something else beside the ruts and mud-holes.

Our stopping-places after the first day were of the ordinary new country class—the very coarsest accommodations by night and by day, and all at the dearest rate. When everybody is buying land and scarce anybody cultivating it, one must not expect to find living either good or cheap: but, I confess, I was surprised at the dearth of comforts which we observed everywhere. Neither milk, eggs, nor vegetables were to be had, and those who could not live on hard salt ham, stewed dried apples, and bread raised with "salt risin'," would necessarily run some risk of starvation.

One word as to this and similar modes of making bread, so much practised throughout this country. It is my opinion that the sin of bewitching snow-white flour by means of either of those abominations, "salt risin'," "milk emptin's," "bran 'east," or any of their odious compounds, ought to be classed with the turning of grain into whiskey, and both made indictable offences. To those who know of no other means of producing the requisite sponginess in bread than the wholesome hop-yeast of the brewer, I may be allowed to explain the mode to which I have alluded with such hearty reprobation. Here follows the recipe:

To make milk emptin's. Take quantum suf. of good sweet milk—add a teaspoon full of salt, and some water, and set the mixture in a warm place till it ferments, then mix your bread with it; and if you are lucky enough to catch it just in the right moment before the fermentation reaches the putrescent stage, you may make tolerably good rolls, but if you are five minutes too late, you will have to open your doors and windows while your bread is baking.—Verbum sap.

"Salt risin'" is made with water slightly salted and fermented like the other; and becomes putrid rather sooner; and "bran 'east" is on the same plan. The consequences of letting these mixtures stand too long will become known to those whom it may concern, when they shall travel through the remoter parts of Michigan; so I shall not dwell upon them here—but I offer my counsel to such of my friends as may be removing westward, to bring with them some form of portable yeast (the old-fashioned dried cakes which mothers and aunts can furnish, are as good as any)—and also full instructions for perpetrating the same; and to plant hops as soon as they get a corner to plant them in. "And may they better reck the rede, Than ever did th' adviser."

The last two days of our slow journey were agreeably diversified with sudden and heavy showers, and intervals of overpowering sunshine. The weather had all the changefulness of April, with the torrid heat of July. Scarcely would we find shelter from the rain which had drenched us completely—when the sunshine would tempt us forth; and by the time all the outward gear was dried, and matters in readiness for a continuation of our progress, another threatening cloud would drive us back, though it never really rained till we started.

We had taken a newly opened and somewhat lonely route this time, in deference to the opinion of those who ought to have known better, that this road from having been less travelled would not be quite so *deep* as the other. As we went farther into the wilderness the difficulties increased. The road had been but little "worked," (the expression in such cases) and in some parts was almost in a state of nature. Where it wound round the edge of a marsh, where in future times there will be a bridge or drain, the wheels on one side would be on the dry ground while the others were sinking in the long wet grass of the marsh—and in such places it was impossible to discern inequalities which yet might overturn us in an instant. In one case of this sort we were obliged to dismount the "live lumber"—as the man who helped us through phrased it, and let the loaded waggon pass on, while we followed in an empty one which was fortunately at hand—and it was, in my eyes, little short of a miracle that our skilful friend succeeded in piloting safely the top-heavy thing which seemed thrown completely off its centre half a dozen times.

At length we came to a dead stand. Our driver had received special cautions as to a certain *mash* that "lay between us and our home"—to "keep to the right"—to "follow the travel" to a particular point, and then "turn up stream:" but whether the very minuteness and reiteration of the directions had puzzled him, as is often the case, or whether his good genius had for once forsaken him, I know not. We had passed the deep centre of the miry slough, when by some unlucky hair's-breadth swerving, in went our best horse—our sorrel—our "Prince,"—the "off haus," whose value had been speered three several times since we left Detroit, with magnificent offers of a "swop!" The noble fellow, unlike the tame beasties that are used to such occurrences, shewed his good blood by kicking and plunging, which only made his case more desperate. A few moments more would have left us with a "single team," when his master succeeded in cutting the traces with his penknife. Once freed, Prince soon made his way out of the boghole and pranced off, far up the green swelling hill which lay before us—out of sight in an instant—and there we sat in the marsh.

There is but one resource in such cases. You must mount

your remaining horse if you have one, and ride on till you find a farmer and one, two, or three pairs of oxen—and all this accomplished, you may generally hope for a release in time.

The interval seemed a *leetle* tedious, I confess. To sit for three mortal hours in an open waggon, under a hot sun, in the midst of a swamp, is not pleasant. The expanse of inky mud which spread around us, was hopeless, as to any attempt at getting ashore. I crept cautiously down the tongue, and tried one or two of the tempting green tufts, which looked as if they *might* afford foothold; but alas! they sank under the slightest pressure. So I was fain to re-gain my low chair, with its abundant cushions, and lose myself in a book. The children thought it fine fun for a little while, but then they began to want a drink. I never knew children who did not, when there was no water to be had.

There ran through the very midst of all this black pud-ding, as clear a stream as ever rippled, and the waggon stood almost in it!—but how to get at it? The basket which had contained, when we left the city, a store of cakes and oranges, which the children thought inexhaustible, held now, nothing but the napkins, which had enveloped those departed joys, and those napkins, suspended corner-wise, and soaked long and often in the crystal water, served for business and pleasure, till Papa came back.

"They're coming! They're coming!" was the cry, and with the word, over went Miss Alice, who had been reaching as far as she could, trying how large a proportion of her nap-kin she could let float on the water.

On, the shrieks and the exclamations! how hard Papa rode, and how hard Mamma scolded! but the little witch got no harm beyond a thorough wetting, and a few streaks of black mud, and felt herself a heroine for the rest of the day.

62

11

LIFE IN A LOGGERY

THE NIGHT DEWS were falling chill and heavy when we crossed the last log-causeway, and saw a dim glimmering in the distance. The children were getting horribly cross and sleepy. The unfortunate anchoring in the black swamp had deranged our plans by about three hours, and when we reached our destined resting-place, which was the log-house where I had been so happy as to make the acquaintance of Miss Irene Ketchum, and her dignified mamma, the family had retired to rest, except Mr. Ketchum, who rested without retiring.

The candle, a long twelve I should judge, was standing on the table, and wasting rapidly under the influence of a very long snuff, which reclined upon its side. Upon the same table, and almost touching the tall iron candlestick, was a great moppy head; and this head rested in heavy slumber on the brawny arms of the master of the house.

"Ketchum! Ketchum!" echoed a shrill voice from within the pinned-up sheets in one corner, and I might have thought the woman was setting the dog at us, if I had not recognized the dulcet-treble of the fair Irene from the other bed—"Pa, Pa, get up, can't you?"

Thus conjured, the master of the mansion tried to overcome the still potent effects of his evening potations, enough to understand what was the matter, but in vain. He could only exclaim, "What the devil's got into the women?" and down went the head again.

Mrs. Ketchum had, by this time, exchanged the night for the day cap, and made herself, otherwise, tolerably presentable. She said she had supposed we were not coming, it was so late; (it was just half-past eight,) and then, like many other poor souls I have known, tried hard to hide her husband's real difficulty.

"He was *so* tired!" she said.

How long the next hour seemed! A summer day in some company I wot of, would not seem half as tedious. It took all Papa's ingenuity, and more than all Mamma's patience to amuse the poor children, till matters were arranged; but at length the important matter of supper being in some sort concluded, preparations were made for "*retiracy.*"

Up the stick-ladder we all paced "slowly and sadly." Miss Irene preceding us with the remnant of the long twelve, leaving all below in darkness. The aspect of our lodging-place was rather portentous. Two bedsteads, which looked as if they might, by no very violent freak of nature, have grown into their present form, a good deal of bark being yet upon them, occupied the end opposite the stairs; and between them was a window, without either glass or shutter—that is to say, politeness aside, a square hole in the house. Three beds spread upon the floor, two chests, and a spinning-wheel, with reels and swifts, completed the plenishing of the room. Two of the beds were already tenanted, as the vibrations of the floor might have told us without the aid of ears, (people snore incredibly after ploughing all day,) and the remainder were at our service. The night air pouring in at the aperture seemed to me likely to bring death on its dewy wings, and when I looked up and saw the stars shining through the crevices in the roof, I thought I might venture to have the wider rent closed, although I had been sensible of some ill resulting from the close quarters at Danforths. So a quilt, that invaluable resource in the woods, was stuck up before the window, and the unhinged cover of one of the chests was used as a lid for the stair-way, for fear the children might fall down. Sheets served to partition off a "tyring room" round my bed—an expedient frequently resorted to—and so dangerous that it is wonderful that so few houses are burnt down in this country. And thus passed my first night in Montacute.

I do not remember experiencing, at any time in my life, a sense of more complete uncomfortableness than was my lot, on awakening the next morning. It seemed to arise entirely from my anticipations of the awkward and tedious inconveniences of our temporary sojourn at this place, where everything was so different from our ideas of comfort, or even decency. But I have since been convinced, that sleeping in an exhausted atmosphere, of which those who slept on the bedsteads felt the effect more sensibly than those who lay on the floor, had no small agency in producing this depression of spirits, so unusual with me.

Be this as it may, my troubles, when the children were to be washed and dressed, became real and tangible enough; for, however philosophical grown people may sometimes be under disagreeables consequent upon a change of habits, children are very epicures, and will put up with nothing that is unpleasant to them, without at least making a noise, which I do detest and dread; though I know mothers ought to "get used to such things." I have heard that eels get accustomed to being skinned, but I doubt the fact.

That morning was the first and last time I ever attempted to carry through the ordinary nursery routine, in a log-hut, without a servant, and with a skillet for a wash-basin.

The little things did get dressed after a while, however, and were safely escorted down the stick-ladder, and it was really a pleasure to see them careering round the house, rioting in their freedom, and to hear now and then a merry laugh, awakening the echoes. Children are the true *bijouterie* of the woods and wilds. How weary would my last three years have been, without the cares and troubles they have brought me?

Our breakfast, of undistinguishable green tea, milk-rising bread, and salt ham, did not consume much time, and most fortunately we here found milk for the children, who of course made out sumptuously. It was the first time since we left Detroit, that we had been able to procure more than a small allowance for the tea.

My first care was to inquire where I might be able to procure a domestic, for I saw plainly I must not expect any aid from Miss Irene or her younger sister, who were just such "captive-princess" looking damsels as Miss Martineau mentions having seen at a country inn somewhere on her tour.

"Well, I don't know," said Mrs. Ketchum in reply to my questions; "there was a young lady here yesterday that was saying she didn't know but she'd live out a spell till she'd bought her a new dress."

"Oh! but I wish to get a girl who will remain with me; I should not like to change often."

Mrs. Ketchum smiled rather scornfully at this, and said there were not many girls about here that cared to live out long at a time.

My spirits fell at this view of the matter. Some of my dear theorizing friends in the civilized world had dissuaded me most earnestly from bringing a maid with me.

"She would always be discontented and anxious to return; and you'll find plenty of good farmer's daughters ready to live with you for the sake of earning a little money."

Good souls! how little did they know of Michigan! I have since that day seen the interior of many a wretched dwelling, with almost literally nothing in it but a bed, a chest, and a table; children ragged to the last degree, and potatoes the only fare; but never yet saw I one where the daughter was willing to own herself obliged to live out at service. She would "hire out" long enough to buy some article of dress perhaps, or "because our folks have been sick, and want a little money to pay the doctor," or for some such special reason; but never as a regular calling, or with an acknowledgment of inferior station.

This state of things appalled me at first; but I have learned a better philosophy since. I find no difficulty now in getting such aid as I require, and but little in retaining it as long as I wish, though there is always a desire of making an occasional display of independence. Since living with one for wages is considered by common consent a favor, I take it as a favor; and this point once conceded, all goes well. Perhaps I have been peculiarly fortunate; but certainly with one or two exceptions, I have little or nothing to complain of on this essential point of domestic comfort.

To be sure, I had one damsel who crammed herself almost to suffocation with sweetmeats and other things which she esteemed very nice; and ate up her own pies and cakes, to the exclusion of those for whom they were intended; who would put her head in at a door, with—"*Miss* Clavers, did you holler? I thought I *heered* a yell."

And another who was highly offended, because room was not made for her at table with guests from the city, and that her company was not requested for tea-visits. And this latter high-born damsel sent in from the kitchen a circumstantial account *in writing*, of the instances wherein she considered herself aggrieved; well written it was too, and expressed with much *naïveté*, and abundant respect. I answered it in the way which "turneth away wrath." Yet it was not long before this fiery spirit was aroused again, and I was forced to part with my country belle. But these instances are not very tremendous even to the city habits I brought with me; and I cannot say I regret having been obliged to relinquish what was, after all, rather a silly sort of pride. But bless me! how I get before my story! I viewed the matter very differently when I was at Ketchum's. My philosophy was of slow growth.

On reflection, it was thought best not to add another sleeper to the loft, and I concluded to wait on myself and the children while we remained at Ketchum's, which we hoped would be but a day or two. I can only say, I contrived to *simplify* the matter very much, when I had no one to depend on but myself. The children had dirty faces, and aprons which would have effected their total exclusion from genteel society more than half the time; and I was happy to encourage the closest intimacy between them and the calves and chickens, in order to get some peace within doors. Mrs. Ketchum certainly had her own troubles during our sojourn under her leaky roof; for the two races commingled not without loud and long effervescence, threatening at times nothing short of a Kilkenny cat battle, ending in mutal extermination.

My office, on these occasions, was an humble imitation of the plan of the celestials in ancient times; to snatch away the combatant in whom I was most interested, and then secrete him for a while, using as a desert island one of the beds in the loft, where the unfortunate had to dree a weary penance, and generally came down quite tame.

12

A NEW HOME—WHO'LL FOLLOW?

THE LOG-HOUSE, which was to be our temporary home, was tenanted at this time; and we were obliged to wait while the incumbent could build a framed one; the materials for which had been growing in the woods not long before; I was told it would take but a short time, as it was already framed.

What was my surprise, on walking that way to ascertain the progress of things, to find the materials still scattered on the ground, and the place quite solitary.

"Did not Mr. Ketchum say Green's house was framed?" said I to the *dame du palais,* on my return; "the timbers are all lying on the ground, and nobody at work."

"Why, la! so they be all framed, and Green's gone to —— for the sash. They'll be ready to raise tomorrow."

It took me some time to understand that *framing* was nothing more than cutting the tenons and mortices ready for putting the timbers together, and that these must be *raised* before there could be a frame. And that "sash," which I in my ignorance supposed could be but for one window, was a *generic* term.

The "raising" took place the following afternoon, and was quite an amusing scene to us cockneys, until one man's thumb was frightfully mashed, and another had a severe blow upon the head. A jug of whiskey was pointed out by those who understood the matter, as the true cause of these disasters, although the Fates got the blame.

69

"Jem White always has such bad luck!" said Mr. Ketchum, on his return from the raising, "and word spake never more," for that night at least; for he disappeared behind the mysterious curtain, and soon snored most sonorously.

The many raisings which have been accomplished at Montacute, without that ruinous ally, strong drink, since the days of which I speak, have been free from accidents of any sort; Jem White having carried his "bad luck" to a distant county, and left his wife and children to be taken care of by the public.

Our cottage bore about the same proportion to the articles we had expected to put into it, that the "lytell hole" did to the fiend whom Virgilius cajoled into its narrow compass; and the more we reflected, the more certain we became that without the magic powers of necromancy, one half of our moveables at least must remain in the open air. To avoid such necessity, Mr. Clavers was obliged to return to Detroit and provide storage for sundry unwieldy boxes which could by no art of ours be conjured into our cot.

While he was absent, Green had enclosed his new house; that is to say put on the roof and the siding, and laid one floor, and forthwith he removed thither without door, window or chimney, a course by no means unusual in Michigan.

As I was by this time, truth to speak, very nearly starved, I was anxious to go as soon as possible to a place where I could feel a little more at home; and so completely had my nine days at Ketchum's brought down my ideas, that I anticipated real satisfaction in a removal to this hut in the wilderness. I would not wait for Mr. Clavers's return; but insisted on setting up for myself at once.

But I should in vain attempt to convey to those who know nothing of the woods, any idea of the difficulties in my way. If one's courage did not increase, and one's invention brighten under the stimulus of such occasions, I should have given up at the outset, as I have often done with far less cause.

It was no easy matter to get a "lady" to clean the place, and ne'er had place more need of the tutelary aid of the goddess of scrubbing brushes. Then this lady must be provided with the necessary utensils, and here arose dilemma upon dilemma. Mrs. Ketchum rendered what aid she could, but there was little superfluous in her house.

And then, such racing and chasing, such messages and requisitions! Mrs. Jennings "couldn't do nothin' without a mop," and I had not thought of such a thing and was obliged to sacrifice on the spot sundry nice towels, a necessity which made all the house-keeping blood in my veins tingle.

After one day's experience of this sort, I decided to go myself to the scene of action, so as to be at hand, for these trying occasions; and I induced Mr. Ketchum to procure a waggon and carry to our new home the various articles which we had piled in a hovel on his premises.

Behold me then seated on a box, in the midst of as anomalous a congregation of household goods as ever met under one roof in the back-woods, engaged in the seemingly hopeless task of calling order out of chaos, attempting occasionally to throw out a hint for the instruction of Mrs. Jennings, who uniformly replied by requesting me not to fret, as she knew what she was about.

Mr. Jennings, with the aid of his sons, undertook the release of the pent up myriads of articles which crammed the boxes, many of which though ranked when they were put in as absolutely essential, seemed ridiculuosly superfluous when they came out. The many observations made by the spectators as each new wonder made its appearance, though at first rather amusing, became after a while quite vexatious; for the truth began to dawn upon me that the common sense was all on their side.

"What on airth's them gimcracks for?" said my lady, as a nest of delicate japanned tables were set out upon the uneven floor.

I tried to explain to her the various convenient uses to which they were applicable; but she looked very scornfully

71

after all and said "I guess they'll do better for kindlin's than anything else, here." And I began to cast a disrespectful glance upon them myself, and forthwith ordered them up stairs, wondering in my own mind how I could have thought a log house would afford space for such superfluities.

All this time there was a blazing fire in the chimney to accommodate Mrs. Jennings in her operations, and while the doors and windows were open we were not sensible of much discomfort from it. Supper was prepared and eaten— beds spread upon the floor, and the children stowed away. Mrs. Jennings and our other "helps" had departed, and I was prepared to rest from my unutterable weariness, when I began to be sensible of the suffocating heat of the place. I tried to think it would grow cooler in a little while, but it was absolutely insufferable to the children as well as myself, and I was fain to set both doors open, and in this exposed situation passed the first night in my western home, alone with my children and far from any neighbor.

If I could live a century, I think, that night will never fade from my memory. Excessive fatigue made it impossible to avoid falling asleep, yet the fear of being devoured by wild beasts, or poisoned by rattlesnakes, caused me to start up after every nap with sensations of horror and alarm, which could hardly have been increased by the actual occurrence of all I dreaded. Many wretched hours passed in this manner. At length sleep fairly overcame fear, and we were awakened only by a wild storm of wind and rain which drove in upon us and completely wetted everything within reach.

A doleful morning was this—no fire on the hearth— streams of water on the floor, and three hungry children to get breakfast for. I tried to kindle a blaze with matches, but alas! even the straw from the packing-boxes was soaked with the cruel rain; and I was distributing bread to the hungry, hopeless of anything more, when Mr. Jennings made his appearance.

"I was thinking you'd begin to be sick o' your bargain by this time," said the good man, "and so I thought I'd come and help you a spell. I reckon you'd ha' done better to have waited till the old man got back."

"What old man?" asked I, in perfect astonishment.

"Why, *your* old man to be sure," said he laughing. I had yet to learn that in Michigan, as soon as a man marries he becomes "th'old man," though he may be yet in his minority. Not long since I gave a young bride the how d' ye do in passing, and the reply was, "I'm pretty well, but my old man's sick a-bed."

But to return, Mr. Jennings kindled a fire which I took care should be a very moderate one; and I managed to make a cup of tea to dip our bread in, and then proceeded to find places for the various articles which strewed the floor. Some auger-holes bored in the logs received large and long pegs, and these served to support boards which were to answer the purpose of shelves. It was soon found that the multiplicity of articles which were to be accommodated on these shelves would fill them a dozen times.

"Now to my thinkin'," said my good genius, Mr. Jennings, "that 'ere soup-t'reen, as you call it, and them little ones, and these here great glass-dishes, and all *sich,* might jist as well go up chamber for all the good they'll ever do you here."

This could not be gainsaid; and the good man proceeded to exhalt them to another set of extempore shelves in the upper story; and so many articles were included in the same category, that I began to congratulate myself on the increase of clear space below, and to fancy we should soon begin to look very comfortable.

My ideas of comfort were by this time narrowed down to a well-swept room with a bed in one corner, and cooking-apparatus in another—and this in some fourteen days from the city! I can scarcely, myself, credit the reality of the change.

It was not till I had occasion to mount the ladder that I realized that all I had gained on the confusion below was most hopelessly added to the confusion above, and I came down with such a sad and thoughtful brow, that my good aid-de-camp perceived my perplexity.

"Hadn't I better go and try to get one of the neighbor's *gals* to come and help you for a few days?" said he.

I was delighted with the offer, and gave him carte-blanche as to terms, which I afterwards found was a mistake, for, where sharp bargains are the grand aim of everybody, those who express something like indifference on the subject, are set down at once as having more money than they know what to do with; and as this was far from being my case, I found reason to regret having given room for the conclusion.

The damsel made her appearance before a great while— a neat looking girl with "scarlet hair and belt to match;" and she immediately set about "reconciling" as she called it, with a good deal of energy and ingenuity. I was forced to confess that she knew much better than I how to make a log-house comfortable.

She began by turning out of doors the tall cupboard, which had puzzled me all the morning, observing very justly, "When there ain't no room for a thing, why, there ain't;" and this decision cut the Gordian knot of all my plans and failures in the disposal of the ungainly convenience. It did yeoman's service long afterwards as a corn-crib.

When the bedsteads were to be put up, the key was among the missing; and after we had sent far and wide and borrowed a key, or the substitute for one, no screws could be found, and we were reduced to the dire necessity of trying to keep the refractory posts in their places by means of ropes. Then there were candles, but no candle-sticks. This seemed at first rather inconvenient, but when Mr. Jennings had furnished blocks of wood with auger-holes bored in them for sockets, we could do nothing but praise the ingenuity of the substitute.

My rosy-haired Phillida who rejoiced in the euphonius appellation of Angeline, made herself entirely at home, looking into my trunks, &c., and asking the price of various parts of my dress. She wondered why I had not my hair cut off, and said she reckoned I would before long, as it was all the fashion about here.

"When d'ye expect *Him?*" said the damsel, with an air of sisterly sympathy, and ere I could reply becomingly, a shout of "tiny joy" told me that Papa had come.

I did not cry for sorrow this time.

13

THE CLAVERS BUILD A DREAM HOUSE

DIFFICULTIES began to melt away like frosty rime after this. Some were removed, but to many we became habituated in a far shorter time than I could have imagined possible. A carpenter constructed a narrow flight of board-steps which really seemed magnificent after the stick-ladder. The screws came before the bedsteads were quite spoiled, and the arrival of my bureau—the unpacking of the box among whose multifarious contents appeared the coffee-mill, the smoothing-irons, the snuffers, gave more real delight than that of any case of splendid Parisian millinery that ever drew together a bevy of belles at Mrs. ——'s show-rooms. I never before knew the value of a portable desk, or realized that a bottle of ink might be reckoned among one's treasures.

Our preparations for residence were on a very limited scale, for we had no idea of inhabiting the loggery more than six weeks or two months at farthest. Our new dwelling was to be put up immediately, and our arrangements were to be only temporary. So easily are people deluded!

The Montacute mill was now in progress, and had grown (on paper) in a short time from a story and a half to four stories; its capabilities of all sorts being proportionably increased. The tavern was equally fortunate, for Mr. Mazard had undertaken its erection entirely on his own account, as a matter of speculation, feeling, he said, quite certain of selling it for double its cost whenever he should wish. The plan of the public-house was the production of his teeming brain, and exhibited congenial intricacies; while the windows resembled his own eyes in being placed too near together, and looking all manner of ways. Several smaller buildings were also in progress, and for all these workmen at a high rate of wages were to be collected and provided for.

I could not but marvel how so many carpenters had happened to "locate" within a few miles of each other in this favored spot; but I have since learned that a plane, a chisel, and two dollars a day make a carpenter in Michigan.

Mill-wrights two are remarkably abundant; but I have never been able to discover any essential difference between them and carpenters, except that they receive three dollars per diem, which, no doubt, creates a distinction in time.

Our mill-wright was a little round-headed fellow with a button nose, a very Adonis, in his own eyes, and most aptly named Puffer, since never did a more consequential dignitary condescend to follow a base mechanical calling. His statements, when he condescended to make any, were always given with a most magisterial air; and no suggestion, however skilfully insinuated or gently offered, was ever received without an air of insulted dignity, and a reiteration of his own conviction that it was probable he understood his business.

It is to be ascribed to this gentleman's care and accuracy that Mr. Clavers has since had the satisfaction of appearing as defendant in several suits at law, brought by those of his neighbors whose property had been doubled in value by the erection of the mill, and who therefore thought they might as well see what else they could get, to recover the value of sundry acres of wet marsh made wetter by the flowing back of the pond, while Mr. Puffer's calculations and levels prove most satisfactorily (on paper) that the pond had no business to flow back so far, and that therefore malice itself could ascribe no fault to his management.

But to return. Our own dwelling was to be built at the same time with all those I have mentioned; and materials for the whole were to be brought by land carriage from two to thirty miles. To my inexperienced brain, these undertakings seemed nothing less than gigantic. I used to dream of the pyramids in Egypt, and the great wall of China, and often thought, during my waking hours, of the "tower on Shinar's plain," and employed myself in conjectural comparisons between the confusion which punished the projectors of that edifice, and the difficulties which beset the builders of Montacute.

"No brick come yet, sir! Dibble couldn't get no white wood lumber at I——, (thirty miles off,) so he stopt and got what lime there was at Jones's; but they hadn't only four bushels, and they wouldn't burn again till week after next; and that 'ere sash that came from —— is all of three inches too large for the window frames; and them doors were made of such green stuff, that they won't go together no how."

"Well, you can go on with the roof surely!"

"Why, so we could; but you know, sir, oak-shingle wouldn't answer for the mill, and there's no pine shingle short of Detroit."

"Can't the dwelling-house be raised to-day then?"

"Why, we calc'lated to raise to-day, sir; but that fellow never came to dig the cellar."

"Go on with the blacksmith's shop, then, since nothing else can be done."

"Yes, sir, certainly. Shall we take that best white wood siding? for you know the oak siding never came from Tacker's mill."

"Send Thomson for it, then."

"Well, Thomson's best horse is so lame that he can't use him to-day, and the other is a-drawin' timber for the dam."

"Let John go with my horses."

"John's wife's sick, and he's got your horses and gone for the doctor."

But if I should fill pages with these delays and disappointments, I should still fail to give any idea of the real vexations of an attempt to build on any but the smallest scale in a new country. You discover a thousand requisites that you had never thought of, and it is well if you do not come to the angry conclusion that everybody is in league against you and your plans. Perhaps the very next day after you have by extra personal exertion, an offer of extra price, or a bonus in some other form, surmounted some prodigious obstacle, you walk down to survey operations with a comfortable feeling of self-gratulation, and find yourself in complete solitude, every soul having gone off to election or town meeting. No matter at what distance these important affairs are transacted, so fair an excuse for a *ploy* can never pass unimproved; and the virtuous indignation which is called forth by any attempt at dissuading one of the sovereigns for exercising "the noblest privilege of a freeman," to forward your business and his own, is most amusingly provoking.

I once ventured to say, in my feminine capacity merely, and by way of experiment, to a man whose family I knew to be suffering for want of the ordinary comforts:

"I should suppose it must be a great sacrifice for you, Mr. Fenwick, to spend two days in going to election."

The reply was given with the air of Forrest's William Tell, and in a tone which would have rejoiced Miss Martineau's heart—"Yes, to be sure; but ought not a man to do his duty to his country?"

This was unanswerable, of course. I hope it consoled poor Mrs. Fenwick, whose tattered gown would have been handsomely renewed by those two days' wages.

As may be conjectured from the foregoing slight sketch of our various thwartings and hinderances, the neat framed house which had been pictured on my mind's eye so minutely, and which I coveted with such enthusiasm, was not built in a month, nor in two, nor yet in three;—but I anticipate again.

The circumstance of living all summer, in the same apartment with a cooking fire, I had never happened to see alluded to in any of the elegant sketches of western life which had fallen under my notice. It was not until I actually became the inmate of a log-dwelling in the wilds, that

79

I realized fully what "living all in one room" meant. The sleeping apparatus for the children and the sociable Angeline, were in the loft; but my own bed, with its cunning fence of curtains; my bureau, with its "Alps on Alps" of boxes and books; my entire cooking array; my centre-table, which bore, sad change! the remains of to-day's dinner, and the preparations for to-morrow, all covered mysteriously under a large cloth, the only refuge from the mice: these and ten thousand other things, which a summer's day would not suffice me to enumerate, cumbered this one single apartment; and to crown the whole was the inextinguishable fire, which I had entirely forgotten when I magnanimously preferred living in a log-house, to remaining in Detroit till a house could be erected. I had, besides the works to which I have alluded, dwelt with delight on Chateaubriand's Atala, where no such vulgar inconvenience is once hinted at; and my floating visions of a home in the woods were full of important omissions, and always in a Floridian clime, where fruits serve for *vivers*.

The inexorable dinner hour, which is passed *sub silentio* in imaginary forests, always recurs, in real woods, with distressing iteration, once in twenty-four hours, as I found to my cost. And the provoking people for whom I had undertaken to provide, seemed to me to get hungry oftener than ever before. There was no end to the bread that the children ate from morning until night—at least it seemed so; while a tin reflector was my only oven, and the fire required for baking drove us all out of doors.

Washing days, proverbial elsewhere for indescribable horrors, were our times of jubilee. Mrs. Jennings, who long acted as my factotum on these occasions, always performed the entire operation, *al fresco,* by the side of the creek, with "a kettle slung Between two poles, upon a stick transverse."

I feel much indebted to Cowper for having given a poetical grace to the arrangement. "The shady shadow of an umbrageous tree" (I quote from an anonymous author) served for a canopy, and there the bony dame generally made a pic-nic meal, which I took care to render as agreeable as possible, by sending as many different articles as the basket could be persuaded to receive, each contained in that characteristic of the country, a pint bowl.

But, oh! the ironing days! Memory shrinks from the review. Some of the ordinary household affairs could be managed by the aid of a fire made on some large stones at a little distance from the house; and this did very well when the wind sat in the right quarter; which it did not always, as witness the remains of the pretty pink gingham which fell a sacrifice to my desire for an afternoon cup of coffee. But the ironing and baking were imperious; and my forest Hecate, who seemed at times to belong to the salamander tribe, always made as much fire as the stick-chimney, with its crumbling clay-lining, would possibly bear. She often succeeded in bringing to a white heat the immense stone which served as a chimney-back, while the deep gaps in the stone hearth, which Alice called the Rocky Mountains, were filled with burning coals out to the very floor. I have sometimes suspected that the woman loved to torment me, but perhaps I wrong her. She was used to it, I dare say, for she looked like one exsiccated in consequence of ceaseless perspiration.

When the day declined, and its business was laid aside, it was our practice to walk to and fro before the door, till the house had been thoroughly cooled by the night-air; and these promenades, usually made pleasant by long talks about home, and laughing conjectures as to what —— and —— would say if they could see our new way of life, were frequently prolonged to a late hour. And to this most imprudent indulgence we could not but trace the agues which soon prostrated most of us.

We had, to be sure, been warned by our eastern friends that we should certainly have the ague, do what we might, but we had seen so many persons who had been settled for years in the open country, and who were yet in perfect health, that we had learned to imagine ourselves secure. I am still of the opinion that care and rational diet will enable most persons to avoid this terrible disease; and I record this grave medical view of things for the encouragement and instruction of such of my city friends as may hereafter find themselves borne westward by the irresistible current of affairs; trusting that the sad fate of their predecessors will deter them from walking in the open air till ten o'clock at night without hat or shawl.

14

DOMESTIC MANNERS ON THE FRONTIER

WHEN ANGELINE left me, which she did after a few days, I was obliged to employ Mrs. Jennings to "chore round," to borrow her own expression; and as Mr. Clavers was absent much of the time, I had the full enjoyment of her delectable society with that of her husband and two children, who often came to meals very sociably, and made themselves at home with small urgency on my part. The good lady's habits required strong green tea at least three times a day; and between these three times she drank the remains of the tea from the spout of the tea-pot, saying "it tasted better so." "If she hadn't it," she said "she had the 'sterics so that she wasn't able to do a chore." And her habits were equally imperious in the matter of dipping with her own spoon or knife into every dish on the table. She would have made out nobly on kibaubs, for even that unwieldly morsel a boiled ham, she grasped by the hock and cut off in mouthfuls with her knife, declining all aid from the carver, saying cooly that she made out very well. It was in vain one offered her anything, she replied invariably with a dignified nod; "I'll help myself, I thank ye. I never want no waitin' on." And this reply is the universal one on such occasions, as I have since had vexatious occasion to observe.

Let no one read with an incredulous shake of the head, but rather let my sketch of these peculiar habits of my neighbors be considered as a mere beginning, a shadow of what might be told. I might "amaze indeed, the very faculty of eyes and ears," but I forbear.

If "grandeur hear with a disdainful smile"—thinking it would be far better to starve than to eat under such circumstances, I can only say such was not my hungry view of the case; and that I often found rather amusing exercise for my ingenuity in contriving excuses and plans to get the old lady to enjoy her meals alone. To have offered her outright a separate table, though the board should groan with all the delicacies of the city, would have been to secure myself the unenviable privilege of doing my own "chores," at least till I could procure a "help" from some distance beyond the reach of my friend Mrs. Jennings' tongue.

It did not require a very long residence in Michigan, to convince me that it is unwise to stem directly the current of society, even in the wilderness, but I have since learned many ways of *wearing round* which give me the opportunity of living very much after my own fashion, without offending, very seriously, anybody's prejudices.

No settlers are so uncomfortable as those who, coming with abundant means as they suppose, to be comfortable, set out with a determination to live as have they been accustomed to live. They soon find that there are places where the "almighty dollar" is almost powerless; or rather, that powerful as it is, it meets with its conqueror in the jealous pride of those whose services must be had in order to live at all.

"Luff when it blows," is a wise and necessary caution. Those who forget it and attempt to carry all sail set and to keep an unvarying course, blow which way it will, always abuse Michigan, and are abused in their turn. Several whom we have known to set out with this capital mistake, have absolutely turned about again in despair, revenging themselves by telling very hard stories about us nor'westers.

Touchstone's philosophy is your only wear for this meridian.

"*Corin.* And how like you this shepherd's life, Master Touchstone?

"*Touch.* Truly, shepherd, in respect of itself it is a good life; but in respect it is a shepherd's life, it is naught. In respect that it is solitary, I like it very well; but in respect that it is private, it is a very vile life. Now, in respect that it is in the fields, it pleaseth me well; but in respect that it is not in the court, it is tedious. As it is a spare life, look you, it fits my humour well; but as there is no plenty in it, it goes much against my stomach. Hast any philosophy in thee, shepherd?

Nobody will quarrel with this view of things. You may say anything you like of the country or its inhabitants: but beware how you raise a suspicion that you despise the homely habits of those round you. This is never forgiven.

It would be in vain to pretend that this state of society can ever be agreeable to those who have been accustomed to the more rational arrangements of the older world. The social character of the meals, in particular, is quite destroyed, by the constant presence of strangers, whose manners, habits of thinking, and social connexions are quite different from your own, and often exceedingly repugnant to your taste. Granting the correctness of the opinion which may be read in their countenances that they are "as good as you are," I must insist, that a greasy cook-maid, or a redolent stable-boy, can never be, to my thinking, an agreeable table companion—putting pride, that most terrific bug-bear of the woods, out of the question.

If the best man now living should honor my humble roof with his presence—if he should happen to have an unfortunate *penchant* for eating out of the dishes, picking his teeth with his fork, or using the fireplace for a pocket handkerchief, I would prefer he take his dinner *solus* or with those who did as he did.

But I repeat it; those who find these inconveniences most annoying while all is new and strange to them, will by the

85

exertion of a little patience and ingenuity, discover ways and means of getting aside of what is most unpleasant, in the habits of their neighbors: and the silent influence of example is daily affecting much towards reformation in many particulars. Neatness, propriety, and that delicate forbearance of the least encroachment upon the rights or the enjoyments of others, which is the essence of true elegance of manner, have only to be seen and understood to be admired and imitated; and I would fain persuade those who are groaning under certain inflictions to which I have but alluded, that the true way of overcoming all the evils of which *they* complain is to set forth in their own manners and habits, all that is kind, forbearing, true, lovely, and of good report. They will find ere long that their neighbors have taste enough to love what is so charming, even though they see it exemplified by one who sits *all day* in a carpeted parlor, teaches her own children instead of sending them to the district school, hates "the breath of garlic-eaters," and —oh fell climax!—knows nothing at all of soap-making.

15

MR. MAZARD ABSCONDS

SEVERAL LOTS had already been purchased in Montacute and some improvement marked each succeeding day. The mill had grown to its full stature, the dam was nearly completed; the tavern began to exhibit promise of its present ugliness, and all seemed prosperous as our best dreams, when certain rumors were set afloat touching the solvency of our disinterested friend Mr. Mazard. After two or three days' whispering, a tall black-browed man who "happened in" from Gullsborough, the place which had for some time been honored as the residence of the Dousterswivel of Montacute, stated boldly that Mr. Mazard had absconded; or, in western language "cleared." It seemed passing strange that he should run away from the large house which was going on under his auspices; the materials all on the ground and the work in full progress. Still more unaccountable did it appear to us that his workmen should go on so quietly, without so much as expressing any anxiety about their pay.

Mr. Clavers had just been telling me of these things, when the long genius above mentioned, presented himself at the door of the loggery. His *abord* was a singular mixture of coarseness, and an attempt at being civil; and he sat for some minutes looking round and asking various questions before he touched the main-spring of his visit.

At length, after some fumbling in his pocket, he produced a dingy sheet of paper, which he handed to Mr. Clavers.

"There; I want you to read that, and tell me what you think of it."

I did not look at the paper, but at my husband's face, which was black enough. He walked away with the tall man, "and I saw no more of them at that time."

Mr. Clavers did not return until late in the evening, and it was then I learned that Mr. Mazard had been getting large quantities of lumber and other materials on his account, and as his agent; and that the money which had been placed in the agent's hands, for the purchase of certain lands to be flowed by the mill-pond, had gone into government coffers in payment for sundry eighty acre lots, which were intended for his, Mr. Mazard's, private behoof and benefit. These items present but a sample of our amiable friend's trifling mistakes. I will not fatigue the reader by dwelling on the subject. The result of all this was most unpleasant to us. Mr. Clavers found himself involved to a large amount; and his only remedy seemed to prosecute Mr. Mazard. A consultation with his lawyer, however, convinced him, that even by this most disagreeable mode, redress was out of the question, since he had through inadvertence rendered himself liable for whatever that gentleman chose to buy or engage in his name. All that could be done, was to get out of the affair with as little loss as possible, and to take warning against land sharks in future.

An immediate journey to Detroit became necessary, and I was once more left alone, and in no overflowing spirits. I sat, "revolving in *my* altered soul The various turns of fate below," when a tall damsel, of perhaps twenty-eight or thirty, came in to make a visit. She was tastefully attired in a blue gingham dress, with broad cuffs of black morocco, and a black cambric apron edged with orange worsted lace. Her oily black locks were cut quite short round the ears, and confined close to her head by a black ribbon, from one side of which depended, almost in her eye, two very long tassels of black silk, intended to do duty as curls. Prunelle slippers with high heels, and a cotton handkerchief tied under the chin, finished the costume, which I have been thus particular in describing, because I have observed so many that were nearly similar.

The lady greeted me in the usual style, with a familiar nod, and seated herself at once in a chair near the door.

"Well, how do you like Michi*gan?*"

This question received the most polite answer which my conscience afforded; and I asked the lady in my turn, if she were one of my neighbors?

"Why, massy, yes!" she replied, "don't you know me? I tho't everybody know'd me. Why, I'm the school-ma'am, Simeon Jenkins' sister, Cleory Jenkins."

Thus introduced, I put all my civility in requisition to entertain my guest, but she seemed quite independent, finding amusement for herself, and asking questions on every possible theme.

"You're doing your own work now, a'n't ye?"

This might not be denied; and I asked if she did not know of a girl whom I might be likely to get.

"Well, I don't know; I'm looking for a place where I can board and do chores myself. I have a good deal of time before school, and after I get back; and I didn't know but I might suit ye for a while."

I was pondering on this proffer, when the sallow damsel arose from her seat, took a short pipe from her bosom, (not "Pan's reedy pipe," reader) filled it with tobacco, which she carried in her "work-pocket," and reseating herself, began to smoke with the greatest gusto, turning ever and anon to spit at the hearth.

Incredible again? alas, would it were not true! I have since known a girl of seventeen, who was attending a neighbor's sick infant, smoke the live-long day, and take snuff besides; and I can vouch for it, that a large proportion of the married women in the interior of Michigan use tobacco in some form, usually that of the odious pipe.

I took the earliest decent opportunity to decline the offered help, telling the school-ma'am plainly, that an inmate who smoked would make the house uncomfortable to me,

89

"Why, law!" said she, laughing; "that's nothing but pride now: folks is often too proud to take comfort. For my part, I couldn't do without my pipe to please nobody."

Mr. Simeon Jenkins, the brother of this independent young lady now made his appearance on some trifling errand; and his sister repeated to him what I had said.

Mr. Jenkins took his inch of cigar from his mouth, and asked if I really disliked tobacco-smoke, seeming to think it scarcely possible.

"Don't your old man smoke?" said he.

"No, indeed," said I, with more than my usual energy; "I should hope he never would."

"Well," said neighbor Jenkins, "I tell you what, I'm *boss* at home; and if my old woman was to stick up in that fashion, I'd keep the house so blue she couldn't see to snuff the candle."

His sister laughed long and loud at this sally, which was uttered rather angrily, and with an air of most manful bravery; and Mr. Jenkins, picking up his end of cigar from the floor, walked off with an air evidently intended to be as expressive as the celebrated and oft-quoted nod of Lord Burleigh in the Critic.

Miss Jenkins was still arguing on the subject of her pipe, when a gentleman approached, whose dress and manner told me that he did not belong to our neighborhood. He was a red-faced, jolly-looking person, evidently "well to do in the world," and sufficiently consequential for any meridian. He seated himself quite unceremoniously; for who feels ceremony in a log-house? said he understood Mr. Clavers was absent—then hesitated; and, as Miss Jenkins afterwards observed, "hummed and hawed," and seemed as if he would fain say something, but scarce knew how.

At length Miss Cleora took the hint—a most necessary point of delicacy, where there is no withdrawing room. She gave her parting nod, and disappeared; and the old gentleman proceeded.

He had come to Montacute with the view of settling his son, "a wild chap," he said, a lawyer by profession, and not very fond of work of any sort; but as he himself had a good deal of land in the vicinity, he thought his son might find employment in attending to it, adding such professional business as might occur.

"But what I wished particularly to say, my dear madam," said he, "regards rather my son's wife than himself. She is a charming girl, and accustomed to much indulgence; and I have felt afraid that a removal to a place so new as this might be too trying to her. I knew you must be well able to judge of the difficulties to be encountered here, and took the liberty of calling on that account."

I was so much pleased with the idea of having a neighbor, whose habits might in some respects accord with my own, that I fear I was scarcely impartial in the view which I gave Mr. Rivers, of the possibilities of Montacute. At least I communicated only such as rises before my own mind, while watching perhaps a glorious sunset reflected in the glassy pond; my hyacinths in all their glory; the evening breeze beginning to sigh in the tree-tops; the children just coming in after a fine frolic with D'Orsay on the grass; and Papa and Prince returning up the lane. At such times, I always conclude, that Montacute is, after all, a dear little world; and I am probably quite as near the truth, as when, —"on some cold rainy day, When the birds cannot show a dry feather;" when Arthur comes in with a pound of mud on each foot, D'Orsay at his heels, bringing in as much more; little Bell crying to go out to play; Charlie prodigiously fretful with his prospective tooth; and some gaunt marauder from "up north," or "out west," sits talking on "bis'ness," and covering my andirons with tobacco juice; I determine sagely, that a life in the woods is worse than no life at all. One view is, I insist, as good as the other; but I told Mr. Rivers he must make due allowance for my desire to have his fair daughter-in-law for a neighbor, with which he departed; and I felt that my gloom had essentially lightened in consequence of his visit.

16

SNAKES, TOADS AND AGUES

Mr. Clavers at length returned; and the progress of the village, though materially retarded by the obliquities of Mr. Mazard's course, was still not entirely at a stand. If our own operations were slow and doubtful, there were others whose building and improving went on at a rapid rate; and before the close of the summer, several small tenements were enclosed and rendered in some sort habitable. A store and a public-house were to be ready for business in a very short time.

I had the pleasure of receiving early in the month of September, a visit from a young city friend, a charming lively girl, who unaffectedly enjoyed the pleasures of the country, and whose taste for long walks and rides was insatiable. I curtained off with the unfailing cotton sheets a snow-white bower for her in the loft, and spread a piece of carpeting, a relic of former magnificence, over the loose boards that served for a floor. The foot square window was shaded by a pink curtain, and a bed-side chair and a candle-stand completed a sleeping apartment which she declared was perfectly delightful.

So smoothly flowed our days during that charming visit that I had begun to fear my fair guest would be obliged to return to —— without a single adventure worth telling, when one morning as we sat sewing, Arthur ran in with a prodigious snake-story, to which, though we were at first disposed to pay no attention, we were at length obliged to listen.

"A most beautiful snake," he declared, "was coming up to the back door."

To the back door we ran; and there, to be sure, was a large rattlesnake, or massasauga, lazily winding its course towards the house, Alice standing still to admire it, too ignorant to fear.

My young friend snatched up a long switch, whose ordinary office was to warn the chickens from the dinner-table, and struck at the reptile which was not three feet from the door. It reared its head at once, made several attempts to strike, or spring, as it is called here, though it never really springs. Fanny continued to strike; and at length the snake turned for flight, not however without a battle of at least two minutes.

"Here's the axe, cousin Fanny," said Arthur, "don't let him run away!" and while poor I stood in silent terror, the brave girl followed, struck once ineffectually, and with another blow divided the snake, whose writhings turned to the sun as many hues as the windings of Broadway on a spring morning—and Fanny was a heroine.

It is my opinion that next to having a cougar spring at one, the absolute killing of a rattlesnake is peculiarly appropriate to constitute a Michigan heroine;—and the cream of my snake-story is, that it might be sworn to, chapter and verse, before the nearest justice. What cougar story can say as much?

But the nobler part of the snake ran away with far more celerity than it had displayed while it "could a *tail* unfold," and we exalted the *coda* to a high station on the logs at the corner of the house—for fear none of the scornful sex would credit our prowess.

That snake absolutely haunted us for a day or two; we felt sure that there were more near the house, and our ten days of happiness seemed cut short like those of Seged, and by a cause not very dissimilar. But the gloom consequent upon confining ourselves, children and all, to the house, in delicious weather, was too much for our prudence; and we soon began to venture out a little, warily inspecting every nook, and harassing the poor children with incessant cautions.

We had been watching the wheelings and flittings of a flock of prairie hens, which had alighted in Mr. Jenkins' corn-field, turning ever and anon a delighted glance westward at the masses of purple and crimson which make sunset so splendid in the region of the great lakes. I felt the dew, and warning all my companions, stepped into the house. I had reached the middle of the room, when I trod upon something soft, which eluded my foot. I shrieked "a snake! a snake!" and fell senseless to the floor.

When I recovered myself I was on the bed, and well sprinkled with camphor, that never failing specific in the woods.

"Where is it?" said I, as soon as I could utter a word. There was a general smile. "Why, Mamma," said Alice, who was exalted to a place on the bed, "don't you recollect that great toad that always sits behind the flour-barrel in the corner?"

I did not repent my fainting though it was not a snake, for if there is anything besides a snake that curdles the blood in my veins it is a toad. The harmless wretch was carried to a great distance from the house, but the next morning, there it sat again in the corner catching flies. I have been told by some persons here that they "liked to have toads in the room in fly time." Truly may it be said, "What's one man's meat—" Shade of Chesterfield, forgive me!—but that anybody *can* be willing to live with a toad! To my thinking nothing but a *toady* can be more odious.

The next morning I awoke with a severe head-ache, and racking pains in every bone. Dame Jennings said it was the "*agur.*" I insisted that it could be nothing but the toad. The fair Fanny was obliged to leave us this day, or lose her escort home—a thing not to be risked in the wilderness. I thought I should get up to dinner, and in that hope bade

94

her a gay farewell, with a charge to make the most of the
snake story for the honor of the woods.

I did *not* get up to dinner, for the simple reason that I
could not stand—and Mrs. Jennings consoled me by telling
me every ten minutes, "Why, you've got th'agur! woman
alive! Why, I know the fever-agur as well as I know beans!
It a'n't nothin' else!"

But no chills came. My pains and my fever became intense, and I knew but little about it after the first day, for
there was an indistinctness about my perceptions, which
almost, although not quite, amounted to delirium.

A physician was sent for, and we expected, of course,
some village Galen, who knew just enough to bleed and
blister, for all mortal ills. No such thing! A man of first-rate
education, who had walked European hospitals, and who
had mother-wit in abundance, to enable him to profit by
his advantages. It is surprising how many such people one
meets in Michigan. Some, indeed, we have been led to suppose, from some traits in their American history, might
have "left their country for their country's good:"—others
appear to have forsaken the old world, either in consequence of some temporary disgust, or through romantic
notions of the liberty to be enjoyed in this favored land. I
can at this moment call to mind, several among our ten-
mile neighbors, who can boast university honors, either
European or American, and who are reading men, even
now. Yet one might pass any one of these gentlemen in the
road without distinguishing between him and the Corydon
who curries his horses, so complete is their outward trans-
formation.

Our medical friend treated me very judiciously; and by
his skill, the severe attack of rheumatic-fever, which my
sunset and evening imprudences had been kindling in my
veins, subsided after a week, into a daily ague; but Mrs.
Jennings was not there to exult in this proof of her sagacity.
She had been called away to visit a daughter, who had
been taken ill at a distance from home, and I was left without a nurse.

My neighbors showed but little sympathy on the occasion. They had imbibed the idea that we held ourselves above them, and chose to take it for granted, that we did not need their aid. There were a good many cases of ague too, and, of course, people had their own troubles to attend to. The result was, that we were in a sad case enough. Oh! for one of those feminine men who can make good gruel, and wash the children's faces! Mr. Clavers certainly did his best, and who can more? But the hot side of the bowl always *would* come to his fingers—and the sauce-pan *would* overset, let him balance it ever so nicely. And then—such hungry children! They wanted to eat all the time. After a day's efforts, he began to complain that stooping over the fire made him very dizzy. I was quite self-absorbed, or I should have noticed such a complaint from one who makes none without cause; but the matter went on, until, when I asked for my gruel, he had very nearly fallen on the coals, in the attempt to take it from the fire. He staggered to the bed, and was unable to sit up for many days after.

When matters reached this pitch—when we had, literally, no one to prepare food, or look after the children—little Bell added to the sick-list, too—our physician proved our good genius. He procured a nurse from a considerable distance; and it was through his means that good Mrs. Danforth heard of our sad condition, and sent us a maiden of all-work, who materially amended the aspect of our domestic affairs.

Our agues were tremendous. I used to think I should certainly die in my ten or twelve hours' fever—and Mr. Clavers confidently asserted, several times, that the upper half of his head was taking leave of the lower. But the event proved we were both mistaken; for our physician verified his own assertion, that an ague was as easily managed as a common cold, by curing us both in a short time after our illness had assumed the intermittent form. There is, however, one important distinction to be observed between a cold and the ague—the former does not recur after every

96

trifling exertion, as the latter is sure to do. Again and again, after we seemed entirely cured, did the insidious enemy renew his attacks. A short ride, a walk of two or three miles, and we were prostrated for a week or two. Even a slight alarm, or anything that occasioned an unpleasant surprise, would be followed by a chill and fever.

These things are, it must be conceded, very discouraging. One learns to feel as if the climate must be a wretched one, and it is not till after these first clouds have blown over, that we have resolution to look around us—to estimate the sunny skies of Michigan, and the ruddy countenances of its older inhabitants as they deserve.

The people are obstinately attached to some superstitious notions respecting agues. They hold that it is unlucky to break them. "You should let them run on," say they, "till they wear themselves out." This has probably arisen from some imprudent use of quinine, (or "Queen Ann,") and other powerful tonics, which are often taken before the system is properly prepared. There is also much prejudice against "Doctor's physic;" while Lobelia, and other poisonous plants, which happen to grow wild in the woods, are used with the most reckless rashness. The opinion that each region produces the medicines which its own diseases require, prevails extensively,—a notion which, though perhaps theoretically correct to a certain extent, is a most dangerous one for the ignorant to practise upon.

These agues are, as yet, the only diseases of the country. Consumption is almost unknown, as a Michigan evil. Indeed many, who have been induced to forsake the seaboard, by reason of too sensitive lungs, find themselves renovated after a year in the peninsula. Our sickly season, from August till October, passed over without a single death within our knowledge.

To be sure, a neighbor told me, not long ago, that her old man had a complaint of "the lights," and that "to try to work any, gits his lights all up in a heap." But as this is a disease beyond the bounds of my medical knowledge, I can only "say the tale as't was said to me," hoping, that none of my emigrating friends may find it contagious:— any disease which is brought on by *working*, being certainly much to be dreaded in this western country!

17

MRS. RIVERS

It was on one of our superlatively doleful ague days, when a cold drizzling rain had sent mildew into our unfortunate bones; and I lay in bed, burning with fever, while my stronger half sat by the fire, taking his chill with his great-coat, hat, and boots on, that Mr. Rivers came to introduce his young daughter-in-law. I shall never forget the utterly disconsolate air, which, in spite of the fair lady's politeness, would make itself visible in the pauses of our conversation. She *did* try not to cast a curious glance round the room. She fixed her eyes on the fire-place—but there were the clay-filled sticks, instead of a chimney-piece—the half-consumed wooden *crane*, which had, more than once, let our dinner fall—the Rocky-Mountain hearth, and the reflector, baking biscuits for tea—so she thought it hardly polite to appear to dwell too long there. She turned towards the window: there were the shelves, with our remaining crockery, a grotesque assortment! and, just beneath, the unnameable iron and tin affairs, that are reckoned among the indispensables, even of the half-civilized state. She tried the other side, but there was the ladder, the flour-barrel, and a host of other things—rather odd parlor furniture— and she cast her eyes on the floor, with its gaping cracks, wide enough to admit a massasauga from below, and its inequalities, which might trip any but a sylph. The poor thing looked absolutely confounded, and I exerted all the energy my fever had left me, to try to say something a little encouraging.

"Come to-morrow morning, Mrs. Rivers," said I, "and you shall see the aspect of things quite changed; and I shall be able to tell you a great deal in favor of this wild life."

She smiled faintly, and tried not to look miserable, but I saw plainly that she was sadly depressed, and I could not feel surprised that she should be so. Mr. Rivers spoke very kindly to her, and filled up all the pauses in our forced talk with such cheering observations as he could muster.

He had found lodgings, he said, in a farm-house, not far from us, and his son's house would, ere long, be completed, when we should be quite near neighbors.

I saw tears swelling in the poor girl's eyes, as she took leave, and I longed to be well for her sake. In this newly-formed world, the earlier settler has a feeling of hostess-ship toward the new comer. I speak only of women—men look upon each one, newly arrived, merely as an additional business-automaton—a somebody more with whom to try the race of enterprize, i.e. money-making.

The next day Mrs. Rivers came again, and this time her husband was with her. Then I saw at a glance why it was that life in the wilderness looked so peculiarly gloomy to her. Her husband's face shewed but too plainly the marks of early excess; and there was at intervals, in spite of an evident effort to play the agreeable, an appearance of absence, of indifference, which spoke volumes of domestic history. He made innumerable inquiries, touching the hunting and fishing facilities of the country around us, expressed himself enthusiastically fond of those sports, and said the country was a living death without them, regretting much that Mr. Clavers was not of the same mind.

Meanwhile I had begun to take quite an interest in his little wife. I found that she was as fond of novels and poetry, as her husband was of field-sports. Some of her flights of sentiment went quite beyond my sobered-down views. But I saw we should get on admirably, and so we have done ever since. I did not mistake that pleasant smile, and that

100

soft sweet voice. They are even now as attractive as ever. And I had a neighbor.

Before the winter had quite set in, our little nest was finished, or as nearly finished as anything in Michigan; and Mr. and Mrs. Rivers took possession of their new dwelling, on the very same day that we smiled our adieux to the loggery.

Our new house was merely the beginning of a house, intended for the reception of a front building, Yankee-fashion, whenever the owner should be able to enlarge his borders. But the contrast with our sometime dwelling, made even this humble cot seem absolutely sumptuous. The children could do nothing but admire the conveniences it afforded. Robinson Crusoe exulted not more warmly in his successive acquisitions than did Alice in "a kitchen, a real kitchen! and a pantry to put the dishes!" while Arthur found much to praise in the wee bed-room which was allotted as his sanctum in the "hic, haec, hoc," hours. Mrs. Rivers, who was fresh from "the settlements," often curled her pretty lip at the deficiencies in her little mansion, but we had learned to prize anything which was even a shade above the wigwam, and dreamed not of two parlors or a piazza.

Other families removed to Montacute in the course of the winter. Our visiting list was considerably enlarged, and I used all my influence with Mrs. Rivers to persuade her that her true happiness lay in making friends of her neighbors. She was very shy, easily shocked by those sins against Chesterfield, which one encounters here at every turn, did not conceal her fatigue when a neighbor happened in after breakfast to make a three hours' call, forgot to ask those who came at one o'clock to take off their things and stay to tea, even though the knitting needles might peep out beneath the shawl. For these and similar omissions I lectured her continually but with little effect. It was with the greatest difficulty I could persuade her to enter any house but ours, although I took especial care to be impartial in my own visiting habits, determined at all sacrifice to live down

101

the impression that I felt *above* my neighbors. In fact, however we may justify certain exclusive habits in populous places, they are strikingly and confessedly ridiculous in the wilderness. What can be more absurd than a feeling of proud distinction, where a stray spark of fire, a sudden illness, or a day's contre-temps, may throw you entirely upon the kindness of your humblest neighbor? If I treat Mrs. Timson with neglect to-day can I with any face borrow her broom to-morrow? And what would become of me, if in revenge for my declining her invitation to tea this afternoon, she should decline coming to do my washing on Monday?

It was as a practical corollary to these my lectures, that I persuaded Mrs. Rivers to accept an invitation that we received for the wedding of a young girl, the sister of our cooper, Mr. Whitefield. I attired myself in white, considered here as the extreme of festal elegance, to do honor to the occasion; and called for Mrs. Rivers in the ox-cart at two o'clock.

I found her in her ordinary neat home-dress; and it required some argument on my part to induce her to exchange it for a gay chally with appropriate ornaments.

"It really seems ridiculous," she said, "to *dress* for such a place! and besides, my dear Mrs. Clavers, I am afraid we shall be suspected of a desire to outshine."

I assured her we were in more danger of that other and far more dangerous suspicion of undervaluing our rustic neighbors.

"I s'pose they didn't think it worth while to put on their best gowns for country-folks!"

I assumed the part of Mentor on this and many similar occasions; considering myself by this time quite an old resident, and of right entitled to speak for the natives.

Mrs. Rivers was a little disposed to laugh at the ox-cart; but I soon convinced her that, with its cushion of straw overspread with a buffalo-robe, it was far preferable to a more ambitious carriage.

"No letting down of steps, no ruining one's dress against

a muddy wheel! no gay horses tipping one into the gutter!"

She was obliged to acknowledge the superiority of our vehicle, and we congratulated ourselves upon reclining *à la* Lalla Rookh and Lady Mary Wortley Montague. Certainly a cart is next to a palanquin.

The pretty bride was in white cambric, worn over pink glazed muslin. The prodigiously stiff under-dress with its large cords (not more than three or four years behind the fashion) gave additional slenderness to her taper waist, bound straitly with a sky-blue zone. The fair hair was decorated, not covered, with a cap, the universal adjunct of full dress in the country, placed far behind the ears, and displaying the largest puffs, set off by sundry gilt combs. The unfailing high-heeled prunelle shoe gave the finishing-touch, and the whole was scented, *à l'outrance,* with essence of lemon.

After the ceremony, which occupied perhaps three minutes, fully twice as long as is required by our state laws, tea was served, absolutely handed on a salver, and by the master of the house, a respectable farmer. Mountains of cake followed. I think either pile might have measured a foot in height, and each piece would have furnished a meal for a hungry school-boy. Other things were equally abundant, and much pleasant talk followed the refreshments. I returned home highly delighted, and tried to persuade my companion to look on the rational side of the thing, which she scarcely seemed disposed to do, so *outré* did the whole appear to her. I, who had begun to claim for myself the dignified character of a cosmopolite, a philosophical observer of men and things, consoled myself for this derogatory view of Montacute gentility, by thinking, "All city people are so cockneyish!"

18

THE DOUBLEDAYS

"MOTHER WANTS your sifter," said Miss Ianthe Howard, a young lady of six years' standing, attired in a tattered calico, thickened with dirt; her unkempt locks straggling from under that hideous substitute for a bonnet, so universal in the western country, a dirty cotton handkerchief, which is used, *ad nauseam*, for all sorts of purposes.

"Mother wants your sifter, and she says she guesses you can let her have some sugar and tea, 'cause you've got plenty."

This excellent reason, "'cause you've got plenty," is conclusive as to sharing with your neighbors. Whoever comes to Michigan with nothing, will be sure to better his condition; but wo to him that brings with him anything like an appearance of abundance, whether of money or mere household conveniences. To have them, and not be willing to share them in some sort with the whole community, is an unpardonable crime. You must lend your best horse to *qui que ce soit*, to go ten miles over hill and marsh, in the darkest night, for a doctor; or your team to travel twenty after a "gal;" your wheel-barrows, your shovels, your utensils of all sorts, belong, not to yourself, but to the public, who do not think it necessary even to *ask* a loan, but take it for granted. The two saddles and bridles of Montacute spend most of their time travelling from house to house a-manback; and I have actually known a stray martingale to be traced to four dwellings, two miles apart, having been lent from one to another, without a word to the original proprietor, who sat waiting, not very patiently, to commence a journey.

Then within doors, an inventory of your plenishing of all sorts, would scarcely more than include the articles which you are solicited to lend. Not only are all kitchen utensils as much your neighbors as your own, but bedsteads, beds, blankets, sheets, travel from house to house, a pleasant and effectual mode of securing the perpetuity of certain efflorescent peculiarities of the skin, for which Michigan is becoming almost as famous as the land "'twixt Maidenkirk and John o'Groat's." Sieves, smoothing irons, and churns run about as if they had legs; one brass kettle is enough for a whole neighborhood; and I could point to a cradle which has rocked half the babies in Montacute. For my own part, I have lent my broom, my thread, my tape, my spoons, my cat, my thimble, my scissors, my shawl, my shoes; and have been asked for my combs and brushes: and my husband, for his shaving apparatus and his pantaloons.

But the cream of the joke lies in the manner of the thing. It is so straight-forward and honest, none of your hypocritical civility and servile gratitude! Your true republican, when he finds that you possess anything which would contribute to his convenience, walks in with "Are you going to use your horses *to-day?*" if horses happen to be the thing he needs.

"Yes, I shall probably want them."

"Oh, well; if you want them——I was thinking to get 'em to go up north a piece."

Or perhaps the desired article comes within the female department.

"Mother wants to get some butter: that 'ere butter you bought of Miss Barton this mornin'."

And away goes your golden store, to be repaid perhaps with some cheesy, greasy stuff, brought in a dirty pail, with "Here's your butter!"

A girl came in to borrow a "wash-dish," "because we've got company." Presently she came back: "Mother says you've forgot to send a towel."

105

"The pen and ink and a sheet o' paper and a wafer," is no unusual request; and when the pen is returned, you are generally informed that you sent "an awful bad pen."

I have been frequently reminded of one of Johnson's humorous sketches. A man returning a broken wheel-barrow to a Quaker, with, "Here I've broke your rotten wheel-barrow usin' on't. I wish you'd get it mended right off, 'cause I want to borrow it again this afternoon." The Quaker is made to reply, "Friend, it shall be done:" and I wish I possessed more of his spirit.

But I did not intend to write a chapter on involuntary loans; I have a story to tell.

One of my best neighbors is Mr. Philo Doubleday, a long, awkward, honest, hard-working Maine-man, or Mainote I suppose one might say; so good-natured, that he might be mistaken for a simpleton; but that must be by those that do not know him. He is quite an old settler, came in four years ago, bringing with him a wife who is to him as vinegar-bottle to oil-cruet, or as mustard to the sugar which is used to soften its biting qualities. Mrs. Doubleday has the sharpest eyes, the sharpest nose, the sharpest tongue, the sharpest elbows, and above all, the sharpest voice that ever "penetrated the interior" of Michigan. She has a tall, straight, bony figure, in contour somewhat resembling two hard-oak planks fastened together and stood on end: and, strange to say! she was full five-and-thirty when her mature graces attracted the eye and won the affections of the worthy Philo. What eclipse had come over Mr. Doubleday's usual sagacity when he made choice of his Polly, I am sure I could never guess; but he is certainly the only man in the wide world who could possibly have lived with her; and he makes her a most excellent husband.

She is possessed with a neat devil; I have known many such cases; her floor is scoured every night, after all are in bed but the unlucky scrubber, Betsey, the maid of all work; and wo to the unfortunate "indiffidle," as neighbor Jenkins says, who first sets dirty boot on it in the morning. If men come in to talk over road business, for Philo is much sought

106

when "the public" has any work to do, or school-business, for that being very troublesome, and quite devoid of profit, is often conferred upon Philo, Mrs. Doubleday makes twenty errands into the room, expressing in her visage all the force of Mrs. Raddle's inquiry, "*Is* them wretches going?" And when at length their backs are turned, out comes the bottle vengeance. The sharp eyes, tongue, elbow, and voice, are all in instant requisition.

"Fetch the broom, Betsey! and the scrub-broom, Betsey! and the mop, and that 'ere dish of soap, Betsey; and why on earth didn't you bring some ashes? You didn't expect to clean such a floor as this without ashes, did you?"—"What time are you going to have dinner, my dear?" says the imperturbable Philo, who is getting ready to go out.

"Dinner! I'm sure I don't know! there's no time to cook dinner in this house! nothing but slave, slave, slave, from morning till night, cleaning up after a set of nasty, dirty," &c. &c. "Phew!" says Mr. Doubleday, looking at his fuming helpmate with a calm smile, "It'll all rub out when it's dry, if you'll only let it alone."

"Yes, yes; and it would be plenty clean enough for you if there had been forty horses in here."

Philo on some such occasion waited till his Polly had stepped out of the room, and then with a bit of chalk wrote on the broad black-walnut mantel-piece:

> Bolt and bar hold gate of wood,
> Gate of iron springs make good,
> Bolt nor spring can bind the flame,
> Woman's tongue can no man tame.

and then took his hat and walked off.

This is his favorite mode of vengeance—"poetical justice" he calls it; and as he is never at a loss for a rhyme of his own or other people's, Mrs. Doubleday stands in no small dread of these efforts of genius. Once, when Philo's crony, James Porter, the black-smith, had left the print of his blackened knuckles on the outside of the oft-scrubbed

107

door, and was the subject of some rather severe remarks from the gentle Polly, Philo, as he left the house with his friend, turned and wrote over the offended spot:

> Knock not here!
> Or dread my dear.
>   P.D.

and the very next person that came was Mrs. Skinner, the merchant's wife, all drest in her red merino, to make a visit. Mrs. Skinner, who did not possess an unusual share of tact, walked gravely round to the back-door, and there was Mrs. Doubleday up to the eyes in soap-making. Dire was the mortification, and point-blank were the questions as to how the visitor came to go round that way; and when the warning couplet was produced in justification, we must draw a veil over what followed—as the novelists say.

Sometimes these poeticals came in aid of poor Betsey; as once, when on hearing a loud crash in the little shanty-kitchen, Mrs. Doubleday called in her shrillest tones, "Betsey! what on earth's the matter?" Poor Betsey, knowing what was coming, answered in a deprecatory whine, "The cow's kicked over the buck-wheat batter!"

When the clear, hilarious voice of Philo from the yard, where he was chopping, instantly completed the triplet—

"Take up the pieces and throw 'em at her!" for once the grim features of his spouse relaxed into a smile, and Betsey escaped her scolding.

Yet, Mrs. Doubleday is not without her excellent qualities as a wife, a friend, and a neighbor. She keeps her husband's house and stockings in unexceptionable trim. Her *emptin's* are the envy of the neighborhood. Her vinegar is, as how could it fail? the *ne plus ultra* of sharpness; and her pickles are greener than the grass of the field. She will watch night after night with the sick, perform the last sad offices for the dead, or take to her home and heart the little ones whose mother is removed forever from her place at the fire-side. All this she can do cheerfully, and she will not repay herself as many good people do by recounting every word of the querulous sick man, or the desolate mourner with added hints of tumbled drawers, closets all in heaps, or *awful* dirty kitchens.

I was sitting one morning with my neighbor Mrs. Jenkins, who is a sister of Mr. Doubleday, when Betsey, Mrs. Doubleday's "hired girl" came in with one of the shingles of Philo's handiwork in her hand, which bore in Mr. Doubleday's well-known chalk marks—

> Come quick, Fanny!
> And bring the granny,
> For Mrs. Double-
> day's in trouble.

And the next intelligence was of a fine new pair of lungs at that hitherto silent mansion. I called very soon after to take a peep at the "latest found;" and if the suppressed delight of the new papa was a treat, how much more was the softened aspect, the womanized tone of the proud and happy mother. I never saw a being so completely transformed. She would almost forget to answer me in her absorbed watching of the breath of the little sleeper. Even when she was trying to be polite, and to say what the occasion demanded, her eyes would *not* be withdrawn from the tiny face. Conversation on any subject but the ever-new theme of "babies" was out of the question. Whatever we began upon whirled sooner or later to the one point. The needle may tremble, but it turns not with the less constancy to the pole.

As I pass for an oracle in the matter of paps and possets, I had frequent communication with my now happy neighbor, who had forgotten to scold her husband, learned to let Betsey have time to eat, and omitted the nightly scouring of the floor, lest so much dampness might be bad for the baby. We were in deep consultation one morning on some important point touching the well-being of this sole object of Mrs. Doubleday's thoughts and dreams, when the very same little Ianthe Howard, dirty as ever, presented herself. She sat down and stared awhile without speaking, *à l'ordinaire;* and then informed us that her mother "wanted Miss Doubleday to let her have her baby for a little while, 'cause Benny's mouth's so sore that"— but she had not time to finish the sentence.

"LEND MY BABY!!!"—and her utterance failed. The new mother's feelings were fortunately too big for speech, and Ianthe wisely disappeared before Mrs. Doubleday found her tongue. Philo, who entered on the instant, burst into one of his electrifying laughs with—"ask my Polly, To lend her dolly!"—and I could not help thinking that one must come "west" in order to learn a little of everything.

The identical glass-tube which I offered Mrs. Howard, as a substitute for Mrs. Doubleday's baby, and which had already, frail as it is, threaded the country for miles in all directions, is, even as I write, in demand; a man on horseback comes from somewhere near Danforth's, and asks in mysterious whispers for—but I shall not tell what he calls it. The reader must come to Michigan.

19

A GENTLEMAN SETTLER

THE WINTER—the much dreaded winter in the woods, strange to tell, flew away more rapidly than any previous winter of my life. One has so much to do in the country. The division of labor is almost unknown. If in absolutely savage life, each man is of necessity "his own tailor, tent-maker, carpenter, cook, huntsman, and fisherman;"—so in the state of society which I am attempting to describe, each woman is, at times at least, her own cook, chamber-maid and waiter; nurse, seamstress and school-ma'am; not to mention various occasional callings to any one of which she must be able to turn her hand at a moment's notice. And every man, whatever his circumstances or resources, must be qualified to play groom, teamster, or boot-black, as the case may be; besides "tending the baby" at odd times, and cutting wood to cook his dinner with. If he has good sense, good nature, and a little spice of practical philoso-phy, all this goes exceedingly well. He will find neither his mind less cheerful, nor his body less vigorous for these lit-tle sacrifices. If he is too proud or too indolent to submit to such infringements upon his dignity and ease, most es-sential deductions from the daily comfort of his family will be the mortifying and vexatious result of his obstinate adherence to early habits.

We witnessed by accident so striking a lesson on this subject, not long after our removal to Montacute, that I must be allowed to record the impression it made upon my

111

mind. A business errand called Mr. Clavers some miles from home; and having heard much of the loveliness of the scenery in that direction, I packed the children into the great waggon and went with him.

The drive was a charming one. The time, midsummer, and the wilderness literally "blossoming as the rose." In a tour of ten miles we saw three lovely lakes, each a lonely gem set deep in masses of emerald green, which shut it in completely from all but its own bright beauty. The road was a most intricate one "through bush—through briar," and the ascents, the "pitches," the "sidlings" in some places quite terrific. At one of the latter points, where the road wound, as so many Michigan roads do, round the edge of a broad green marsh, I insisted upon getting out, as usual. The place was quite damp; but I thought I could pick my way over the green spots better than trust myself in the waggon, which went along for some rods at an angle (*I* said so at least,) of forty-five. Two men were mowing the marsh, and seemed highly amused at my perplexity, when after watching the receding vehicle till it ascended a steep bank on the farther side, I began my course. For a few steps I made out tolerably, but then I began to sink most inconveniently. Silly thin shoes again. Nobody should ever go one mile from home in thin shoes in this country, but old Broadway habits are *so* hard to forget.

At length, my case became desperate. One shoe had provokingly disappeared. I had stood on one foot as long as ever a goose did, but no trace of the missing Broqua could I find, and down went the stocking six inches into the black mud. I cried out for help; and the mowers, with "a long and a loud guffaw," came leisurely towards me. Just then appeared Mr. Clavers on the green slope above mentioned. It seems his high mightiness had concluded by this time that I had been sufficiently punished for my folly, (all husbands are so tyrannical!) and condescended to come to my rescue. I should have been very sulky; but then, there were the children. However, my spouse did try to find a road which should less frequently give rise to those troublesome terrors of mine. So we drove on and on, through ancient woods, which I could not help admiring; and, at length, missing our way, we came suddenly upon a log-house, very different from that which was the object of our search. It was embowered in oaks of the largest size; and one glance told us that the hand of refined taste had been there. The under-brush had been entirely cleared away, and the broad expanse before the house looked like a smooth-shaven lawn, deep-shadowed by the fine trees I have mentioned. Gleams of sunset fell on beds of flowers of every hue; curtains of French muslin shaded the narrow windows, and on a rustic seat near the door lay a Spanish guitar, with its broad scarf of blue silk. I could not think of exhibiting my inky stocking to the inmates of such a cottage, though I longed for a peep; and Mr. Clavers went alone to the house to inquire the way, while I played *tiger* and held the horses.

I might have remained undiscovered, but for the delighted exclamations of the children, who were in raptures with the beautiful flowers, and the lake which shone, a silver mirror, immediately beneath the bank on which we were standing. Their merry talk echoed through the trees, and presently out came a young lady in a *demi-suisse* costume; her dark hair closely braided and tied with ribbons, and the pockets of her rustic apron full of mosses and wild flowers. With the air rather of Paris than of Michigan, she insisted on my alighting; and though in awkward plight, I suffered myself to be persuaded. The interior of the house corresponded in part with the impressions I had received from my first glance at the exterior. There was a harp in a recess, and the white-washed log-walls were hung with a variety of cabinet pictures. A tasteful drapery of French chintz partly concealed another recess, closely filled with books; a fowling piece hung over the chimney, and before a large old-fashioned looking-glass stood a French pier-table, on which were piled fossil specimens, mosses, vases of flowers, books, pictures, and music. So far all was well; and two young ladies seated on a small sofa near the table, with netting and needle-work were in keeping with the romantic side of the picture. But there was more than all this.

The bare floor was marked in every direction with that detestable yellow dye which mars everything in this country, although a great box filled with sand stood near the hearth, melancholy and fruitless provision against this filthy visitation. Two great dirty dogs lay near a large rocking-chair, and this rocking-chair sustained the tall person of the master of the house, a man of perhaps forty years or thereabouts, the lines of whose face were such, as he who runs may read. Pride and passion, and reckless self-indulgence were there, and fierce discontent and determined indolence. An enormous pair of whiskers, which surmounted the whole lower part of the countenance, afforded incessant employment for the long slender fingers, which showed no marks of labor, except very dirty nails. This gentleman had, after all, something of a high-bred air, as if one did not look at the floor, and could forget certain indications of excessive carelessness discernible in his dress and person.

We had not yet seen the lady of the cottage; the young girl who had ushered me in so politely was her sister, now on a summer visit. Mrs. B—— shortly after entered in an undress, but with a very lady-like grace of manner, and the step of a queen. Her face, which bore the traces of beauty, struck me as one of the most melancholy I had ever seen; and it was over-spread with a sort of painful flush, which did not conceal its habitual paleness.

We had been conversing but a few minutes, when a shriek from the children called everyone out of doors in an instant. One of Mr. B——'s sons had ventured too near the horses, and received a kick from our "old Tom," who is a little roguish, a kick on the arm. He roared most lustily, and everybody was very much frightened, and ran in all directions seeking remedies. I called upon a boy, who seemed to be a domestic, to get some salt and vinegar, (for the mother was disabled by terror;) but as he only grinned and stared at me, I ran into the kitchen to procure it myself. I opened a closet door, but the place seemed empty or nearly so; I sought everywhere within ken, but all was equally desolate; I opened the door of a small bed-room, but I saw in a moment that I ought not to have gone there, and shut it again instantly. Hopeless of finding what I sought, I returned to the parlor, and there the little boy was holding a vinaigrette to his mother's nose, while the young ladies were chafing her hands. She had swooned in excessive alarm, and the kick had, after all, produced only a trifling bruise.

After Mrs. B—— had recovered herself a little, she entered at some length, and with a good deal of animation on a detail of her Michigan *experiences;* not, as I had hoped at the beginning, "in equal scale weighing delight and dole;" but giving so depressing a view of the difficulties of the country, that I felt almost disposed for the moment to regret my determination of trying a woodland life. She had found all barren. They had no neighbors, or worse than none—could get no domestics—found every one disposed to deal unfairly, in all possible transactions; and though last not least, could get nothing fit to eat.

Mr. B——'s account, though given with a careless, off-hand air, had a strong dash of bitterness in it—a sort of fierce defiance of earth and heaven, which is apt to be the resource of those who have wilfully thrown away their chances of happiness. His remarks upon the disagreeables which we had to encounter, were carried at least as far as those of his wife; and he asserted that there was but one alternative in Michigan—cheat or be cheated.

We were not invited to remain to tea; but took our leave with many polite hopes of further acquaintance. Mr. Clavers found the spot he had been seeking, and then, taking another road home, we called to see Mrs. Danforth; whom we considered even then in the light of the very good friend which she has since so often proved herself. I told of our accidental visit and learned from the good lady some particulars respecting this family, whose condition seemed so strange and contradictory, even in the western country,

115

where every element enters into the composition of that anomalous mass called society.

Mr. B——, was born to a large fortune, a lot which certainly seems in our country to carry a curse with it in a large proportion of instances. Feeling quite above the laborious calling by which his father had amassed wealth, the son's only aim had been to spend his money, like a gentleman; and in this he had succeeded so well that by the time he had established himself, at the head of the ton in one of our large Eastern cities, and been set down as an irreclaimable *roué* by his sober friends, he found that a few more losses at play would leave him stranded. But he had been quite the idol of the "good society" into which he had purchased admission, and the one never-failing resource in such cases—a rich wife, was still perhaps in his power. Before his altered fortunes were more than whispered by his very particular friends, he had secured the hand of an orphan heiress, a really amiable and well-bred girl; and it was not until she had been his wife for a year or more that she knew that her thousands had done no more than prop a falling house.

Many efforts were made by the friends on both sides, to aid Mr. B—— in establishing himself in business, but his pride and indolence proved insuperable difficulties; and after some years of those painful struggles between pride and poverty, which so many of the devotees of fashion can appreciate from their own bitter experience, a retreat to the West was chosen as the least of prospective evils.

Here the whole country was before him "where to choose." He could have bought at government price any land in the region to which he had directed his steps. Water-power of all capabilities was at his command, for there was scarce a settler in the neighborhood. But he scorned the idea of a place for *business*. What he wanted was a charming spot for a gentlemanly residence. There, with his gun and his fishing rod he was to live; a small income which still remained of his wife's fortune furnishing the only dependence.

116

And this income, small as it was, would have been, in prudent and industrious hands, a subsistence at least; so small is the amount really requisite for a frugal way of life in these isolated situations. But unfortunately Mr. B——'s character had by no means changed with his place of residence. His land, which by cultivation would have yielded abundant supplies for his table, was suffered to lie unimproved, because he had not money to pay laborers. Even a garden was too much trouble; the flower-beds I had seen were made by the hands of Mrs. B——, and her sisters; and it was asserted that the comforts of life were often lacking in this unfortunate household, and would have been always deficient but for constant aid from Mrs. B——'s friends.

Mrs. B—— had done as women so often do in similar situations, making always a great effort to keep up a certain appearance, and allowing her neighbors to discover that she considered them far beneath her; she had still forgotten her delicate habits, and that they were delicate and lady-like, no one can doubt who had ever seen her, and labored with all her little strength for the comfort of her family. She had brought up five children on little else beside Indian meal and potatoes; and at one time the neighbors had known the whole family live for weeks upon bread and tea without sugar or milk;—Mr. B—— sitting in the house smoking cigars, and playing the flute, as much of a gentleman as ever.

And these people, bringing with them such views and feelings as make straitened means productive of absolute wretchedness anywhere, abuse Michigan, and visit upon their homely neighbors the bitter feelings which spring from that fountain of gall, mortified yet indomitable pride. Finding themselves growing poorer and poorer, they persuade themselves that all who thrive, do so by dishonest gains, or by mean sacrifices; and they are teaching their children, by the irresistible power of daily example, to despise plodding industry, and to indulge in repining and feverish longings after unearned enjoyments.

117

But I am running into an absolute homily! I set out to say only that we had been warned at the beginning against indulging in certain habits which darken the whole course of country life; and here I have been betrayed into a chapter of sermonizing. I can only beg pardon and resume my broken thread.

20

A GARDEN IN MONTACUTE

I BELIEVE I was recurring to the rapidity with which our first winter in the wilds slipped away. We found that when the spring came we were not half prepared to take advantage of it; but armed with the "American Gardener," and quantities of choice seeds received in a box of treasures from home during the previous autumn, we set about making something like a garden. It would seem that in our generous soil this could not be a difficult task; but our experience has taught us quite differently. Besides the eradication of stumps, which is a work of time and labor anywhere, the "grubs" present a most formidable hindrance to all gardening efforts in the "oak-openings." I dare say my reader imagines a "grub" to be a worm, a destructive wretch that spoils peach trees. In Michigan, it is quite another affair. Grubs are, in western parlance, the gnarled roots of small trees and shrubs, with which our soil is interlaced in some places almost to a solidity. When these are disturbed by the immense "breaking up" plough, with its three or four yoke of oxen, the surface of the ground wears everywhere the appearance of chevaux-de-frise; and to pile in heaps for burning, such of these serried files as have been fairly loosened by the plough, is a work of much time and labor. And after this is done in the best way, your *potagère* will still seem to be full of grubs; and it will take two or three years to get rid of these troublesome proofs of the fertiliy of your soil. But your incipient Eden will

119

afford much of interest and comfort before this work is accomplished, and I sincerely pity those who lack a taste for this primitive source of pleasure.

On the opening day of our first spring, the snow had scarcely disappeared ere the green tops of my early bulbs were peeping above the black soil in which they had been buried on our first arrival; and the interest with which I watched each day's development of these lovely children of the sun, might almost compare with that which I felt in the daily increasing perfection of my six months' old Charlie, whose rosy cheeks alone, could, in my view at least, outblush my splendid double hyacinths.

Whatever of a perennial kind we could procure, we planted at once, without waiting until our garden should be permanently arranged. All that we have since regretted on this point is that we had not made far greater efforts to increase our variety; since one year's time is well worth gaining, where such valuables are in question.

On the subject of flowers, I scarcely dare trust my pen with a word, so sure am I that my enthusiastic love for them would, to most readers, seem absolutely silly or affected. But where the earth produces spontaneously such myriads of splendid specimens, it would seem really ungrateful to spare the little time and pains required for their cultivation. This is a sin which I at least shall avoid; and I lose no opportunity of attempting to inspire my neighbors with some small portion of my love for everything which can be called a flower, whether exotic or home-bred.

The ordinary name with us for a rose is "a rosy-flower;" our vase of flowers usually a broken-nosed pitcher, is a "posy-pot;" and "yaller lilies" are among the most dearly-prized of all the gifts of Flora. A neighbor after looking approvingly at a glass of splendid tulips, of which I was vain-glorious beyond all justification, asked me if I got "them blossoms out of these here woods." Another cooly broke off a spike of my finest hyacinths, and after putting it to his undiscriminating nose, threw it on the ground with a "pah!" as contemptuous as Hamlet's. But I revenged myself when I set him sniffing at a crown imperial—so we are at quits now.

A lady to whom I offered a cutting of my noble balm geranium, with leaves larger than Charlie's hand, declined the gift, saying, "she never know'd nobody make nothin' by raisin' sich things." One might have enlightened her a little as to their moneyed value, but I held my peace and gave her some sage-seed.

Yet, oddly enough, if anything could be odd in Michigan—there is, within three miles of us, a gardener and florist of no mean rank, and one whose aid can be obtained at any time for some small consideration of "rascal counters;" so that a hot-bed, or even a green-house is within our reach.

I have sometimes thought that there could scarcely be a trade or profession which is not largely represented among the farmers of Michigan, judging from the somewhat extensive portion of the state with which we have become familiar. I was regretting the necessity of a journey to Detroit for the sake of a gold filling; when lo! a dentist at my elbow, with his case of instruments, his gold foil, and his skill, all very much at my service.

Montacute, half-fledged as it is, afford facilities that one could scarcely expect. Besides the blacksmith, the cooper, the chair-maker, the collar-maker, and sundry carpenters and masons, and three stores, there is the mantua-maker for your dresses, the milliner for your bonnets, not mine, the "hen tailor" for your little boy's pantaloons; the plain seamstress, plain enough sometimes, for all the sewing you can't possibly get time for, and "the spinners and the knitters in the sun," or in the chimney-corner, for all your needs in the winter hosiery line. Is one of your guests dependent upon a barber? Mr. Jenkins can shave. Does your husband get *too* shaggy? Mr. Jenkins cuts hair. Does he demolish his boot upon a *grub?* Mr. Jenkins is great at a *rifacciamento*. Does Billy lose his cap in the pond? Mr. Jenkins makes caps *comme il y en a peu*. Does your bellows get the asthma? Mr. Jenkins is a famous Francis Flute.

121

Then there is Philemon Greenly has been apprenticed to a baker, and he can make you crackers, baker's-bread and round-hearts, the like of which—, but you should get *his* story. And I certainly can make long digressions, if nothing else. Here I am wandering like another Eve from my dearly beloved garden.

A bed of asparagus—I mean a dozen of them, should be among the very first cares of spring; for you must recollect, as did the Cardinal De Retz at Vincennes, that asparagus takes three years to come to the beginnings of perfection. Ours, seeded down after the Shaker fashion, promise to be invaluable. They grew so nobly the first year that the *haulm* was almost worth mowing, like the fondly-prized down on the chin of sixteen. Then, what majestic palm-leaf rhubarb, and what egg-plants! Nobody can deny that our soil amply repays whatever trouble we may bestow upon it. Even on the first turning up, it furnishes you with all the humbler luxuries in the vegetable way, from the earliest pea to the most delicate cauliflower, and the golden pumpkin, larger than Cinderella's grandmother ever saw in her dreams. Enrich it properly, and you need lack nothing that will grow north of Charlestown.

Melons, which attain a delicious perfection in our rich sandy loam, are no despicable substitute for the peaches of the older world; at least during the six or seven summers which must elapse before the latter can be abundant. I advise a prodigious melon-patch.

A fruit sometimes despised elsewhere, is here among the highly-prized treasures of the summer. The whortle-berry of Michigan is a different affair from the little half-starved thing which bears the same name elsewhere. It is of a deep rich blue, something near the size of a rifle bullet, and of a delicious sweetness. The Indians bring in immense quantities slung in panniers or mococks of bark on the sides of their wild-looking ponies; a squaw, with any quantity of papooses, usually riding a *l'Espagnole* on the ridge between them.

"Schwap? Nappanee?" is the question of the queen of

the forest; which means, "Will you exchange, or *swap*, for flour:" and you take the whortle-berries in whatever vessel you choose, returning the same measured quantity of flour.

The spirit in which the Indians buy and sell is much the same now as in the days of the renowned Wouter Van Twiller, when "the hand of a Dutchman weighed a pound, and his foot two pounds." The largest haunch of venison goes for two fingers, viz. twenty-five cents, and an entire deer for one hand, one dollar. Wild strawberries of rare size and flavor, "schwap-nappanee," which always means equal quantities. A pony, whatever be his age or qualities, two hands held up twice, with the fingers extended, twenty dollars. If you add to the price an old garment, or a blanket, or a string of glass beads, the treasure is at once put on and worn with *such* an air of "look at me." Broadway could hardly exceed it.

The Indians bring in cranberries too; and here again Michigan excels. The wild plum, so little prized elsewhere, is valued where its civilized namesake is unattainable; and the assertion frequently made that "it makes excellent *saase*," is undeniably true. But grapes! One must see the loads of grapes in order to believe.

The practical conclusion I wish to draw from all this wandering talk is that it is well worth while to make a garden in Michigan. I hope my reader will not be disposed to reply in that terse and forceful style which is cultivated at Montacute, and which has more than once been employed in answer to my enthusiastic lectures on this subject. "Taters grows in the field, and 'taters is good enough for me."

21

TINKERVILLE

I HAVE NOT SAID a single word as yet of our neighbor Tinkerville; a village whose rising fortunes have given occasion for more discussion in the select circles of Montacute than anything but the plan of the new school-house. I know this rambling gossiping style, this going back to take up dropped stitches, is not the orthodox way of telling one's story; and if I thought I could do any better, I would certainly go back and begin at the very beginning; but I feel conscious that the truly feminine sin of talking "about it and about it," the unconquerable partiality for wandering wordiness would cleave to me still; so I proceed in despair of improvement to touch upon such points in the history of Tinkerville as have seemed of vital and absorbing interest to the citizens of Montacute.

Tinkerville was originally one of the many speculations of the enterprising Mr. Mazard, and it differed from most of his landed property, in having been purchased at second hand. This fact was often mentioned in his proffers of sale, as a reason why the tract could not be afforded *quite* so low as was his general practice. He omitted to state, that he bought of a person who, having purchased at the land-office without viewing, was so entirely discouraged when he saw the woody swamp in which he was to pitch his tent, that he was glad to sell out to our speculator at a large discount, and try elsewhere on the old and sound principle of "look before you leap." The tract contained, as Mr. Mazard's advertisement fairly set forth, "almost every variety of land;" and as he did not say which kind predominated, nobody could complain if imagination played tricks, as is sometimes the case in land-purchases.

An old gentleman of some property in Massachusetts became the fortunate owner of the emblazoned chart, which Mr. Mazard had caused to set forth the advantages of his choice location. There were canals and rail-roads, with boats and cars at full speed. There was a steam-mill, a wind-mill or two; for even a land-shark did not dare to put a stream where there was scarce running water for the cattle; and a state-road, which had at least been talked of, and a court-house and other county buildings, "all very grand;" for, as the spot was not more than ten miles from the centre of the county, it might some day become the county-seat. Besides all this, there was a large and elegantly-decorated space for the name of the happy purchaser, if he chose thus to dignify his future capital.

Mr. Tinker was easily persuaded that the cherished surname of his ancestors would blend most musically with the modern and very genteel termination in which so many of our western villages glory; so Tinkerville was appointed to fill the trump of fame and the blank on the chart; and Mr. Mazard furnished with full powers, took out the charter, staked out the streets, where he could get at them, and peddled out the lots, and laid out the money, all very much to his own satisfaction; Mr. Tinker rejoicing that he had happened to obtain so "enterprising" an agent.

We were not informed what were the internal sensations of the lot-holders, when they brought their families, and came to take possession of their various "stands for business." They were wise men; and having no money to carry them back, they set about making the best of what they could find. And it is to be doubted whether Mr. Mazard's multifarious avocations permitted him to visit Tinkerville after the settlers began to come in. Many of them expressed themselves quite satisfied that there was an abundance of water there to duck a land-shark, if they could catch him near it; and Mr. Mazard was a wise man too.

While the little settlement was gradually increasing, and a store had been, as we were told, added to its many advantages and attractions, we heard that the padrone of Tinkerville had sold out; but whether from the fear that the income from his Michigan property would scarce become tangible before his great grandson's time, or whether some Bangor Mr. Mazard had offered him a tempting bargain nearer home, remains to us unknown. It was enough for Montacute to discover that the new owners were "enterprising men." This put us all upon the alert.

The Tinkervillians, who were obliged to come to us for grinding until their wind-mills could be erected, talked much of a new hotel, a school-house, and a tannery; all which, they averred, were "going up" immediately. They turned up their noses at our squint-eyed "Montacute house," expressing themselves certain of getting the county honors, and ended by trying to entice away our blacksmith. But our Mr. Porter, who "had a soul above buttons," scorned their arts, and would none of their counsel. Mr. Simeon Jenkins did, I fear, favorably incline to their side; but on its being whispered to him that Montacute had determined upon employing a singing-master next winter; he informed the ambassadors, who were no doubt spies in disguise, that he would never be so selfish as to prefer his own interest to the public good. No one thought of analyzing so patriotic a sentiment, or it might have been doubted whether Mr. Jenkins sacrificed so much in remaining to exercise his many trades, where there were twice as many people to profit by them as he would find at Tinkerville.

22

THE GRANDEUR THAT WAS TINKERVILLE

MRS. RIVERS and I had long been planning a ride on horse-back; and when the good stars were in conjunction, so that two horses and two saddles were to be had at one time, we determined to wend our resolute way as far as Tinkerville, to judge for ourselves of the state of the enemy's preparations. We set out soon after breakfast in high style; my Eclipse being Mr. Jenkins's "old Governor," seventeen last grass; and my fair companion's a twenty-dollar Indian pony, age undecided—men's saddles of course, for the settlement boasts no other as yet; and, by way of luxury, a large long-woolled sheepskin strapped over each.

We jogged on charmingly, now through woods cool and moist as the grotto of Undine, and carpeted everywhere with strawberry vines and thousands of flowers; now across strips of open land where you could look through the straight-stemmed and scattered groves for miles on each side. A marsh or two were to be passed, so said our most minute directions, and then we should come to the trail through deep woods, which would lead us in a short time to the emerging glories of our boastful neighbor.

We found the marshes, without difficulty, and soon afterwards the trail, and D'Orsay's joyous bark, as he ran far before us, told that he had made some discovery. "Deer, perhaps," said I. It was only an Indian, and when I stopped and tried to inquire whether we were in the right track, he could not be made to understand but gave the usual assenting grunt and passed on.

When I turned to speak to my companion she was so ashy pale that I feared she must fall from her horse.

"What *is* the matter, my dearest madam!" said I, going as near her as I could coax old Governor.

"The Indian! the Indian!" was all she could utter. I was terribly puzzled. It had never occurred to me that the Indians would naturally be objects of terror to a young lady who had scarcely ever seen one; and I knew we should probably meet dozens of them in the course of our short ride.

I said all I could, and she tried her best to seem courageous, and, after she had rallied her spirits a little, we proceeded, thinking the end of our journey could not be distant, especially as we saw several log-houses at intervals which we supposed were the outskirts of Tinkerville.

But we were disappointed in this; for the road led through a marsh, and then through woods again, and such tangled woods, that I began to fear, in my secret soul, that we had wandered far from our track, betrayed by D'Orsay's frolics.

I was at length constrained to hint to my pale companion my misgivings, and to propose a return to the nearest log hut for information. Without a word she wheeled her shaggy pony, and, in a few minutes, we found ourselves at the bars belonging to the last log-house we had passed.

A wretched looking woman was washing at the door.

"Can you tell us which is the road to Tinkerville?"

"Well, I guess you can't miss it if you follow your own tracks. It a'n't long since you came through it. That big stump is the middle of the public square."

23

THE MYSTERY OF BECKWORTH'S WIFE

WE RETURNED by a different and less lonely route, the Tinkervillians having very civilly directed us to one on which we should not at any point be far distant from a dwelling. The single Indian we had encountered in the morning had been quite sufficient to spoil Mrs. Rivers' ride; and we hurried on at the best pace of our sober steeds.

The country through which we were passing was so really lovely that even my timid little friend forgot her fears at times and exclaimed like a very enthusiast. At least two small lakes lay near our way; and these, of winding outline, and most dazzling brightness, seemed, as we espied them now and then through the arched vistas of the deep woods, multiplied to a dozen or more. We saw grape-vines which had so embraced large trees that the long waving pennons flared over their very tops; while the lower branches of the sturdy oaks was one undistinguishable mass of light green foliage, without an inch of bark to be seen. The roadside was piled like an exaggerated velvet with exquisitely beautiful ferns of almost every variety; and some open spots gleamed scarlet with those wild strawberries so abundant with us, and which might challenge the world for flavor.

Birds of every variety and song and hue, were not wanting, nor the lively squirrel, that most joyous of nature's pensioners; and it cost us some little care to keep D'Orsay in his post of honor as sole escort through these lonely passes. But alack! "'twas ever thus!" We had scarcely sauntered two miles when a scattered drop or two foretold that we were probably to try the melting mood. We had not noticed a cloud, but thus warned we saw portentous gatherings of these bug-bears of life.

Now if our ponies would only have gone a little faster! But they would not, so we were wet to the skin—travelling *jets d'eau*—looking doubtless very much like the western settler taking his stirrup-cup in one of Mrs. Trollope's true pictures.

When we could be no further soaked we reached a farmhouse—not a Michigan farm-house, but a great, noble, yankee "palace of pine boards," looking like a cantle of Massachusetts or western New-York dropped *par hazard,* in these remote wilds. To me who had for a long while seen nothing of dwelling kind larger than a good sized chickencoop, the scene was quite one of *eastern* enchantment. A large barn with shed and stables and poultry-yard and all! Fields of grain, well fenced and stumpless, surround this happy dwelling; and a most inviting door-yard, filled to profusion with shrubs and flowers, seemed to invite our entrance.

"A honey-suckle! absolutely a honey-suckle on the porch!" Mrs. Rivers was almost too forlorn to sympathize with me: but then she had not been quite so long from home. I have been troubled with a sort of home calenture at times since we removed westward.

We stayed not for urging, but turned our graceless steeds into the shady lane, and dismounting, not at the front entrance, but, *a la Michigan,* at the kitchen door, we were received with much grave but cordial politeness by the comely mistress of the mansion, who was sharing with her pretty daughter the after-dinner cares of the day. Our upper garments were spread to dry, and when we were equipped, with urgent hospitality, in others belonging to our hostesses, we were ushered into the parlor or "keeping room."

130

Here, writing at an old-fashioned *secretary,* sat the master of the house, a hearty, cheerful-looking, middle-aged man; evidently a person of less refinement than his wife, but still of a most prepossessing exterior. He fell no whit behind in doing the honors, and we soon found ourselves quite at our ease. We recounted the adventures of our tiny journey, and laughed at our unlucky over-running of the game.

"Ah! Tinkerville! yes, I think it will be some time yet before those dreams will come to pass. I have told Mr. Jephson there was nothing there to make a village out of."

"You are acquainted then with the present proprietors?"

"With one of them I have been acquainted since we were boys; and he has been a speculator all that time, and is now at least as poor as ever. He has been very urgent with me to sell out here and locate in his village, as he calls it; but we knew rather too much of him at home for that," and he glanced at his fair spouse with some archness. I could scarcely believe that any man could have been impudent enough to propose such an exchange, but nothing is incredible in Michigan.

Mrs. Beckworth was now engaged in getting tea, in spite of our hollow-hearted declarations that we did not wish it. With us, be it known to new comers, whatever be the hour of the day, a cup of tea with *trimmings,* is always in season; and is considered as the orthodox mode of welcoming any guest, from the clergyman to "the maid that does the meanest chores." We were soon seated at a delicately-furnished table.

The countenance of the good lady had something of peculiar interest for me. It was mild, intelligent, and very pleasing. No envious silver streaked the rich brown locks which were folded with no little elegance above the fair brow. A slight depression of the outer extremity of eye-lid, and of the delicately-pencilled arch above it, seemed to tell of sorrow and meek endurance. I was sure that like so many western settlers, the fair and pensive matron had a story; and when I had once arrived at this conclusion, I determined to make a brave push to ascertain the truth of my conjecture.

I began, while Mrs. Beckworth was absent from the parlor, by telling everything I could think of; this being the established mode of getting knowledge in this country. Mr. Beckworth did not bite.

"Is this young lady your daughter, Mr. Beckworth?"

"A daughter of my wife's—Mary Jane Harrington."

"Oh! ah! a former marriage; and the fine young man who brought us into such good quarters is a brother of Miss Harrington's I'm sure."

"A half brother—Charles Boon."

"Mrs. Beckworth thrice married! impossible!" was my not very civil but quite natural exclamation.

Our host smiled quietly, a smile which enticed me still further. He was, fortunately for my reputation for civility, too kindly polite not to consent to gratify my curiosity, which I told him sincerely had been awakened by the charming countenance of his wife, who was evidently the object of his highest admiration.

As we rode through the freshened woods with Mr. Beckworth, who had, with ready politeness, offered to see us safely a part of the way, he gave us the particulars of his early history; and to establish my claim to the character of a physiognomist, I shall here recount what he told me; and, as I cannot recollect his words, I must give this romance of rustic life in my own, taking a new chapter for it.

24

BECKWORTH TELLS HIS STORY

HENRY BECKWORTH, the eldest son of a Massachusetts farmer, of small means and many mouths, was glad to accept a situation as clerk in the comprehensive "variety store" of his cousin Ellis Irving, who was called a great merchant in the neighboring town of Langton. This cousin Ellis had fallen into the dangerous and not very usual predicament of having everybody's good word; and it was not until he failed in business, that anyone discovered that he had a fault in the world.

While he was yet in his hey-day, and before the world knew he had been so good-natured as to endorse for his wife's harum-scarum brother, his clerk, Henry Beckworth, had never dared to acknowledge, even in his dreams, that he loved to very dizziness his sweet cousin Agnes Irving. But when mortification and apoplexy had done their work upon Mr. Irving, and his delicate wife had ascertained that the remnant of her days must pass in absolute poverty, dependent for food and raiment upon her daughter's needle, Henry found his wits and his tongue, and made so good use of both, that, ere long, his cousin Agnes did not deny that she liked him very well.

Now young ladies who have been at boarding-school and learned to paint water-melons in water colors, and work Rebecca at the well in chenille and gold thread, find real, thrifty, housewifely sewing, very slow and hard work, to earn even bread and salt by; but the dove-eyed Agnes had been the sole care and pride of a genuine New England housewife, who could make hard gingerbread as well as soft, and who had plumed herself on being able to put every stitch into six fine shirts between Sunday evening and Saturday night. And so the fair child, though delicately bred, earned her mother's living and her own, with cheerful and ungrudging industry; and Henry sent all the surplus of his clerkly gains to his father, who sometimes found the cry of "crowdie, crowdie, a' the day," rather difficult to pacify.

But bye-and-bye, Mrs. Irving became so feeble that Agnes was obliged to nurse her instead of plying her skilful needle; and then matters went far astray, so that after a while the kind neighbors brought in almost all that was consumed in that sad little household; Henry Beckworth being then out of employ, and unable for the time to find any way of aiding his cousin, save by his personal services in the sick-room.

He grew almost mad under his distress, and the anxious, careful love which is the nurseling of poverty, and at length seeing Mrs. Irving's health a little amended, he gave a long, sad, farewell kiss to his Agnes and left her with an assurance that she should hear from him soon. He dared not tell her that he was quitting her to go to sea, in order that he might have immediate command of a trifling sum which he could devote to her service.

He made his way to the nearest sea-port, secured a berth before the mast in a vessel about to sail for the East Indies; and then put into a letter all the love, and hope, and fear, and caution, and encouragement, and resolution, and devotedness, that one poor sheet could carry, giving the precious document into the care of a Langton man, who was returning "direct," as he said, to the spot where poor Henry had left his senses.

This said letter told Agnes, among other things, how and when to draw on Messrs. ——, for Henry's wages, which were left subject to her order—and the lover went to sea, with a heavy heart indeed, but with a comforting security that he had done all that poverty would let him, for the idol of his heart.

An East India voyage is very long, and most people experience many a changing mood and many a wayward moment during its course; but Henry Beckworth's heart beat as if it would burst his blue jacket, when he found himself on shore again, and thought of what awaited him at Langton.

He called on Messrs. ——, to ascertain whether anything remained of his pay, and found that every dollar was untouched. At first this angered him a little; "for," as he justly argued, "if Agnes loves me as I love her—but never mind!" This I give as a fair specimen of his thoughts on his homeward journey. All his contemplations, however incoherent or wide of the mark, came invariably to one conclusion—that Agnes would surely be willing to marry him, poor as he was, rather than he should go to sea again.

It was evening, and a very dull, lead-colored evening, when the stage that contained our lover stopped at the only public-house in Langton. The True Blue Hotel, kept, as the oval sign which creaked by its side informed the grateful public, by Job Jephson (at this moment J. Jephson, Esquire, of Tinkerville, in Michigan,) the very Job Jephson to whose kindly care Henry had committed his parting letter. The stage passed on, and Mr. Beckworth paced the tessellated floor of Mr. Jephson's bar-room, until the worthy proprietor and himself were left its sole occupants.

"Why, Henry, my boy, is that you? Do tell! Why your hat was slouched over your eyes so, that I did not know you! Why, man! where on *airth* have you sprung from!"

Henry asked after everybody, and then after Agnes Irving and her mother.

"Agnes Irving!"

"Dead!" said Henry, wildly enough.

"Dead! no, married to be sure! three months ago; and this very day a week ago, her mother was buried."

It is really surprising how instantaneously pride comes to

135

one's aid on some occasions. The flashing thought of the loved one's death, had been anguish intolerable and inconcealable; the certainty of what was far worse only blanched Henry's cheek, and set his teeth firmly together while his lips questioned on, and the loquacious host of the True Blue proceeded.

"Poor Agnes saw hard times after you went away. She had to give up the house you left her in, and take a room at Mr. Truesdell's. And then Mrs. Irving did nothing but pine after the comforts she had lost, for her mind was kind o' broke up by trouble. And Agnes tried to find some other place to board, because her mother took such an awful dislike to Mrs. Truesdell; but there wasn't nobody willing to take them in, because the old lady was so particular. And so, John Harrington—you know John?—made up to her again, though she'd refused him two or three times before; and said he loved her better than ever, and that he would take her mother home and do for her as if she was his own. Now, you see, the neighbors had got pretty much tired of sending in things, because they thought Aggy oughtn't to refuse such a good offer, and so after a while John got her. After all the poor old lady did not seem to enjoy her new home, but pined away faster than ever, and said she knew Aggy had sold herself for her sake, but that was only a notion you know, for John was an excellent match for a poor——"

"Did you give my cousin the letter I handed you?" interrupted Henry.

"I'll just tell you all about that," responded Mr. Jephson, complacently drawing a chair for Henry, and inviting him to sit, as if for a long story. "I'll just tell you how that was. When you and I parted that time, I thought I was all ready for a start home; but there was a chance turned up to spekilate a little, and arter that I went down South to trade away some notions, so that when I got back to Langton it was quite cold weather, and I took off my best coat and laid it away, for where's the use of wearing good clothes under a great coat, you know? and there, to be sure was

136

your letter in the pocket of it. Well, before I found it again Agnes was getting ready to be married; and, thinks I to myself, like enough it's a love-letter, and might break off the match if she got it, gals are so foolish! so I just locked up the letter and said nothing to nobody and"—there lay Mr. Jephson on his bar-room floor.

Henry turned from the place with some glimmering of an intention to seek his lost love and tell her all, but one moment's lapse cured this madness; so he only sat down and looked at Job, who was picking himself up and talking the while.

"Man alive! what do you put yourself into such a plaguy passion for? I done it all for the best; and as to forgetting, who does not forget sometimes? Plague take you! you've given my back such a wrench I sha'n't be able to go to trainin' to-morrow, and tore my best pantaloons besides; and, arter all, you may likely thank me for it as long as you live. There's as good fish in the sea as was ever caught— but I swan! you're as white as the wall, and no mistake," and he caught the poor soul as he was falling from his chair.

"Well, now, if this doesn't beat cock-fighting!" muttered he, as he laid his insensible guest at full length on the floor and ran to the bar for some "camphire," which he administered in all haste, "to take on so about a gal without a cent, but he wont come to after all, and I shall have to bleed him:" saying which he pulled off one sleeve of Henry's jacket and proceeded in due form to the operation.

"He wont bleed, I vow! Hang the fellow! if he dies, I shall be took up for manslaughter. Why, Harry, I say!" shaking him soundly, and dragging at his arm with no gentle force. At last blood came slowly, and Beckworth became once more conscious of misery, and Mr. Jephson's tongue set out as if fresh oiled by the relief of his fears for his own safety.

"Now, Henry, don't make such a fool of yourself! You always used to be a fellow of some sconce. What can't be cured must be endured." But as Henry's lips resumed their color, and he raised himself from the floor, Mr. Jephson's habitual prudence urged him farther and farther from the reach of the well arm. His fears were groundless, however, for all that Henry now wanted was to be alone, that he might weep like a woman.

"Promise me that you will never tell anyone that I have been here this night," said he at length; "this is all I ask. Since Agnes is another man's wife, God forbid I should wish my name mentioned in her presence."

"Why, law! I'll promise that, to be sure; but you shouldn't make so much out o' nothing: Agnes has got the best house in town, and everything comfortable; and it a'n't no ways likely she would fret after *you*." And with this comforting assurance Henry prepared for departure.

"I say, Beckworth!" said Mr. Jephson as his guest left the room with his valise; "I shan't charge you anything for the bleeding."

25

BECKWORTH'S FOLLY

THE WINDOWS of heaven were opened that night. The rain descended in sheets instead of drops; and it was only by an occasional flash of paly lightning that our unfortunate was able to find the house which he well recollected for John Harrington's. There it was in all its fresh whiteness and greenness, and its deep masses of foliage, and its rich screens of honeysuckle and sweet-briar, meet residence for a happy bridegroom and his new-found treasure. The upper half of the parlor shutters were unclosed, and plainly by the clear lamp-light could Henry see the delicate papering of the walls, and the pretty French clock under its glass shade on the mantel-piece. Oh! for one glance at the table, near which he felt sure Agnes was sitting. Wild thoughts of the old song—"we took but ae kiss, an' we tore ourselves away," were coursing through his brain, and he was deliberating upon the chance that the end window, which looked on a piazza, might be free from the envious shutter, when a man ran against him in the dark. The next flash showed a great-coated figure entering the pretty rural gate to the little shrubbery; and in another moment the hall-door opened. Henry saw the interior, light and cheerful; and again all was dark.

It would have been very wrong to set the house on fire and then go and murder Job Jephson; and as Henry could not at the moment decide upon any other course of conduct, which would be at all in unison with his feelings, he set out, a human loco-motive at the top-speed, in the very teeth of the storm, on his way towards the sea-port again. The worse one feels, the faster one travels, hoping to out-run sorrow; so it did not take Henry Beckworth long to reach a neighboring town, where he could find a stage-coach; and he was far at sea again in the course of a very few days.

His *outre-mer* adventures are of no importance to my story—how, as he stood with two or three mess-mates, staring, like a true Yankee, at the Tower of London, a press-gang seized them all, and rowed them to a vessel which lay off the Traitors' Gate, the Americans protesting themselves as such, and the John Bulls laughing at them;—how, when they got on board the man o' war, they showed their pro-tections, and the officer of his Majesty's recruiting service said he could do nothing in the case till the ship returned from her cruize—and how the ship did not return from her cruize, but after cruizing about for some three years or more, was taken by a French first-rate and carried into Brest. All this is but little to the purpose. But when Henry was thrown into a French prison, his American certificate procured his release through the consul's good offices, and he shipped at once for New-York, somewhat weary of a sea life.

At New-York he learned from a townsman whom he met there that Agnes Harrington had been two years a widow.

"Is she rich?" asked Henry. A strange question for a true lover.

"Rich!—Lord bless ye! John Harrington wasn't worth *that;*" snapping his fingers most expressively. "His property was under mortgage to such an extent, that all it would sell for wouldn't clear it. His widow and child will not have a cent after old Horner forecloses, as he is now about doing. And Mrs. Harrington's health is very poor, though to my thinking she's prettier than ever."

Henry's movements were but little impeded by baggage, and the journey to Langton was performed in a short time. Once more was he set down at Job Jephson's; and there

140

was day-light enough this time to see, besides the oval sign before hinted at, which had for years held out hopes of "Entertainment for man and beast," a legend over the door in great white characters, "Post Office,"—"good business for Job," thought Henry Beckworth,—a board in one window setting forth, "Drugs and Medicines," and a card in the other, "Tailoring done here."

Slight salutation contented Henry, when the man of letters made his appearance, and he requested a horse to carry him as far as his father's, saying he would send for his trunk in the morning. Mr. Jephson made some little difficulty and delay, but Henry seemed in fiery haste. In truth he hated the sight of Job beyond all reason; but that complacent personage seemed to have forgotten, very conveniently, all former passages in that memorable bar-room.

"You don't ask after your old friends, Harry," said he. "A good many things has altered here since I see you last. You came that time a little too late."

Henry looked dirks at the fellow, but he went on as coldly as ever.

"Now this time, to my thinkin', you've come a *leetle* too soon."

Henry tried not to ask him what he meant; but for his life he could not help it.

"Why, I mean, if John Harrington's widow has not more sense than I think she has, you've come in time to spoil a good match."

"A match!" was all that Henry could say.

"Aye, a match; for Colonel Boon came from there yesterday, and sent for old Horner here to this blessed house, and took up the mortgage on Harrington's property; and everybody knows he has been after Aggy this twelvemonth, offering to marry her and clear the property, and do well by the child. And if there's a good man on airth, Boon is that man, and everybody knows it."

What did Henry Beckworth now? He un-ordered his horse, and went quietly to bed.

141

26

THE WINNING OF AGNES

HENRY BECKWORTH came from the hand of Nature abundantly furnished with that excellent qualification known and revered throughout New England, under the expressive name of "spunk." This quality at first prompted him, spite of the croakings of the ill-omened Job, to present himself before the one only object of his constant soul, to tell her all, and to ask her to share with him the weal or wo which might yet be in store for him. But he had now seen a good deal of this excellent world, and the very indifferent people who transact its affairs. He had tasted the tender mercies of a British man o' war, and the various *agrémens* of a French prison; and the practical conclusion which had gradually possessed itself of his mind, was, that money is, beyond all dispute, one of the necessaries of life.

No way of making money off-hand occurred to him as he tossed and groaned through the endless hours of that weary night. He had neither house nor land, nor yet a lottery ticket—nor a place under government—and the chest which stood at his bed-side, though it contained enough of this world's goods to keep his fair proportions from the weather; and a sea-journal—a love-log—which he hoped might one day, by some romantic chance, come into the fair hands of his beloved, and give her to guess how his sad life had passed—held as he well knew, nothing which she could in anywise eat, or that she would be probably willing, under any contingency to put on.

142

I feel proud of my hero. He was "a man of deeds, not words." He loved Agnes so well, that before morning shone on his haggard cheek, he had determined to turn his back forever on the home of his youth, the scene of his first love-dream; and to seek his dark fortune far away from the place which held all that his heart prized on earth.

This resolution once taken, he arose and addressed himself to his sad journey, waiting only the earliest beam of light before he wakened Mr. Jephson. This worthy commended much his prudent course, and recommended a long journey; an attempt to discover the North-West Passage, or to ascertain the truth of Capt. Symmes' theory; to take the nonsense out of him and make a little money.

For five long years did Henry Beckworth box the compass; five years of whaling voyages and all their attendant hardships—and when at the end of that time he retouched his native shore, richer than he had ever been before in his life, he heard, as the reader will no doubt anticipate, that Agnes Boon was again unmated; her worthy Colonel having been killed by a fall from his horse in less than two years from his marriage.

Yet did our phoenix of lovers approach the village which he had vowed never to see again, with many more misgivings than he had experienced on former occasions. Years and a rough life he was well aware had changed him much. He thought of his Agnes, fair and graceful as a snow-drop, and feared lest his weather-beaten visage might find no favor in her eyes. Yet he determined that this time nothing, not even that screech-owl Job Jephson, should prevent him from seeing her, face to face, and learning his fate from her own lips.

He approached Langton by a road that passed not near the detested house of man and horse entertainment, and was just emerging from a thick grove which skirted the village on that side, when he came near riding over a man who seemed crouched on the ground as if in search of something, and muttering to himself the while. The face that turned hastily round was Job Jephson's.

"Why, it a'n't! Yes, I'll be switched if it isn't Henry Beck-worth rose from the dead!" said this fated tormentor; and he fastened himself on the bridle-rein in such sort, that Henry could not rid himself of his company without switching him in good earnest.

"Here was I, looking up some little things for my steam doctorin' business," said Mr. Jephson, "and little thinkin' of anybody in the world; and you must come along jist like a sperrit. But I've a notion you've hit it about right this time. I s'pose you know Aggy's a rich widow by this time, don't ye?"

Henry vouchsafed no reply, though he found it very difficult to maintain a dignified reserve, when so many questions were clustering on his lips. But it was all one to Job —question or no question, answer or no answer, he would talk on, and on, and on.

"I'll tell ye what," he continued, "I shouldn't wonder if Aggy looked higher now, for she's a good spec for any man. I see you've smarted up a good deal, but don't be cock-sure—for there's others that would be glad to take her and her two children. I've been a thinkin' myself——"

And now Henry gave Job such a switch across the knuckles as effectually cleared the bridle, and changed the current of the steam-doctor's thoughts. In half an hour he rang at Mrs. Boon's door, and was ushered at once into her presence.

"Mr. Beckworth, ma'am," said the little waiting-maid as she threw open the parlor door.

Agnes, the beloved, rose from her seat—sat down again —tried to speak, and burst into tears; while Henry looked on her countenance—changed indeed, but still lovely in matronly dignity—more fondly than in the days of his lighter youthful love; and seating himself beside her, began at the wrong end of the story, as most people do in such cases, talking as if it were a thing of course that his twice-widowed love should become his wife.

"Marry again! oh, never!"—that was entirely out of the question; and she wiped her eyes and asked her cousin to

144

stay to dinner. But Henry deferred his ultimatum on this important point, till he should have ravelled out the whole web of his past life before the dewy eyes of his still fair mistress, till he should tell her all his love—no, that he could never fully tell, but some of the proofs of it at least, and that first horrible forget of Job Jephson's. And when this was told in many words, Agnes, all sighs and tears, still said no, but so much more faintly that Mr. Beckworth thought he would stay to dinner. And then—but why should I tell the rest, when the reader of my true-love story has already seen Mrs. Beckworth like a fair but full-blown China-rose—Mr. Beckworth with *bien content* written on every line of his handsome middle-aged face—Mary Jane Harrington a comely marriageable lass, and George Boon a strapping youth of eighteen—all flourishing on an oak opening in the depths of Michigan?

Let none imagine that this tale of man's constancy must be the mere dream of my fancy. I acknowledge nothing but the prettinesses. To Henry Beckworth himself I refer the incredulous, and if they do not recognize my story in his, I cannot help it. Even a woman can do no more than her best.

27

MISS ELOISE FIDLER

AN ADDITION to our Montacute first circle had lately appeared in the person of Miss Eloise Fidler, an elder sister of Mrs. Rivers, who was to spend some months "in this peaceful retreat,"—to borrow one of her favorite expressions.

This young lady was not as handsome as she would fain have been, if I may judge by the cataracts of ash-colored ringlets which shaded her cheeks, and the exceeding straitness of the stays which restrained her somewhat exuberant proportions. Her age was at a stand; but I could never discover exactly where, for this point proved an exception to the general communicativeness of her disposition. I guessed it at eight-and-twenty; but perhaps she would have judged this uncharitable, so I will not insist. Certain it is that it must have taken a good while to read as many novels and commit to memory as much poetry, as lined the head and exalted the sensibilities of our fair visitant.

Her dress was in the height of fashion, and all her accoutrements *point de vice*. A gold pencil-case of the most delicate proportions was suspended by a kindred chain round a neck which might be called whity-brown; and a note-book of corresponding lady-like-ness was peeping from the pocket of her highly-useful apron of blue silk— ever ready to secure a passing thought or an elegant quotation. Her album—she was just the person to have an album—was resplendent in gold and satin, and the verses which meandered over its emblazoned pages were of the most unexceptionable quality, overlaid with flowers and gems—love and despair. To find any degree of appropriateness in these various offerings, one must allow the fortunate possessor of the purple volume, at least all the various perfections of an Admirable Crichton, allayed in some small measure by the trifling faults of coldness, fickleness, and deceit; and to judge of Miss Fidler's friends by their hand-writing, they must have been able to offer an edifying variety of bumps to the fingers of the phrenologist. But here is the very book itself at my elbow, waiting these three months, I blush to say, for a contribution which has yet to be pumped up from my unwilling brains; and I have a mind to steal a few specimens from its already loaded pages, for the benefit of the distressed, who may, like myself, be at their wits' end for something to put in just such a book.

The first page, rich with embossed lilies, bears the invocation, written in a great black spattering hand, and wearing the air of defiance. It runs thus:

> If among the names of the stainless few
>   Thine own hath maintain'd a place,
> Come dip thy pen in the sable dew
>   And with it this volume grace.
>
> But oh! if thy soul e'er encouraged a thought
>   Which purity's self might blame,
> Close quickly the volume, and venture not
>   To sully its snows with thy name.

Then we come to a wreath of flowers of gorgeous hues, within whose circle appears in a *miminee piminee* hand, evidently a young lady's—

THE WREATH OF SLEEP.

> Oh let me twine this glowing wreath
>   Amid those rings of golden hair,

'T will soothe thee with its odorous breath
　To sweet forgetfulness of care.

'T is form'd of every scented flower
　That flings its fragrance o'er the night;
And gifted with a fairy power
　To fill thy dreams with forms of light.

'T was braided by an angel boy
　When fresh from Paradise he came
To fill our earth-born hearts with joy—
　Ah! need I tell the cherub's name?

This contributor I have settled in my own mind to be a descendant of Anna Matilda, the high-priestess of the Della-Cruscan order. The next blazon is an interesting view of a young lady, combing her hair. As she seems not to have been long out of bed, the lines which follow are rather appropriate, though I feel sure they come from the expert fingers of a merchant's clerk—from the finished elegance, and very sweeping tails of the chirography.

MORNING.

Awake! arise! art thou slumbering still?
When the sun is above the mapled hill,
And the shadows are flitting fast away,
And the dews are diamond beneath his ray,
And every bird in our vine-roofed bower
Is waked into song by the joyous hour;
Come, banish sleep from thy gentle eyes,
Sister! sweet sister! awake! arise!

Yet I love to gaze on thy lids of pearl,
And to mark the wave of the single curl
That shades in its beauty thy brow of snow,
And the cheek that lies like a rose below;
And to list to the murmuring notes that fall
From thy lips, like music in fairy hall.
But it must not be—the sweet morning flies
Ere thou hast enjoyed it! awake! arise!

148

There is balm on the wings of this freshen'd air;
'T will make thine eyes brighter, thy brow more fair,
And a deep, deep rose on thy cheek shall be
The meed of an early walk with me.
We will seek the shade by the green hill side,
Or follow the clear brook's whispering tide;
And brush the dew from the violet's eyes—
Sister! sweet sister! awake! arise!

This I transcribe for the good advice which it contains.
And what have we here? It is tastefully headed by an engraving of Hero and Ursula in the "pleached bower," and
Beatrice running "like a lap-wing" in the background. It
begins ominously.

TO ——.

Oh, look upon this pallid brow!
    Say, canst thou there discern one trace
Of that proud soul which oft ere now
    Thou'st sworn shed radiance o'er my face?
Chill'd is that soul—its darling themes,
    Thy manly honour, virtue, truth
Prove now to be but fleeting dreams,
    Like other lovely thoughts of youth.

Meet, if thy coward spirit dare,
    This sunken eye; say, dost thou see
The rays thou saidst were sparkling there
    When first its gaze was turn'd on thee?
That eye's young light is quench'd forever;
    No change its radiance can repair:
Will Joy's keen touch relume it? Never!
    It gleams the watch-light of Despair.

I find myself growing hoarse by sympathy, and I shall
venture only a single extract more, and this because Miss
Fidler declares it, without exception, the sweetest thing she
ever read. It is written with a crow-quill, and has other

149

marks of femininity. Its vignette is a little girl and boy playing at battle-door.

BALLAD.

The deadly strife was over, and across the field of fame,
With anguish in his haughty eye, the Moor Almanzor came;
He prick'd his fiery courser on among the scatter'd dead,
Till he came at last to what he sought, a sever'd human head.

It might have seem'd a maiden's, so pale it was, and fair;
But the lip and chin were shaded till they match'd the raven hair.
There lingered yet upon the brow a spirit bold and high,
And the stroke of death had scarcely closed the piercing eagle
    eye.

Almanzor grasp'd the flowing locks, and he staid not in his flight,
Till he reach'd a lonely castle's gate where stood a lady bright.
"Inez! behold thy paramour!" he loud and sternly cried,
And threw his ghastly burden down, close at the lady's side.

"I sought thy bower at even-tide, thou syren, false as fair!
"And would that I had rather died! I found yon stripling there.
"I turn'd me from the hated spot, but I swore by yon dread
    Heaven,
"To know no rest until my sword the traitor's life had riven."

The lady stood like stone until he turn'd to ride away,
And then she oped her marble lips, and wildly did she say:
"Alas, alas! thou cruel Moor, what is it thou hast done?
"This was my brother Rodriguez, my father's only son."

And then before his frenzied eyes, like a crush'd lily bell,
Lifeless upon the bleeding head, the gentle Inez fell.
He drew his glittering ataghan—he sheath'd it in his side—
And for his Spanish ladye-love the Moor Almanzor died.

This is not a very novel incident, but young ladies like stories of love and murder, and Miss Fidler's tastes were peculiarly young-lady-like. She praised Ainsworth and James, but thought Bulwer's works "very immoral," though

I never could discover that she had more than skimmed the story from any of them. Cooper she found "pretty;" Miss Sedgwick, "pretty well, only her characters are such common sort of people."

Miss Fidler wrote her own poetry, so that she had ample employment for her time while with us in the woods. It was unfortunate that she could not walk out much on account of her shoes. She was obliged to make out with diluted inspiration. The nearest approach she usually made to the study of Nature, was to sit on the wood-pile, under a girdled tree, and there, with her gold pencil in hand, and her "eyne, grey as glas," rolled upwards, poefy by the hour. Several people, and especially one marriageable lady of a certain age, felt afraid Miss Fidler was "kind o' crazy."

And, standing marvel of Montacute, no guest at morning or night ever found the fair Eloise ungloved. Think of it! In the very wilds to be always like a cat in nutshells, alone useless where all are so busy! I do not wonder our good neighbors thought the damsel a little touched. And then her shoes! "Saint Crispin Crispianus" never had so self-sacrificing a votary. No shoemaker this side of New-York could make a sole papery enough; no tannery out of France could produce materials for this piece of exquisite feminine foppery. Eternal imprisonment within doors, except in the warmest and driest weather, was indeed somewhat of a price to pay, but it was ungrudged. The sofa and its footstool, finery and novels, *would* have made a delicious world for Miss Eloise Fidler, *if*——

But, alas! "all this availeth me nothing," has been ever the song of poor human nature. The mention of that unfortunate name includes the only real, personal, pungent distress which had as yet shaded the lot of my interesting heroine. Fidler! In the mortification adhering to so unpoetical, so unromantic, so inelegant a surname—a name irredeemable even by the highly classical elegance of the Eloise, or the fair lady herself pronounced it, "Elovees;" in this lay all her wo; and the grand study of her life had been to sink this hated cognomen in one more congenial

151

to her taste. Perhaps this very anxiety had defeated itself; at any rate, here she was at —— I did not mean to touch on the ungrateful guess again, but at least at mateable years; neither married, nor particularly likely to be married.

Mrs. Rivers was the object of absolute envy to the pining Eloise. "Anna had been so fortunate," she said; "Rivers was the sweetest name! and Harley was such an elegant fellow!"

We thought poor Anna had been anything but fortunate. She might better have been Fidler or Fiddle-string all her life than to have taken the name of an indifferent and dissipated husband. But not so thought Miss Fidler. It was not long after the arrival of the elegant Eloise, that the Montacute Lyceum held its first meeting in Mr. Simeon Jenkins's shop, lighted by three candles, supported by candelabra of scooped potatoes; Mr. Jenkins himself sitting on the head of a barrel as president. At first the debates of the institute were held with closed doors; but after the youthful or less practised speakers had tried their powers for a few evenings, the Lyceum was thrown open to the world every Tuesday evening, at six o'clock. The list of members was not very select as to age, character, or standing; and it soon included the entire gentility of the town, and some who scarce claimed rank elsewhere. The attendance of the ladies was particularly requested; and the whole fair sex of Montacute made a point of showing occasionally the interest they undoubtedly felt in the gallant knights who tilted in this field of honor.

But I must not be too diffuse—I was speaking of Miss Fidler. One evening—I hope that beginning prepares the reader for something highly interesting—one evening the question to be debated was the equally novel and striking one which regards the comparative mental capacity of the sexes; and as it was expected that some of the best speakers on both sides would be drawn out by the interesting nature of the subject, everybody was anxious to attend.

Among the rest was Miss Fidler, much to the surprise of

152

A woodcut from the *Western Miscellany* showing how logs were raised into position. This is more fanciful than exact in certain particulars. Casks and jugs in the foreground were the cause of many bad accidents, as Mrs. Kirkland points out. (*Chapter 41*)

A log tavern sketched by a British traveler in Western New York in 1808. It is identical with the more elaborate of the Michigan log taverns of 1837. Note the "stick" chimney, and the bow-top wagons. The garbage disposal system of the frontier is in the foreground. (*Chapter 2*)

The earliest type of Michigan cabin. It was built as a shelter until a more substantial dwelling could be erected. In this instance, after the family had moved into its frame house, the cabin was used as a barn. Later the plank addition was added to enlarge it. Photograph taken in the 1880's, probably as a sentimental record of the original homestead. (*Chapter 5*)

A settler's clearing in Ohio as recorded by the artist Thomas Wharton in 1831. It is identical with similar clearings in Michigan. It is interesting to compare the house-cabin with that previously shown in a photograph. Note fences, and the "spring house" in the foreground, which indicate that these settlers were not

A view of Detroit in 1836 when the Kirklands taught at the Detroit Female Seminary, now the site of City Hall. The city's splendor is somewhat magnified. In 1836, a thousand emigrants a day, during the shipping season alone, poured through Detroit on their way to the interior. (*Chapter 8*)

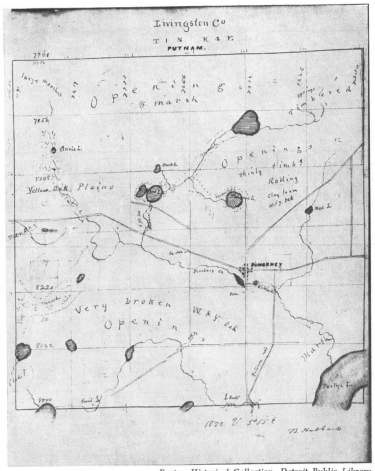

Burton Historical Collection, Detroit Public Library

Township map of Putnam, Livingston County, showing village of
Pinckney about 1838-39. The star, southeast of the village, inscribed
"Kirkland" indicates the millsite. Each rectangle represents a square
mile. Some idea of the prevalence of marshes and swamps can be
gained from this survey map. (*Chapter 3*)

The frame house built by the Kirklands in Pinckney, Michigan, in 1837. Probably the ell was added later. Mrs. Kirkland, in a letter to N. P. Willis in January 1838, speaks of having moved from the loggery, so it is probable that the house was occupied by the end of 1837. Used as a storage catch-all for many years, it was finally torn down in 1925. (*Chapter 13*)

The Hart portrait published in 1852. Mrs. Kirkland would not allow her features to be reproduced. This engraving was made in London apparently during her first trip abroad. A contemporary photograph indicates that her features were sharper, more "Yankee," with an expression of intelligence not so clearly shown in this romanticized drawing. (*Chapter 14*)

Mrs. Campaspe Nippers listening to a whispered confidence from across the room. A Darley illustration for *A New Home.* (*Chapter* 33)

Mrs. Clavers and Mrs. Rivers returning from Tinkersville in the rain. The beast in the foreground is D'Orsay. This and the preceding illustration were made by Darley in 1849 for a forthcoming edition of *A New Home*. In general, Darley's illustrations for Mrs. Kirkland have little reference or distinction as factual frontier pictures.
(*Chapter 23*)

Broadway in 1836 when it was the principal and fashionable thoroughfare in New York. Mrs. Kirkland's
"two girls" Broadway bears in the background of her mind as the civilized contrast.

A tavern in Deerborn, west of Detroit, in 1834. There is little essential difference from the earlier New York State tavern previously shown, although the pigs are no longer unconfined. (From William Nowlin's *The Bark Covered House*, an early narrative of the Michigan frontier.)

A settler's clearing drawn in 1831 by Wharton. Certain refinements, including a porch and additional "stick" chimneys, have been added. The dead trees have died from being girdled, and those in the woods show the continuing clearing. The even growth at the end of the house-ell is apparently an orchard since it is also enclosed by a rail fence to keep out cattle. Its size as well as the additions to the house indicate a settlement

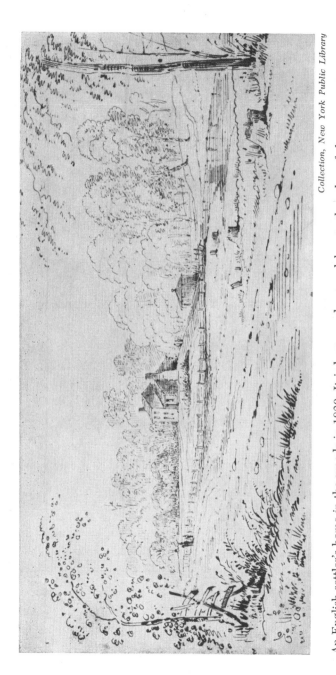

An English settler's home in the woods in 1830. It is larger and more elaborate than that of the average American emigrant. Something of a villa rather than a farm house, its site was chosen partly from aesthetic considerations. This was the Western home of Thomas Wharton, the artist who became later the architect of the much admired U.S. Customs House in New Orleans. (*Chapter 34*)

An Amsterdam interpretation of life on the frontier from the notes of a Dutch settler in Illinois in 1835. Despite the imaginative touches, which seem drawn from more tropical re-gions, it does record an actual practice, in factual detail. (Chapter 18)

The evolved log-house as it continued in use. Its careful construction, in contrast to the earlier type, is indicated by the dovetailing at the corners, the tight liners inserted in the logs before chinking, and the care with which the window frame is fitted. The open loft of which Mrs. Kirkland writes is partially observed in the attic. The porched addition, usually a summer kitchen, was added many years later. Many of these houses still exist, unsuspected by the present occupants, the exterior covered with clapboards. (*Chapter 52*)

Burning trees in a girdled clearing. This was the first step in extensive clearing, particularly for quick pasturage in heavily wooded areas, since grass grew quickly once the shade was removed. The interlacing of roots, however, made it difficult to plough, and both trees and roots had to be removed for tillable fields. (*Chapter 43*)

her sister and myself, who had hitherto been so unfashionable as to deny ourselves this gratification.

"What new whim possesses you, Eloise?" said Mrs. Rivers; "you who never go out in the day-time."

"Oh, just *per passy le tong*," said the young lady, who was a great French scholar; and go she would and did.

The debate was interesting to absolute breathlessness, both of speakers and hearers, and was gallantly decided in favor of the fair by a youthful member who occupied the barrel as president for the evening. He gave it as his decided opinion, that if the natural and social disadvantages under which woman labored and must ever continue to labor, could be removed; if their education could be entirely different, and their position in society the reverse of what it is at present, they would be very nearly, if not quite, equal to the nobler sex, in all but strength of mind, in which very useful quality it was his opinion that man would still have the advantage, especially in those communities whose energies were developed by the aid of debating societies.

This decision was hailed with acclamations, and as soon as the question for the ensuing debate, "which is the more useful animal the ox or the ass?" was announced, Miss Eloise Fidler returned home to rave of the elegant young man who sat on the barrel, whom she had decided to be one of "Nature's aristocracy," and whom she had discovered to bear the splendid appellative of Dacre. "Edward Dacre," said she, "for I heard the rude creature Jenkins call him Ed."

The next morning witnessed another departure from Miss Fidler's usual habits. She proposed a walk; and observed that she had never yet bought an article at the store, and really felt as if she ought to purchase something. Mrs. Rivers chancing to be somewhat occupied, Miss Fidler did me the honor of a call, as she could not think of walking without a chaperon.

Behind the counter at Skinner's I saw for the first time a spruce young clerk, a really well-looking young man, who

153

made his very best bow to Miss Fidler, and served us with much assiduity. The young lady's purchases occupied some time, and I was obliged gently to hint home-affairs before she could decide between two pieces of muslin, which she declared to be so nearly alike, that it was almost impossible to say which was the best.

When we were at length on our return, I was closely questioned as to my knowledge of "that gentleman," and on my observing that he seemed to be a very decent young man, Miss Fidler warmly justified him from any such opinion, and after a glowing eulogium on his firm countenance, his elegant manners and his grace as a debater, concluded by informing me, as if to cap the climax, that his name was Edward Dacre.

I had thought no more of the matter for some time, though I knew Mr. Dacre had become a frequent visitor at Mr. Rivers', when Mrs. Rivers came to me one morning with a perplexed brow, and confided to me her sisterly fears that Eloise was about to make a fool of herself, as she had done more than once before.

"My father," she said, "hoped in this remote corner of creation Eloise might forget her nonsense and act like other people; but I verily believe she is bent upon encouraging this low fellow, whose principal charm in her bewildered eyes is his name."

"His name?" said I, "pray explain;" for I had not then learned all the boundless absurdity of this new Cherubina's fancies.

"Edward Dacre!" said my friend, "this is what enchants my sister, who is absolutely mad on the subject of her own homely appellation."

"Oh, is that all?" said I, "send her to me, then; and I engage to dismiss her cured."

And Miss Fidler came to spend the day. We talked of all novels without exception, and all poetry of all magazines, and Miss Fidler asked me if I had read the "Young Duke." Upon my confessing as much, she asked my opinion of the heroine, and then if I had ever heard so sweet a name. "May

Dacre—May Dacre," she repeated, as if to solace her delighted ears.

"Only think how such names are murdered in this country," said I, tossing carelessly before her an account of Mr. Skinner's which bore, "Edkins Daker" below the receipt. I never saw a change equal to that which seemed to "come o'er the spirit of her dream." I went on with my citations of murdered names, telling how Rogers was turned into Rudgers, Conway into Coniway, and Montague into Montaig, but poor Miss Fidler was no longer in talking mood; and, long before the day was out, she complained of a head-ache and returned to her sister's. Mr. Daker found her "not at home" that evening; and when I called next morning, the young lady was in bed, steeping her long ringlets in tears, real tears.

To hasten to the catastrophe: it was discovered ere long that Mr. Edkins Daker's handsome face, and really pleasant manners, had fairly vanquished Miss Fidler's romance, and she had responded to his professions of attachment with a truth and sincerity, which while it vexed her family inexpressibly, seemed to me to atone for all her follies. Mr. Daker's prospects were by no means despicable, since a small capital employed in merchandize in Michigan, is very apt to confer upon the industrious and fortunate possessor that crowning charm, without which handsome faces, and even handsome names, are quite worthless in our western eyes.

Some little disparity of age existed between Miss Fidler and her adorer; but this was conceded by all to be abundantly made up for by the superabounding gentility of the lady; and when Mr. Daker returned from New-York with his new stock of goods and his stylish bride, I thought I had seldom seen a happier or better mated couple. And at this present writing, I do not believe Eloise, with all her whims, would exchange her very nice Edkins for the proudest Dacre of the British Peerage.

155

28

THE NEWLANDS

THERE IS in our vicinity one class of settlers whose condition has always been inexplicable to me. They seem to work hard, to dress wretchedly, and to live in the most uncomfortable style in all respects, apparently denying themselves and their families everything beyond the absolute necessities of life. They complain most bitterly of poverty. They perform the severe labor which is shunned by their neighbors; they purchase the coarsest food, and are not too proud to ask for an old coat or a pair of cast boots, though it is always with the peculiar air of dignity and "don't care," which is characteristic of the country.

Yet instead of increasing their means by these penurious habits, they grow poorer every day. Their dwellings are more and more out of repair. There are more and more shingles in the windows, old hats and red petticoats cannot be spared; and an increasing dearth of cows, pigs, and chickens. The daughters go to service, and the sons "chore round" for everybody and anybody; and even the mamma, the centre of dignity, is fain to go out washing by the day.

A family of this description had fallen much under our notice. The father and his stout sons had performed a good deal of hard work in our service, and the females of the family had been employed on many occasions when "help" was scarce. Many requests for cast articles, or those of trifling value had been proffered during the course of our acquaintance; and in several attacks of illness, such comforts as our house afforded had been frequently sought, though no visit was ever requested.

They had been living through the summer in a shanty, built against a sloping bank, with a fire-place dug in the hill-side, and a hole pierced through the turf by way of a chimney. In this den of some twelve feet square, the whole family had burrowed since April; but in October, a log-house of the ordinary size was roofed in, and though it had neither door nor window, nor chimney, nor hearth, they removed, and felt much elated with the change. Something like a door was soon after swinging on its leathern hinges, and the old man said they were now quite comfortable, though he should like to get a window!

The first intelligence we received from them after this, was that Mr. Newland, the father, was dangerously ill with inflammation of the lungs. This was not surprising, for a quilt is but a poor substitute for a window during a Michigan November. A window was supplied, and such alleviations as might be collected were contributed by several of the neighbors. The old man lingered on, much to my surprise, and after two or three weeks we heard that he was better, and would be able to "kick round" pretty soon.

It was not long after, that we were enjoying the fine sleighing, which is usually so short-lived in this lakey region. The roads were not yet much beaten, and we had small choice in our drives, not desiring the troublesome honor of leading the way. It so happened that we found ourselves in the neighborhood of Mr. Newland's clearing; and though the sun was low, we thought we might stop a moment to ask how the old man did.

We drove to the door, and so noiseless was our approach, guiltless of bells, that no one seemed aware of our coming. We tapped, and heard the usual reply, "Walk!" which I used to think must mean "Walk off."

I opened the door very softly, fearing to disturb the sick man; but I found this caution quite mal-apropos. Mrs. Newland was evidently in high holiday trim. The quilts had been removed from their stations round the bed, and the old man, shrunken and miserable-looking enough, sat on a chair in the corner. The whole apartment bore the marks of expected hilarity. The logs over-head were completely shrouded by broad hemlock boughs fastened against them; and evergreens of various kinds were disposed in all directions, while three tall slender candles, with the usual potato supporters, were placed on the cupcoard shelf.

On the table, a cloth seemed to cover a variety of refreshments; and in front of this cloth stood a tin pail, nearly full of a liquid whose odor was but too discernible; and on the whiskey, for such it seemed, swam a small tin cup. But I forget the more striking part of the picture, the sons and daughters of the house. The former flaming in green stocks and scarlet watch-guards, whilst the cut of their long dangling coats showed that whoever they might once have fitted, they were now exceedingly out of place; the latter decked in tawdry, dirty finery, and wearing any look but that of the modest country maiden, who, "in choosing her garments, counts no bravery in the world like decency."

The eldest girl, Amelia, who had lived with me at one time, had been lately at a hotel in a large village at some distance, and had returned but a short time before, not improved either in manners or reputation. Her tall commanding person was arrayed in far better taste than her sisters', and by contrast with the place and circumstances, she wore really a splendid air. Her dress was of rich silk, made in the extreme mode, and set off by elegant jewelry. Her black locks were drest with scarlet berries; most elaborate pendants of wrought gold hung almost to her shoulders; and above her glittering basilisk eyes, was a gold chain with a handsome clasp of coral. The large hands were covered with elegant gloves, and an embroidered handkerchief was carefully arranged in her lap.

I have attempted to give some idea of the appearance of things in this wretched log-hut, but I cannot pretend to paint the confusion into which our ill-timed visit threw the family, who had always appeared before us in such different characters. The mother asked us to sit down, however, and Mr. Newland muttered something, from which I gathered, that "the girls thought they must have a kind of a house-warmin' like."

We made our visit very short, of course; but before we could make our escape, an old fellow came in with a violin, and an ox-sled approached the door, loaded with young people of both sexes, who were all "spilt" into the deep snow, by a "mistake on purpose" of the driver. In the scramble which ensued, we took leave; wondering no longer at the destitution of the Newlands, or of the other families of the same class, whose young people we had recognized in the mêlée.

The Newland family did not visit us as usual after this. There was a certain consciousness in their appearance when we met, and the old man more than once alluded to our accidental discovery with evident uneasiness. He was a person not devoid of shrewdness, and he was aware that the utter discrepancy between his complaints, and the appearances we had witnessed, had given us but slight opinion of his veracity; and for some time we were almost strangers to each other.

How was I surprised some two months after at being called out of bed by a most urgent message from Mrs. Newland, that Amelia, her eldest daughter, was dying! The messenger could give no account of her condition, but that she was now in convulsions, and her mother despairing of her life.

I lost not a moment, but the way was long, and ere I entered the house, the shrieks of the mother and her children told me I had come too late. Struck with horror, I almost hesitated whether to proceed, but the door was opened, and I went in. Two or three neighbors with terrified countenances stood near the bed, and on it lay the remains of the poor girl, swollen and discolored, and already so changed in appearance that I should not have recognized it elsewhere.

I asked for particulars, but the person whom I addressed shook her head and declined answering; and there was altogether an air of horror and mystery which I was entirely unable to understand. Mrs. Newland, in her lamentations, alluded to the suddenness of the blow, and when I saw her a little calmed, I begged to know how long Amelia had been ill, expressing my surprise that I had heard nothing of it. She turned upon me as if I had stung her.

"What, you've heard their lies too, have ye?" she exclaimed fiercely, and she cursed in no measured terms those who meddled with what did not concern them. I felt much shocked; and disclaiming all intention of wounding her feelings, I offered the needful aid, and when all was finished, returned home uninformed as to the manner of Amelia Newland's death.

Yet I could not avoid noticing that all was not right. "Oft have I seen a timely-parted ghost Of ashy semblance, meagre, pale and bloodless—" but the whole appearance of this sad wreck was quite different from that of any corpse I had ever viewed before. Nothing was done, but much was said or hinted on all sides. Rumor was busy as usual; and I have been assured by those who ought to have warrant for their assertions, that this was but one fatal instance out of the *many cases,* wherein life was perilled in the desperate effort to elude the "slow unmoving finger" of public scorn.

That the class of settlers to which the Newlands belong, a class but too numerous in Michigan, is a vicious and degraded one, I cannot doubt: but whether the charge to which I have but alluded, is in any degree just, I am unable to determine. I can only repeat, "I say the tale as 't was said to me," and I may add that more than one instance of a similar kind, though with results less evidently fatal, has since come under my knowledge.

The Newlands have since left this part of the country, driving off with their own, as many of their neighbors' cattle and hogs as they could persuade to accompany them; and not forgetting one of the train of fierce dogs which have not only shown ample sagacity in getting their own

160

living, but, "gin a' tales be true," assisted in supporting the family by their habits of nightly prowling.

I passed by their deserted dwelling. They had carried off the door and window, and some boys were busy pulling the shingles from the roof to make quail-traps. I trust we have few such neighbors left. Texas and the Canada war have done much for us in this way; and the wide west is rapidly drafting off those whom we shall regret as little as the Newlands.

29

A FOREST FIRE AND A BROKEN DAM

As I HAVE NEVER MADE any remarkable progress in the heights and depths of meteorology, I am unable to speak with confidence as to the concatenation of causes which may withhold from this fertile peninsula the treasures of the clouds, in the early Spring-time, when our land elsewhere is saturated even to repletion with the "milky nutriment." In plain terms, I cannot tell anything about the reason why we have such dry Springs in Michigan, I can only advert to the fact as occasioning scenes rather striking to the new comer.

In April, instead of the "misty-moisty morning," which proverbially heralds the "uncertain glory" of the day in that much belied month, the sun, day after day, and week after week, shows his jolly red face, at the proper hour, little by little above the horizon, casting a scarlet glory on the leafless trees, and investing the well-piled brush-heaps with a burning splendor before their time. Now and then a brisk shower occurs, but it is short-lived, and not very abundant; and after being here through a season or two, one begins to wonder that the soil is so fertile. My own private theory is, that when the peninsula was covered with water, as it doubtless was before the Niagara met with such a fall, the porous mass became so thoroughly soaked, that the sun performs the office of rain, by drawing from below to the rich surface, the supplies of moisture which, under ordinary circumstances, are necessarily furnished from the aerial reservoirs. Such are my views, which I offer with the diffidence becoming a tyro; but at the same time avowing frankly that I shall not even consider an opposing hypothesis, until my antagonist shall have traversed the entire state, and counted the marshes and cat-holes from which I triumphantly draw my conclusion.

Leaving this question, then, I will make an effort to regain the floating end of my broken thread. These exceedingly dry Spring-times—all sun a very little east-wind—leave every tree, bush, brier and blade of grass, dry as new tinder. They are as combustible as the heart of a Sophomore; as ready for a blaze as a conclave of ancient ladies who have swallowed the first cup of Hyson, and only wait one single word to begin.

At this very suitable time, it is one of the customs of the country for every man that has an acre of marsh, to burn it over, in order to prepare for a new crop of grass; and a handful of fire thus applied, wants but a small cap-full of wind, to send it miles in any or all directions. The decayed trees, and those which may have been some time felled, catch the swift destruction, and aid the roaring flame; and while the earth seems covered with writhing serpents of living fire, ever and anon an undulating pyramid flares wildly upward, as if threatening the very skies, only to fall the next moment in crashing fragments, which serve to further the spreading ruin.

These scenes have a terrible splendor by night; but the effect by day is particularly curious. The air is so filled with the widely-diffused smoke, that the soft sunshine of April is mellowed into the ruddy glow of Autumn, and the mist which seems to hang heavy over the distant hills and woods, completes the illusion. One's associations are those of approaching winter, and it seems really a solecism to be making a garden under such a sky. But this is not all.

We were all busy in the rough, pole-fenced acre, which we had begun to call our garden;—one with a spade, another with a hoe or rake, and the least useful,—videlicet,

I—with a trowel and a paper of celery-seed, when a rough neighbor of ours shouted over the fence:—

"What be you a potterin' there for? You'd a plaguy sight better be a fighting fire, *I* tell ye! The wind is this way, and that fire'll be on your hay-stacks in less than no time, if you don't mind."

Thus warned, we gazed at the dark smoke which had been wavering over the north-west all day, and saw that it had indeed made fearful advances. But two well-travelled roads still lay between us and the burning marshes, and these generally prove tolerably effectual barriers when the wind is low. So our operatives took their way toward the scene of action, carrying with them the gardening implements, as the most efficient weapons in "fighting fire."

They had to walk a long distance, but the fire was very obliging and advanced more than two steps to meet them. In short, the first barrier was overleapt before they reached the second, and the air had become so heated that they could only use the hoes and spades in widening the road nearest our dwelling, by scraping away the leaves and bushes; and even there they found it necessary to retreat more rapidly than was consistent with a thorough performance of the work. The winds, though light, favored the destroyer, and the more experienced of the neighbors, who had turned out for the general good, declared there was nothing now but to make a "back-fire!" So homeward all ran, and set about kindling an opposing serpent which should "swallow up the rest;" but it proved too late. The flames only reached our stable and haystacks the sooner, and all that we could now accomplish was to preserve the cottage and its immediate appurtenances.

I scarce remember a blanker hour. I could not be glad that the house and the horses were safe, so vexed did I feel to think that a rational attention to the advance of that black threatening column, would have prevented the disaster. I sat gazing out of the back window, watching the gradual blackening of the remains of our stores of hay— scolding the while most vehemently, at myself and everybody else, for having been so stupidly negligent; declaring that I should not take the slightest interest in the garden which had so engrossed us, and wishing most heartily that the fellow who set the marsh on fire, could be detected and fined "not more than one thousand dollars," as the law directs; when our neighbor, long Sam Jennings, the slowest talker in Michigan, came sauntering across the yard with his rusty fowling-piece on his shoulder, and drawled out—

"I should think your dam was broke some; I see the water in the creek look dreadfully muddy." And while Sam took his leisurely way to the woods, the tired fire-fighters raced, one and all, to the dam, where they found the water pouring through a hole near the head-gate at a rate which seemed likely to carry off the entire structure in a very short time.

But I have purposely refrained from troubling the reader with a detail of any of the various accidents which attended our own particular debût, in the back-woods. I mentioned the fire because it is an annual occurrence throughout the country, and often consumes wheat-stacks, and even solitary dwellings; and I was drawn in to record the first breach in the mill-dam, as occurring on the very day of the disaster by fire.

I shall spare my friends any account of the many troubles and vexatious delays attendant on repairing that necessary evil, the dam; and even a transcript of the first three astounding figures which footed the account of expenses on the occasion. I shall only observe, that if long Sam Jennings did not get a ducking for not giving intelligence of the impending evil a full half-hour before it suited his convenience to stroll our way, it was not because he did not richly deserve it—and so I close my chapter of accidents.

30

MOONLIGHT AND AGUE: THE TITMOUSES

"Ah! who can tell how hard it is to" *say*—anything about an unpretending village like ours, in terms suited to the delicate organization of "ears polite." How can one hope to find anything of interest about such common-place people? Where is the aristocratic distinction which makes the kind visit of the great lady at the sick-bed of suffering indigence so great a favor, that all the inmates of the cottage behave picturesquely out of gratitude—form themselves into a *tableaux,* and make speeches worth recording? Here are neither great ladies nor humble cottagers. I cannot bring to my aid either the exquisite boudoir of the one class, with its captivating *bijouterie*—its velvet couches and its draperies of rose-colored satin, so becoming to the complexions of one's young-lady-characters—nor yet the cot of the other more simple but not less elegant, surrounded with clustering eglantine and clematis, and inhabited by goodness, grace, and beauty. These materials are denied me; but yet I must try to describe something of Michigan cottage life, taking care to avoid myself of such delicate periphrasis as may best veil the true homeliness of my subject.

Moonlight and the ague are, however, the same everywhere. At least I meet with no description in any of the poets of my acquaintance which might not be applied, without reservation, to Michigan moonlight; and as for the ague, did not great Caesar shake "when the fit was on him?"

166

> T'is true this god did shake:
> His coward lips did from their colour fly—

And in this important particular poor Lorenzo Titmouse was just like the inventor of the laurel crown. We—Mrs. Rivers and I—went to his father's, at his urgent request, on just such a night as is usually chosen for romantic walks by a certain class of lovers. We waited not for escort, although the night had already fallen, and there was a narrow strip of forest to pass in our way; but leaving word whither we had gone, we accompanied the poor shivering boy, each carrying what we could. And what does the gentle reader think we carried? A custard or a glass of jelly each, perhaps; and a nice sponge-cake, or something equally delicate, and likely to tempt the faint appetite of the invalid. No such thing. We had learned better than to offer such nick-nacks to people who "a'n't us'd to sweetnin'." My companion was "doubly arm'd:" a small tin pail of cranberry sauce in one hand, a bottle of vinegar in the other. I carried a modicum of "hop 'east," and a little bag of crackers; a scrap of Hyson, and a box of quinine pills. Odd enough; but we had been at such places before.

We had a delicious walk; though poor Lorenzo, who had a bag of flour on his shoulders, was fain to rest often. This was his "well day," to be sure; but he had some eight or ten fits of ague, enough to wither anybody's pith and marrow, as those will say who have tried it. That innate politeness which young rustics, out of books as well as in them, are apt to exhibit when they are in good humor, made Lorenzo decline, most vehemently, our offers of assistance. But we at length fairly took his bag from him, and passing a stick through the string, carried it between us; while the boy disposed of our various small articles by the aid of his capacious pockets. And a short half mile from the bridge brought us to his father's.

It was an ordinary log house, but quite old and dilapidated; the great open chimney occupying most of one end

167

of the single apartment, and two double-beds with a trundle-bed, the other. In one of the large beds lay the father and eldest son; in the other, the mother and two little daughters, all ill with ague, and all sad and silent, save my friend Mrs. Titmouse, whose untameable tongue was too much even for the ague. Mrs. Titmouse is one of those fortunate beings who can talk all day without saying anything. She is the only person whom I have met in these regions who appears to have paid her devoirs at Castle Blarney.

"How d'ye do, ladies,—how d'ye do? Bless my soul! if ever I thought I'd be catch'd in sitch a condition, and by sich grand ladies too! Not a chair for you to sit down on. I often tell Titmouse that we live jist like the pigs; but he ha'n't no ambition. I'm sure I'm under a thousand compliments to ye for coming to see me. We're expecting a mother of his'n to come and stay with us, but she ha'n't come yet— and I in sitch a condition; can't show ye no civility. Do sit down, ladies, if you *can* sit upon a chest—ladies like you. I'm sure I'm under a thousand compliments—" and so the poor soul ran on till she was fairly out of breath, in spite of our efforts to out-talk her with our assurances that we could accommodate ourselves very well, and could stay but a few minutes.

"And now, Mrs. Titmouse," said Mrs. Rivers, in her sweet, pleasant voice, "tell us what we can do for you."

"Do for me! Oh, massy! Oh, nothing, I thank ye. There a'n't nothing that ladies like you can do for me. We make out very well—"

"What do you say so for!" growled her husband from the other bed. "You know we ha'n't tasted a mouthful since morning, nor hadn't it, and I sent Lorenzo myself—"

"Well, I never!" responded his help-mate; "you're always doing just so: troubling people. You never had no ambition, Titmouse; you know I always said so. To be sure, we ha'n't had no tea this good while, and tea *does* taste dreadful good when a body's got the agur; and my bread is gone, and I ha'n't been able to set no emptin; but—"

Here we told what we had brought, and prepared at once to make some bread; but Mrs. Titmouse seemed quite horrified, and insisted on getting out of bed, though she staggered, and would have fallen if we had not supported her to a seat.

"Now tell *me* where the water is, and I will get it myself," said Mrs. Rivers, "and do you sit still and see how soon I will make a loaf."

"Water!" said the poor soul; "I'm afraid we have not water enough to make a loaf. Mr. Grimes brought us a barrel day before yesterday, and we've been dreadful careful of it, but the agur is so dreadful thirsty—I'm afraid there a'n't none."

"Have you no spring?"

"No, ma'am; but we have always got plenty of water down by the *mash* till this dry summer."

"I should think that was enough to give you the ague. Don't you think the marsh water unwholesome?"

"Well, I don't know but it is; but you see *he* was always a-going to dig a well; but he ha'n't no ambition, nor never had, and I've always told him so. And as to the agur, if you've got to have it, why you can't get clear of it."

There was, fortunately, water enough left in the barrel to set the bread and half-filled the tea-kettle; and we soon made a little blaze with sticks, which served to boil the kettle to make that luxury of the woods, a cup of green tea.

Mrs. Titmouse did not need the tea to help her talking powers, for she was an independent talker, whose gush of words knew no ebb nor exhaustion. "Alike to her was tide or time, Moonless midnight or matin prime." Her few remaining teeth chattered no faster when she had the ague than at any other time. The stream flowed on "in one weak, washy, everlasting flood."

When we had done what little we could, and were about to depart, glad to escape her overwhelming protestations of eternal gratitude, her husband reminded her that the cow had not been milked since the evening before, when "Miss Grimes" had been there. Here was a dilemma! How we regretted our defective education, which prevented our rendering so simple yet so necessary a service to the sick poor.

We remembered the gentleman who did not know whether he could read Greek, as he had never tried; and set ourselves resolutely at work to ascertain our powers in the milking line.

But alas! the "milky mother of the herd" had small respect for timid and useless town ladies. "Crummie kick'd, and Crummie flounced, And Crummie whisk'd her tail."

In vain did Mrs. Rivers hold the pail with both hands, while I essayed the arduous task. So sure as I succeeded in bringing ever so tiny a stream, the ill-mannered beast would almost put out my eyes with her tail, and then oblige us both to jump up and run away; and after a protracted struggle, the cow gained the victory, as might have been expected, and we were fain to retreat into the house.

The next expedient was to support Mrs. Titmouse on the little bench, while she tried to accomplish the mighty work; and having been partially successful in this, we at length took our leave, promising aid for the morrow, and hearing the poor woman's tongue at intervals till we were far in the wood.

"Lord bless ye! I'm sure I'm under an everlastin' compliment to ye; I wish I know'd how I could pay ye. Such ladies to be waitin' on the likes of me; I'm sure I never see nothing like it," &c. &c.

And now we began to wonder how long it would be before we should see our respected spouses, as poor Lorenzo had fallen exhausted on the bed, and was in no condition to see us even a part of the way home. The wood was very dark, though we could see glimpses of the mill-pond lying like liquid diamonds in the moon-light.

We had advanced near the brow of the hill which descends toward the pond, when strange sounds met our ears. Strange sounds for our peaceful village! Shouts and howlings—eldritch screams—Indian yells—the braying of tin horns, and the violent clashing of various noisy articles.

170

We hurried on, and soon came in sight of a crowd of persons, who seemed coming from the village to the pond. And now loud talking, threats—"Duck him! duck the impudent rascal!" what could it be?

Here was a mob! a Montacute mob! and the cause? I believe all mobs pretend to have causes. Could the choice spirits have caught an abolitionist? which they thought, as I had heard, meant nothing less than a monster.

But now I recollected having heard that a ventriloquist, which I believe most of our citizens considered a beast of the same nature, had sent notices of an exhibition for the evening; and the truth flashed upon us at once.

"In with him! in with him!" they shouted as they approached the water, just as we began to descend the hill. And then the clear fine voice of the dealer in voice was distinctly audible above the hideous din—

"Gentlemen, I have warned you; I possess the means of defending myself, you will force me to use them."

"Stop his mouth," shouted a well-known bully, "he lies; he ha'n't got nothing! in with him!" and a violent struggle followed, some few of our more sober citizens striving to protect the stranger.

One word to Mrs. Rivers, and we set up a united shriek, a screech like an army of sea-gulls. "Help, help!" and we stopped on the hillside, our white dresses distinctly visible in the clear, dazzling moonlight.

We "stinted not nor staid" till a diversion was fairly effected. A dozen forms seceded at once from the crowd, and the spirit of the thing was at an end.

We waited on the spot where our artifice began, certain of knowing every individual who should approach; and the very first proved those we most wished to see. And now came the very awkward business of explaining our *ruse,* and Mrs. Rivers was rather sharply reproved for *her* part of it. Harley Rivers was not the man to object to anything like a *lark,* and he had only attempted to effect the release of the ventriloquist, after Mr. Clavers had joined him on the way to Mr. Titmouse's. The boobies who had

171

been most active in the outrage would fain have renewed the sport; but the ventriloquist had wisely taken advantage of our diversion in his favor, and was no where to be found. The person at whose house he had put up told afterwards that he had gone out with loaded pistols in his pocket; so even a woman's shrieks, hated of gods and men, may sometimes be of service.

Montacute is far above mobbing now. This was the first and last exhibition of the spirit of the age. The most mobbish of our neighbors have flitted westward, seeking more congenial association. I trust they may be so well satisfied that they will not think of returning; for it is not pleasant to find a dead pig in one's well, or a favorite dog hung up at the gate-post; to say nothing of cows milked on the marshes, hen-roosts rifled, or melon-patches cleared in the course of the night.

We learned afterwards the "head and front" of the ventriloquist's offence. He had asked twenty-five cents a-head for the admisson of the sovereign people.

31

TINKERVILLE'S WILD CAT

THE VERY NEXT intelligence from our urban rival came in the shape of a polite note to Mr. Clavers, offering him any amount of stock in the "Merchants' and Manufacturers' Bank of Tinkerville." My honorable spouse—I acknowledge it with regret—is anything but "an enterprising man." But our neighbor, Mr. Rivers, or his astute father for him, thought this chance for turning paper into gold and silver too tempting to be slighted, and entered at once into the business of making money on a large scale.

I looked at first upon the whole matter with unfeigned indifference, for money had never seemed so valueless to me as since I have experienced how little it will buy in the woods; but I was most unpleasantly surprised when I heard that Harley Rivers, the husband of my friend, was to be exalted to the office of President of the new bank.

"Just as we were beginning to be so comfortable, to think you should leave us," said I to Mrs. Rivers.

"Oh! dear no," she replied; "Harley says it will not be necessary for us to remove at present. The business can be transacted just as well here, and we shall not go until the banking-house and our own can be erected."

This seemed odd to a novice like myself; but I rejoiced that arrangements were so easily made which would allow me to retain for a while so pleasant a companion.

As I make not the least pretension to regularity, but only an attempt to "body forth" an unvarnished picture of the times, I may as well proceed in this place to give the initiated reader so much of the history of the Tinkerville Bank, as has become the property of the public; supposing that the effects of our "general Banking Law" may not be as familiarly known elsewhere as they unfortunately are in this vicinity.

When our speculators in land found that the glamor had departed, that the community had seen the ridicule of the delusion which had so long made "The cobwebs on a cottage wall Seem tapestry in lordly hall; A nutshell seem a gilded barge, A sheeling seem a palace large, And youth seem age and age seem youth." And poverty seem riches, and idleness industry, and fraud enterprise; some of these cunning magicians set themselves about concocting a new species of gramarye, by means of which the millions of acres of wild land which were left on their hands might be turned into *bonâ fide* cash—paper cash at least, to meet certain times of payment of certain moneys borrowed at certain rates of interest during the fervor of the speculating mania. The "General Banking Law" of unenviable notoriety, which allowed any dozen of men who could pledge real estate to a nominal amount, to assume the power of making money of rags; this was the magic cauldron, whose powers were destined to transmute these acres of wood and meadow into splendid metropolitan residences, with equipages of corresponding elegance. It was only "bubble-bubble," and burr-oaks were turned into marble tables, tall tamaracks into draperied bedsteads, lakes into looking-glasses, and huge expanses of wet marsh into velvet couches, and carpets from the looms of Agra and Ind.

It is not to be denied that this necromantic power had its limits. Many of these successful wizards seemed after all a little out of place in their palaces of enchantment; and one could hardly help thinking, that some of them would have been more suitably employed in tramping, with cow-hide boot, the slippery marshes on which their greatness was based, than in treading mincingly the piled carpets which

174

were the magical product of those marshes. But that was nobody's business but their own. They considered themselves as fulfilling their destiny.

Some thirty banks or more were the fungous growth of the new political hot-bed; and many of these were of course without a "local habitation," though they might boast the "name," it may be, of some part of the deep woods, where the wild cat had hitherto been the most formidable foe to the unwary and defenseless. Hence the celebrated term "Wild Cat," justified fully by the course of these cunning and stealthy blood-suckers; more fatal in their treacherous spring than ever was their forest prototype. A stout farmer might hope to "whip" a wild cat or two; but once in the grasp of a "Wild Cat bank," his struggles were unavailing. Hopeless ruin has been the consequence in numerous instances, and everyday adds new names to the list.

But I have fallen into the sin of generalizing, instead of journalizing, as I promised. The interesting nature of the subject will be deemed a sufficient justification, by such of my readers as may have enjoyed the pleasure of making alumets of bank-notes, as so many Michiganians have done, or might have done if they had not been too angry.

Of the *locale* of the Merchants' and Manufacturers' Bank of Tinkerville, I have already attempted to give some faint idea; and I doubt not one might have ridden over many of the new banks in a similar manner, without suspecting their existence. The rubicand and smooth-spoken father-in-law of my friend was the main-spring of the institution in question; and his son Harley, who "did not love work," was placed in a conspicuous part of the panorama as President. I thought our Caleb Quotem neighbor, Mr. Simeon Jenkins, would have found time to fulfil the duties of cashier, and he can write "S. Jenkins" very legibly; so there would have been no objection on that score: but it was thought prudent to give the office to a Tinkervillian— a man of straw, for aught I know to the contrary; for all I saw or heard of him was his name, "A. Bite," on the bills. A fatal mistake this, according to Mr. Jenkins. He can demonstrate, to anybody who feels an interest in the facts of the case, that the bank never would have "flatted out," if he had had a finger in the pie.

Just as our Wild Cat was ready for a spring, the only obstacle in her path was removed, by the abolition of the old-fashioned-and-troublesome-but-now-exploded plan of specie payments; and our neighbors went up like the best rocket from Vauxhall. The Tinkerville Astor House, the County Offices, the Banking House, were all begun simultaneously, as at the waving of a wand of power. Montacute came at once to a dead stand; for not a workman could be had for love or flour. These beautifully engraved bills were too much for the public spirit of most of us, and we forgot our Montacute patriotism for a time. "Real estate pledge;" of course, the notes were better than gold or silver, because they were lighter in the pocket.

Time's whirligig went round. Meanwhile all was prosperous at the incipient capital of our rising county. Mr. President Rivers talked much of removing to the bank; and in preparation, sent to New-York for a complete outfit of furniture, and a pretty carriage; while Mrs. Rivers astonished the natives in our log meeting-house, and the woodchucks in our forest strolls, by a Parisian bonnet of the most exquisite rose-color, her husband's taste. Mr. Rivers, senior, and sundry other gentlemen, some ruddy-gilled and full-pocketed like himself, others looking so lean and hungry, that I wondered anybody would trust them in a bank— a place where, as I supposed in my greenness, "in bright confusion open rouleaux lie," made frequent and closeted sojourn at Montacute.

Our mill whirred merely, and toll-wheat is a currency that never depreciates; but in other respects, we were only moderately prosperous. Our first merchant, Mr. Skinner, did not clear above three thousand dollars the first year. Slow work for Michigan; and somehow, Mr. Jenkins was far from getting rich as fast as he expected.

One bright morning, as I stood looking down Main-street, thinking I certainly saw a deer's tail at intervals flying through the woods, two gentlemen on horse-back rode deliberately into town. They had the air of men who were on serious business; and as they dismounted at the door of the Montacute House, a messenger was despatched in an instant to Mr. Rivers. Ere long, I discovered the ruddy papa wending his dignified way towards the Hotel, while the President, on his famous trotter Greenhorn, emerged from the back-gate, and cleared the ground in fine style towards Tinkerville.

A full hour elapsed before the elder Mr. Rivers was ready to accompany the gentlemen on their ride. He happened to be going that way, which was very convenient, since the Bank Commissioners, for our portly strangers were none other, did not know in what part of the unsurveyed lands the new city lay. The day was far spent when the party returned to take tea with Mrs. Rivers. All seemed in high good humor. The examination prescribed by our severe laws had been exceedingly satisfactory. The books of the Bank were in apple-pie order. Specie certificates, a newly-invented kind of gold and silver, were abundant. A long row of boxes, which contained the sinews of peace as well as of war, had been viewed and "hefted" by the Commissioners. The liabilities seemed as nothing compared with the resources; and the securities were as substantial as earth and stone could make them.

If the height of prosperity could have been heightened, Tinkerville would have gone on faster than ever after this beneficent visitation. Mr. Rivers' new furniture arrived, and passed through our humble village in triumphal procession, pile after pile of huge boxes, provokingly impervious to the public eye; and, last of all, the new carriage, covered as closely from the vulgar gaze as a celebrated belle whose charms are on the wane. The public buildings at the county seat were proclaimed finished, or *nearly* finished, a school-house begun, a meeting-house talked of; but for the latter, it was supposed to be *too early*—rather premature.

32

TINKERVILLE'S BUBBLE BURSTS

ALL TOO SOON came the period when I must part with my pleasant neighbor Mrs. Rivers, the opening brilliancy of whose lot seemed to threaten a lasting separation, from those whose way led rather through the "cool, sequestered vale," so much praised, and so little coveted.

Mr. Rivers had for some time found abundant leisure for his favorite occupations of hunting and fishing. The signing of bills took up but little time, and an occasional ride to the scene of future glories, for the purpose of superintending the various improvements, was all that necessarily called him away. But now, final preparations for a removal were absolutely in progress; and I had begun to feel really sad at the thought of losing the gentle Anna, when the Bank Commissioners again paced in official dignity up Main-street, and, this time, alighted at Mr. Rivers' door.

The President and Greenhorn had trotted to Tinkerville that morning, and the old gentleman was not in town; so our men of power gravely wended their way towards the newly painted and pine-pillared honors of the Merchants' and Manufacturers' Banking-house, not without leaving behind them many a surmise as to the probable object of this new visitation.

It was Mr. Skinner's opinion, and Mr. Skinner is a longheaded Yankee, that the Bank had issued too many bills; and for the sincerity of his judgment, he referred his hearers to the fact, that he had for some time been turning the splendid notes of the Merchants' and Manufacturers' Bank of Tinkerville into wheat and corn as fast as he conveniently could.

A sly old farmer, who had sold several hundred bushels of wheat to Mr. Skinner, at one dollar twenty-five cents a bushel, winked knowingly as the merchant mentioned this proof of his own far-seeing astuteness; and informed the company that he had paid out the last dollar long ago on certain outstanding debts.

Mr. Porter knew that the Tinkerville black-smith had run up a most unconscionable bill for the iron doors, &c. &c., which were necessary to secure the immense vaults of the Bank; that would give, as he presumed, some hint of the probable object of the Commissioners.

Mr. Simeon Jenkins, if not the greatest, certainly the most grandiloquent man in Montacute, didn't want to know any better than he did know, that the Cashier of the Bank was a thick-skull; and he felt very much afraid that the said Cashier had been getting his principals into trouble. Mr. Bite's manner of writing his name was, in Mr. Jenkins' view, proof positive of his lack of capacity; since "nobody in the universal world" as Mr. Jenkins averred, "ever wrote such a hand as that, that know'd anything worth knowing."

But conjectures, however positively advanced, are, after all, not quite satisfactory; and the return of the commissioners was most anxiously awaited even by the very worthies who knew their business so well.

The sun set most perversely soon, and the light would not stay long after him; and thick darkness settled upon this mundane sphere, and no word transpired from Tinkerville. Morning came, and with it the men of the office, but oh! with what lengthened faces!

There were whispers of "an injunction"—horrid sound! —upon the Merchants' and Manufacturers' Bank of Tinkerville.

To picture the dismay which drew into all sorts of shapes

the universal face of Montacute, would require a dozen Wilkies. I shall content myself with saying that there was no joking about the matter.

The commissioners were not very communicative, but in spite of their dignified mystification, something about broken glass and tenpenny nails did leak out before their track was fairly cold.

And where was Harley Rivers? "Echo answers, where!" His dear little wife watered her pillow with her tears for many a night before he returned to Montacute.

It seemed, as we afterwards learned, that the commissioners had seen some suspicious circumstances about the management of the Bank, and returned with a determination to examine into matters a little more scrupulously. It had been found in other cases that certain "specie-certificates" had been loco-motive. It had been rumored, since the new batch of Banks had come into operation, that "Thirty steeds both fleet and wight Stood saddled in the stables day and night—" ready to effect at short notice certain transfers of assets and specie. And in the course of the Tinkerville investigation the commissioners had ascertained by the aid of hammer and chisel, that the boxes of the "real stuff" which had been so loudly vaunted, contained a heavy charge of broken glass and tenpenny nails, covered above and below with half-dollars, principally "bogus." Alas! for Tinkerville, and alas, for poor Michigan!

The distress among the poorer classes of farmers which was the immediate consequence of this and other Bank failures, was indescribable. Those who have seen only a city panic, can form no idea of the extent and severity of the sufferings on these occasions. And how many small farmers are there in Michigan who have *not* suffered from this cause?

The only adequate punishment which I should prescribe for this class of heartless adventurers, would be to behold at one glance all the misery they have occasioned; to be gifted with an Asmodean power, and forced to use it. The

180

hardiest among them, could scarcely, I think, endure to witness the unroofing of the humble log-huts of Michigan, after the bursting of one of these Dead-sea apples. Bitter indeed were the ashes which they scattered!

How many settlers who came in from the deep woods many miles distant where no grain had yet grown, after travelling perhaps two or three days and nights, with a half-starved ox-team, and living on a few crusts by the way, were told when they offered their splendid-looking bank-notes, their hard-earned all, for the flour which was to be the sole food of wife and babes through the long winter, that these hoarded treasures were valueless as the ragged paper which wrapped them! Can we blame them if they cursed in their agony, the soul-less wretches who had thus drained their best blood for the furtherance of their own schemes of low ambition? Can we wonder that the poor, feeling such wrongs as these, learn to hate the rich, and to fancy them natural enemies?

Could one of these heart-wrung beings have been introduced, just as he was, with the trembling yet in his heart, and the curses on his lips, into the gilded saloon of his betrayer, methinks the dance would have flagged, the song wavered, the wine palled, for the moment at least. "Light is the dance and doubly sweet the lays When for the dear delight another pays—" But the uninvited presence of the involuntary paymaster, would have been "the hand on the wall" to many a successful(!) banker.

After public indignation had in some measure subsided, and indeed such occurrences as I have described became too common to stir the surface of society very rudely, Mr. Harley Rivers returned to Montacute, and prepared at once for the removal of his family. I took leave of his wife with most sincere regret, and I felt at the time as if we should never meet again. But I have heard frequently from them until quite lately; and they have been living very handsomely (Mr. Rivers always boasted that he *would* live like a gentleman) in one of the Eastern cities on the spoils of the Tinkerville Wild Cat.

33

THE MONTACUTE FEMALE BENEFICENT SOCIETY

My near neighbor, Mrs. Nippers, whose garden joins ours, and whose "keepin' room," I regret to say it, looks into my kitchen, was most cruelly mortified that she was not elected President of the Montacute Female Beneficent Society. It would have been an office *so* congenial to her character, condition, and habits! 'T was cruel to give it to Mrs. Skinner, "merely," as Mrs. Nippers declares, "because the society wanted to get remnants from the store!"

Mrs. Campaspe Nippers is a widow lady of some thirty-five, or thereabouts, who lives with her niece alone in a small house, in the midst of a small garden, in the heart of the village. I have never noticed anything peculiar in the construction of the house. There are not, that I can discover, any contrivances resembling ears; or those ingenious funnels of sail-cloth which are employed on board-ship to coax fresh air down between-decks. Nor are there large mirrors, nor a telescope, within doors, nor yet a *camera obscura*. I have never detected any telegraphic signals from without. Yet no man sneezes at opening his front door in the morning; no woman sweeps her steps after breakfast; no child goes late to school; no damsel slips into the store; no bottle comes out of it; no family has fried onions for dinner; no hen lays an egg in the afternoon; no horse slips his bridle; no cow is missing at milking-time;

and no young couple after tea; but Mrs. Nippers, and her niece, Miss Artemisia Clinch, know all about it, and tell it to everybody who will listen to them.

A sad rumor was raised last winter, by some spiteful gossip against a poor woman who had taken lodgers to gain bread for her family; and when Mrs. Nippers found it rather difficult to gain credence for her view of the story, she nailed the matter, as she supposed, by whispering with mysterious meaning, while her large light eyes dilated with energy and enjoyment—"I have myself seen a light there after eleven o'clock at night!"

In vain did the poor woman's poor husband, a man who worked hard, but would make a beast of himself at times, protest that malice itself might let his wife escape; and dare any *man* to come forward and say aught against her. Mrs. Nippers only smiled, and stretched her eye-lids so far apart, that the sky-blue whites of her light-grey eyes were visible both above and below the scarce distinguishable iris, and then looked at Miss Artemisia Clinch with such triumphant certainty; observing, that a drunkard's word was not worth much. It is impossible ever to convince her, in anybody's favor.

But this is mere wandering. Association led me from my intent, which was only to speak of Mrs. Nippers as connected with the Montacute Female Beneficent Society. This Association is the prime dissipation of our village, the magic circle within which lies all our cherished exclusiveness, the strong hold of *caste*, the test of gentility, the temple of emulation, the hive of industry, the mart of fashion, and I must add, though reluctantly, the fountain of village scandal, the hot-bed from which springs every root of bitterness among the petticoated denizens of Montacute. I trust the importance of the Society will be enhanced in the reader's estimation, by the variety of figures I have been compelled to use in describing it. Perhaps it would have been enough to have said it is a Ladies' Sewing Society, and so saved all this wordiness; but I like to amplify.

When the idea was first started, by I know not what

fortunate individual—Mrs. Nippers does, I dare say,—this same widow-lady espoused the thing warmly, donned her India-rubbers, and went all over through the sticky mud, breakfasted with me, dined with Mrs. Rivers, took tea with Mrs. Skinner, and spent the intervals and the evening with half-a-dozen other people, not only to recommend the plan, but to give her opinion of how the affair ought to be conducted, to what benevolent uses applied, and under what laws and by-laws; and though last, far from least, who ought to be its *officers*. Five Directresses did she select, two Secretaries, and a Treasurer, Managers and Auditors,—like the military play of my three brothers, who always had "fore-captain," "hind-captain," and "middle-captain," but no privates. But in all this Mrs. Campaspe never once hinted the name of a Lady President. She said, to be sure, that she should be very glad to be of any sort of service to the Society; and that from her position she should be more at leisure to devote time to its business, than almost any other person; and that both herself and her niece had been concerned in a sewing-society in a certain village at "the East," whose doings were often quoted by both ladies, and concluded by inquiring who her hearer thought would be the most suitable President.

In spite of this industrious canvassing, when the meeting for forming the society took place at Mrs. Skinner's, Mrs. Campaspe Nippers' name was perversely omitted in the animated ballot for dignities. No one said a word, but everyone had a sort of undefined dread of so active a member, and, by tacit consent, every office which she had herself contrived, was filled, without calling upon her. Her eyes grew preternaturally pale, and her lips wan as whit-leather, when the result was known; but she did not trust herself to speak. She placed her name on the list of members with as much composure as could be looked for, under such trying circumstances, and soon after departed with Miss Artemisia Clinch, giving a parting glance which seemed to say, with Sir Peter Teazle, "I leave my character behind me."

A pawkie smile dawned on two or three of the sober visages of our village dames, as the all-knowing widow and her submissive niece closed the door, but no one ventured a remark on the killing frost which had fallen upon Mrs. Nippers' anticipated "budding honors," and after agreeing upon a meeting at our house, the ladies dispersed.

The next morning, as I drew my window curtain, to see whether the sun had aired the world enough to make it safe for me to get up to breakfast,—I do not often dispute the *pas* with Aurora—I saw Mrs. Nippers emerge from the little front door of her tiny mansion, unattended by her niece for a marvel, and pace majestically down Main-street. I watched her in something of her own prying spirit, to see whither she could be going so early; but she disappeared in the woods, and I turned to my combs and brushes, and thought no more of the matter.

But the next day, and the next, and the day after, almost as early each morning, out trotted my busy neighbor; and although she disappeared in different directions—sometimes P.S. and sometimes O.P.—she never returned till late in the afternoon. My curiosity began to be troublesome.

At length came the much-desired Tuesday, whose destined event was the first meeting of the society. I had made preparations for such plain and simple cheer as is usual with such feminine gatherings, and began to think of arranging my dress with the decorum required by the occasion, when about one hour before the appointed time, came Mrs. Nippers and Miss Clinch, and ere they were unshawled and unhooded, Mrs. Flyter and her three children—the eldest four years, and the youngest six months. Then Mrs. Muggles and her crimson baby, four weeks old. Close on her heels, Mrs. Briggs and her little boy of about three years' standing, in a long-tailed coat, with vest and decencies of scarlet circassian. And there I stood in my gingham wrapper, and kitchen apron; much to my discomfiture, and the undisguised surprise of the Female Beneficent Society.

185

"I always calculate to be ready to begin at the time appointed," remarked the gristle-lipped widow.

"So do I," responded Mrs. Flyter, and Mrs. Muggles, both of whom sat the whole afternoon with baby on knee, and did not sew a stitch.

"What! isn't there any work ready?" continued Mrs. Nippers with an astonished aspect; "well, I *did* suppose that such smart officers as *we* have, would have prepared all beforehand. We always used to, at the East."

Mrs. Skinner, who is really quite a pattern-woman in all that makes woman indispensable, viz. cooking and sewing, took up the matter quite warmly, just as I slipped away in disgrace to make the requisite reform in my costume.

When I returned, the work was distributed, and the company broken up into little knots or coteries; every head bowed, and every tongue in full play. I took my seat at as great a distance from the sharp widow as might be, though it is vain to think of eluding a person of her ubiquity, and reconnoitred the company who were "done off" (indigenous) "in first-rate style," for this important occasion. There were nineteen women with thirteen babies—or at least "young 'uns" (indigenous,) who were not above gingerbread. Of these thirteen, nine held large chunks of gingerbread, or doughnuts, in trust, for the benefit of the gowns of the society; the remaining four were supplied with bunches of maple sugar, tied in bits of rag, and pinned to their shoulders, or held dripping in the fingers of their mammas.

Mrs. Flyter was "slicked up" for the occasion, in the snuff-colored silk she was married in, curiously enlarged in the back and not as voluminous in the floating part as is the wasteful custom of the present day. Her three immense children, white-haired and blubber-lipped like their amiable parent, were in pink ginghams and blue glass beads. Mrs. Nippers wore her unfailing brown merino, and black apron; Miss Clinch her inevitable scarlet calico; Mrs.

186

Skinner her red merino with baby of the same; Mrs. Daker shone out in her very choicest city finery—where else could she show it, poor thing; and a dozen other Mistresses shone in their "'tother gowns," and their tamboured collars. Mrs. Doubleday's pretty black-eyed Dolly was neatly stowed in a small willow-basket, where it lay looking about with eyes full of sweet wonder, behaving itself with marvellous quietness and discretion, as did most of the other little torments, to do them justice.

Much consultation, deep and solemn, was held as to the most profitable kinds of work to be undertaken by the society. Many were in favor of making up linen, cotton linen of course, but Mrs. Nippers assured the company that shirts never used to sell well at the East, and she was therefore perfectly certain that they would not do here. Pincushions and such like femininities were then proposed; but at these Mrs. Nippers held up both hands, and showed a double share of blue-white around her eyes. Nobody about here needed pincushions, and besides where should we get the materials? Aprons, capes, caps, collars, were all proposed with the same ill success. At length Mrs. Doubleday, with an air of great deference, inquired what Mrs. Nippers would recommend.

The good lady hesitated a little at this. It was more her forte to object to other people's plans, than to suggest better; but after a moment's consideration she said she should think fancy-boxes, watch-cases, and alum baskets would be very pretty.

A dead silence fell on the assembly, but of course it did not last long. Mrs. Skinner went on quietly cutting out shirts, and in a very short time furnished each member with a good supply of work, stating that any lady might take work home to finish if she liked.

Mrs. Nippers took her work and edged herself into a coterie of which Mrs. Flyter had seemed till then magnet. Very soon I heard, "I declare it's a shame!" "I don't know what'll be done about it"; "She told me so with her own mouth;" "Oh but I was there myself!" etc., etc., in many different voices; the interstices well filled with undistinguishable whispers "not loud but deep."

It was not long before the active widow transferred her seat to another corner;—Miss Clinch plying her tongue, not her needle, in a third. The whispers and the exclamations seemed to be gaining ground. The few silent members were inquiring for more work.

"Mrs. Nippers has the sleeve! Mrs. Nippers, have you finished that sleeve?"

Mrs. Nippers colored, said "No," and sewed four stitches. At length "the storm grew loud apace."

"It will break up the society—"

"What *is* that?" asked Mrs. Doubleday, in her sharp treble. "What is it, Mrs. Nippers? *You* know all about it."

Mrs. Nippers replied that she only knew what she had heard, etc., etc., but, after a little urging, consented to inform the company in general, that there was a great dissatisfaction in the neighborhood; that those who lived in log-houses at a little distance from the village, had not been invited to join the society; and also that many people thought twenty-five cents quite too high, for a yearly subscription.

Many looked aghast at this. Public opinion is nowhere so strongly felt as in this country, among new settlers. And as many of the present company still lived in log-houses, a tender string was touched.

At length, an old lady who had sat quietly in a corner all the afternoon, looked up from behind the great woollen sock she was knitting—

"Well now! that's queer!" said she, addressing Mrs. Nippers with an air of simplicity simplified. "Miss Turner told me you went round her neighborhood last Friday, and told how that Miss Clavers and Miss Skinner despised everybody that lived in log-houses; and you know you told Miss Briggs that you thought twenty-five cents was too much; didn't she, Miss Briggs?" Mrs. Briggs nodded.

The widow blushed to the very centre of her pale eyes,

but "e'en though vanquished," she lost not her assurance. "Why, I'm sure I only said that we only paid twelve-and-a-half cents at the East; and as to log-houses, I don't know, I can't just recollect, but I didn't say more than others did."

But human nature could not bear up against the mortification; and it had, after all, the scarce credible effect of making Mrs. Nippers sew in silence for some time, and carry her colors at half-mast for the remainder of the afternoon.

At tea each lady took one or more of her babies into her lap and much grabbing ensued. Those who wore calicoes seemed in good spirits and appetite, for green tea at least, but those who had unwarily sported silks and other unwashables, looked acid and uncomfortable. Cake flew about at great rate, and the milk and water which ought to have gone quietly down sundry juvenile throats, was spirited without mercy into various wry faces. But we got through. The astringent refreshment produced its usual crisping effect upon the vivacity of the company. Talk ran high upon almost all Montacutian themes.

"Do you have any butter now?" "When are you going to raise your barn?" "Is your man a going to kill, this week?" "I ha'n't seen a bit of meat these six weeks." "Was you to meetin' last Sabbath?" "Has Miss White got any wool to sell?" "Do tell if you've been to Detroit!" "Are you out o' candles?" "Well I *should* think Sarah Teals wanted a new gown!" "I hope we shall have milk in a week or two," and so on; for, be it known, that in a state of society like ours, the bare necessities of life are subjects of sufficient interest for a good deal of conversation. More than one truly respectable woman of our neighborhood has told me, that it is not very many years since a moderate allowance of Indian meal and potatoes, was literally all that fell to their share of this rich world for weeks together.

"Is your daughter Isabella well?" asked Mrs. Nippers of me solemnly, pointing to little Bell who sat munching her bread and butter, half asleep, at the fragmentious table.

"Yes, I believe so, look at her cheeks."

"Ah yes! it was her cheeks I was looking at. They are so *very* rosy. I have a little niece who is the very image of her. I never see Isabella without thinking of Jerushy; and Jerushy is most dreadfully scrofulous!"

Satisfied at having made me uncomfortable, Mrs. Nippers turned to Mrs. Doubleday, who was trotting her pretty babe with her usual proud fondness.

"Don't you think your baby breathes rather strangely?" said the tormentor.

"Breathes! how!" said the poor thing, off her guard in an instant.

"Why rather croupish, I think, if *I* am any judge. I have never had any children of my own to be sure, but I was with Mrs. Green's baby when it died, and—"

"Come, we'll be off!" said Mr. Doubleday, who had come for his spouse. "Don't mind the envious vixen"— aside to his Polly.

Just then, somebody on the opposite side of the room happened to say, speaking of some cloth affair, "Mrs. Nippers says it ought to be sponged."

"Well, sponge it then, by all means," said Mr. Doubleday, "nobody else knows half as much about sponging;" and with wife and baby in tow, off walked the laughing Philo, leaving the widow absolutely transfixed.

"What *could* Mr. Doubleday mean by that?" was at length her indignant exclamation.

Nobody spoke.

"I am sure," continued the crest-fallen Mrs. Campaspe, with an attempt at a scornful giggle, "I am sure if anybody understood him, I would be glad to know what he *did* mean."

"Well now, I can tell you;" said the same simple old lady in the corner, who had let out the secret of Mrs. Nippers' morning walks. "Some folks calls that *sponging*, when you go about getting your dinner here and your tea there, and sich like; as you know you and Meesy there does. That was what he meant I guess." And the old

190

lady quietly put up her knitting, and prepared to go home.

There have been times when I have thought that almost any degree of courtly duplicity would be preferable to the *brusquerie* of some of my neighbors: but on this occasion I gave all due credit to a simple and downright way of stating the plain truth. The scrofulous hint brightened my mental and moral vision somewhat.

Mrs. Nippers' claret cloak and green bonnet, and Miss Clinch's ditto ditto, were in earnest requisition, and I do not think either of them spent a day out that week.

34

ENGLISH SETTLERS

MANY ENGLISH FAMILIES reside in our vicinity, some of them well calculated to make their way anywhere; close, penurious, grasping and indefatigable; denying themselves all but the necessaries of life, in order to add to their lands, and make the most of their crops; and somewhat apt in bargaining to overreach even the wary pumpkin-eaters, their neighbors: others to whom all these things seem so foreign and so unsuitable, that one cannot but wonder that the vagaries of fortune should have sent them into so uncongenial an atmosphere. The class last mentioned, generally live retired, and show little inclination to mingle with their rustic neighbors; and of course, they become at once the objects of suspicion and dislike. The principle of "let-a-be for let-a-be" holds not with us. Whoever exhibits any desire for privacy is set down as "praoud," or something worse; no matter how inoffensive, or even how benevolent he may be; and of all places in the world in which to live on the shady side of public opinion, an American back-woods settlement is the very worst, as many of these unfortunately mistaken emigrants have been made to feel.

The better classes of English settlers seem to have left their own country with high-wrought notions of the unbounded freedom to be enjoyed in this; and it is with feelings of angry surprise that they learn after a short residence here, that this very universal freedom abridges their own liberty to do as they please in their individual capacity; that the absolute democracy which prevails in country places, imposes as heavy restraints upon one's free-will in some particulars, as do the over-bearing pride and haughty distinctions of the old world in others; and after one has changed one's whole plan of life, and crossed the wide ocean to find a Utopia, the waking to reality is attended with feelings of no slight bitterness. In some instances within my knowledge these feelings of disappointment have been so severe as to neutralize all that was good in American life, and to produce a sour discontent which increased every real evil and went far towards alienating the few who were kindly inclined toward the stranger.

I ever regarded our very intelligent neighbors the Brents, as belonging to the class who have emigrated by mistake, they seemed so well-bred, so well-off, so amiable and so unhappy. They lived a few miles from us, and we saw them but seldom, far less frequently than I could have wished, for there were few whose society was so agreeable. Mr. Brent was a handsome, noble-looking man of thirty or perhaps a little more, well-read, and passionately fond of literary pursuits; no more fit to be a Michigan farmer than to figure as President of the Texan republic; and his wife a gentle and timid woman, very dependent and very lovely, was as ill fitted to bear the household part of a farmer's lot. But all this seemed well-arranged, for the farm was managed "on shares" by a stout husbandman and his family, tolerably honest and trustworthy people as times go; and Mr. Brent and his pale and delicate Catherine disposed of their hours as they thought proper; not however without many secret and some very audible surmises and wonderings on the part of their immediate neighbors, which were duly reported, devoutly believed, and invariably added to, in the course of their diffusion in Montacute.

I might repeat what I heard at a Montacute tea-party; I might give Mrs. Flyter's view of the probable duration of Mr. Brent's means of living on the occasion of having learned from Mrs. Holbrook that Mrs. Brent did not see to the butter-making, and had never milked a cow in her life. I might repeat Mrs. Allerton's estimate of the cost of Mrs. Brent's dress at meeting on a certain Sunday. But I shall tell only what Mrs. Nippers said, for I consider her as unimpeachable authority in such matters. Her decided and solemn assertion was that Mrs. Brent was jealous.

"Jealous of whom?"

"Why of Mr. Brent to be sure!"

"But it is to be supposed that there is somebody else concerned."

"Ah yes! but I don't know. Mrs. Barton didn't know."

"Oh, it was Mrs. Barton who told you then."

Mrs. Nippers had declined giving her authority, and Mrs. Barton was the wife of Mr. Brent's farmer. So she colored a little, and said that she did not wish it repeated, as Mrs. Barton had mentioned it to her in confidence. But since it *had* come out by mere chance, she didn't know but she might just as well tell that Mrs. Barton was sure that Mrs. Brent was jealous of somebody in England, or somebody that was dead, she didn't know which. She hoped that none of the ladies would mention it.

There were some fourteen or so in company, and they had not yet had tea. After tea the poor Brents were completely "used up," to borrow a phrase much in vogue with us, and the next day I was not much surprised at being asked by a lady who made me a three hours' morning call beginning at nine o'clock, if I had heard that Mr. and Mrs. Brent were going to "part."

I declared my ignorance of anything so terrible, and tried to trace back the news, but it must have passed through several able hands before it came to me.

We rode over to see the Brents that afternoon, found them as usual, save that Mrs. Brent seemed wasting, but she always declared herself quite well; and her husband, whose manner towards her is that of great tenderness, yet not exactly that of husbands in general, a little constrained, was reading aloud to her as she lay on the sofa. They

194

seemed pleased to see us, and promised an afternoon next week to meet "a few friends,"—that is the term, I believe, —but not Mrs. Nippers.

Among those whom I invited to partake our strawberries and cream on the occasion, were Mr. Cathcart and his beautiful wife, English neighbors from a little vine-clad cottage on the hill west of our village; much older residents than the Brents, who had not yet been a year in our vicinity. Mrs. Cathcart is one of the most beautiful women I have ever seen, and certainly a very charming one in all respects, at least to me, who do not dislike a good share of spirit and energy in a lady. Her spouse, though far different, has his good points, and can make himself agreeable enough when he is in the humor; which sometimes occurs, though not often. He is at least twenty years older than his lady, and as ugly as she is handsome, and horribly jealous, I say it myself, of everything and everybody which or whom Mrs. Cathcart may chance to look at or speak to, or take an interest in, gentle and simple, animate or inanimate. It is really pitiable sometimes to see the poor man grin in the effort to suppress the overboiling of his wrath, for he is a very polite person, and generally says the most disagreeable things with a smile.

These neighbors of ours are persons of taste—taste in pictures, in music, in books, in flowers; and thus far they are well mated enough. But there are certain glances and tones which betray to the most careless observer that there *are* points of difference, behind the scenes at least; and little birds have whispered that after Mrs. Cathcart had spent the morning in transplanting flowers, training her honeysuckles and eglantines, and trimming the turf seats which are tastefully disposed round their pretty cottage, Mr. Cathcart has been seen to come out and destroy all she had been doing; ploughing up the neat flower-beds with his knife, tearing down the vines, and covering the turf sofas with gravel. And the same little birds have added, that when Mr. Cathcart, sated with mischief, turned to go into the house again, he found the front-door fastened, and then

195

the back-door fastened; and after striding about for some time till his bald head was well nigh fried, he was fain to crawl in at the little latticed window, and then—but further these deponents say not.

Well! our little strawberry party was to consist of these English neighbors and some others, and I made due provision of the fragrant rubies, and the et-ceteras of a rural tea-visit. Roses of all hues blushed in my vases—a-hem! they were not pitchers, for the handles were broken off,— and forests of asparagus filled the fire-place. Alice and Arthur figured in their Sundays, little Bell had a new calico apron, and Charlie a shining clean face; so we were all ready.

First of all came the Cathcarts, and their one only and odd son of three years old; a child who looked as old as his father, and walked and talked most ludicrously like him. It did seem really a pity that the uncommonly fine eyes of his beautiful mamma had not descended to him; those large-pupilled grey eyes, with their long black lashes! and her richest of complexions, brighter in bloom and contrast than the sunniest side of a ripe peach; and her thousand graces of face and person. But there he was, a frightful little dwarf, just what his father would seem, looked at through a reverse telescope, or in a convex mirror. And Mr. Cathcart was all smiles and politeness, and brought a whole pocket full of literary novelties lately received from "home." And Mrs. Cathcart, always charming, looked lovelier than usual, in a pale-colored silk and very delicate ornaments.

She was sitting at the piano, playing some brilliant waltzes for the children, and Mr. Cathcart looking over some New-York papers which lay on the table, when Mrs. Brent, wan and feeble as usual, glided into the room. I introduced her to my guests, with whom she was evidently unacquainted, and in the next moment Mr. Brent entered.

It needed but one glance to convince me that, to Mrs. Cathcart at least, there was no occasion to introduce the latest comer. She half rose from her seat, painful blushes overspread her beautiful countenance, and instantly sub-

196

siding left it deathly pale, while Mr. Brent seemed equally discomposed, and Mr. Cathcart gazed in undisguised and most angry astonishment. I went through with the ceremony of presentation as well as I could, awkwardly enough, and an embarrassed pause succeeded, when in walked Mrs. Nippers and Miss Clinch.

"Well, good folks," said the widow fanning herself with a wide expanse of turkeys' feathers, which generally hung on her arm in warm weather; "this is what you may call toiling for pleasure, Mrs. Cathcart, how *do* you manage to get out in such melting weather? Well! I declare you *do* all look as if you *was* overcome by the weather or something else!" and she laughed very pleasantly at her own wit.

"Warm or cool, I believe we had better return home, Mrs. Cathcart," said her amiable spouse with one of his ineffable grins. She obeyed mechanically, and began putting her own straw bonnet on little Algernon.

"I declare," said the agreeable Mrs. Campaspe, "I thought—I was in hopes you were going to stay, and we could have had such a nice sociable time;" for Mrs. Nippers was very fond of inviting company—to other people's houses.

"No, Madam!" said Mr. Cathcart, "we must go instantly. Fanny, what are you doing? Can't you tie the child's hat?"

"One word, Sir!" said Mr. Brent, whose fine countenance had undergone a thousand changes in the few moments which have taken so many lines in telling; and he stepped into the garden path, with a bow which Mr. Cathcart returned very stiffly. He followed, however, and, in less than one minute, returned, wished us a very good day with more than the usual proportion of smiles—rather grinnish ones, 'tis true; but very polite; and almost lifting his trembling wife into the vehicle, which still stood at the gate, drove off at a furious rate.

And how looked the pale and gentle Catherine during this brief scene? As one who feels the death-stroke; like a frail blighted lily.

And beside her stood in silence
    One with a brow as pale,
And white lips rigidly compress'd
    Lest the strong heart should fail.

"Your ride has been too much for you, Mrs. Brent," said I; "you must rest awhile;" and I drew her into a small room adjoining the parlor, to avoid the industrious eyes of Mrs. Nippers.

She spoke not, but her eyes thanked me, and I left her, to receive other guests. Mrs. Nippers made a very faint move to depart when she began to perceive that company had been invited.

"Remain to tea, Mrs. Nippers," I said—could one say less—and she simpered, and said she was hardly decent, but—and added in a stage whisper, "If you could lend me a smart cap and cape, I don't know but I would." So she was ushered in due form to my room, with unbounded choice in a very narrow circle of caps and capes, and a pair of thin shoes, and then clean stockings, were successively added as decided improvements to her array. And when she made her appearance in the state-apartments, she looked, as she said herself, "pretty scrumptious;" but took an early opportunity to whisper, "I didn't know where you kept your pocket-handkerchiefs." So Alice was despatched for one, and the lady was complete.

Mr. Brent, with Bella in his arms, paced the garden walk, pretending to amuse the child, but evidently agitated and unhappy.

"Did you ever see anything so odd?" whispered Mrs. Nippers, darting a glance toward the garden.

But, fortunately, the person honored by her notice was all unconscious; and happening to observe his wife as he passed the low window in the little west-room, he stopped a few moments in low and earnest conversation with her. It was not long before Mrs. Brent appeared, and, apologizing with much grace, said, that feeling a little better, she would

198

prefer returning home. I took leave of her with regretful presentiments.

In less than a week, Mrs. Nippers had more than she could attend to. The Brents had left the country, and Mrs. Cathcart was alarmingly ill. The unfortunate strawberry-party so unexpectedly marred by this *rencontre,* was the theme of every convention within five miles, to speak moderately; and by the time the story reached home again, its own mother could not have recognized it.

A letter from Mr. Brent to say farewell and a little more gave us in a few words the outlines of a sad story; and while all Montacute was ringing with one of which not the smallest particular is lacking, I am not at liberty to disclose more of the "OWRE TRUE TALE," than the reader will already have conjectured—"a priory 'tachment."

The way Mrs. Nippers rolls up her eyes when the English are mentioned is certainly "a caution."

35

AGUE: MICHIGAN MALARIA

THE FRENCH CHARACTER has been supposed to surpass all others in flexibility—in the power of adapting itself to circumstances, even the most adverse and uncomfortable, and surely no people have been more fully tried. I think it was a practical philosopher of that race who asserted that a change of condition, however severe, ceased to be keenly felt after the first three months. The truth of this remark has been questioned, but I believe many, who have emigrated to these new countries, will be ready to confirm it by their own experience. It appears to me indeed that we must partake, in no slight degree, of the mobility of the French character, in order to maintain even a moderate share of spirits and resolution, under a change of situation which is certainly what, in their superfine phrase, is termed *vraiment desolant,* though it must be confessed that to say in plain English, *desolating,* too much might be implied. No English word that I can remember does express precisely this compulsory uprooting of all ancient memories, and the substitution of new and not very attractive associations in their honored place.

I know not whether we may not push still further our claim to the philosophical character, and consider ourselves as surpassing our prototype; for the French in their lowest estate have usually contrived so to place themselves as never to lack that elixir of life—society. A faithful friend or two—and they are too imaginative a people not to be tender and faithful in friendship—a friend or two and something to talk about, rank next to shelter and before food in their estimate of the comforts of life. But the emigrant to the wilderness must dispense even with society, as well as almost everything else which he has been accustomed to consider essential to happiness, and it is only after a weary interval of solitary rule that he may hope for neighbors and *de quoi causer*.

And happy would it be if even this were the worst. But what would the lively Frenchman say of his lot if he had witnessed, as so many of us have, the complete prostration of his family by agues? if he and his wife and his children, his man-servant and his maid-servant, and the good neighbor who tried to alleviate their sufferings, should be successively deprived of health, and reduced to a state of the most dispiriting helplessness, until scarce a hand retained power to draw water for the sick?

Such things are experienced annually by many of the settlers in the Western country; and, to finish the picture to the life, we must add the entire failure of the supply of *quinine*, on which alone we can rely for relief. This medicine, which acts like a charm on intermittents, is sometimes not to be procured in the interior at any price, and many lives are doubtless lost in consequence.

The cures wrought by means of this powerful agent are wonderful, and yet there exists a violent prejudice against its use. Agues are often suffered to "run," as we phrase it, the whole year round, in preference to curing them in two or three days with quinine, and it is perhaps only when the miserable patient is reduced to the last extreme of pallor and emaciation, and the grave seems opening to receive its prey, that the cure will be resorted to. A thousand prescriptions are in circulation, each of which is infallible in the estimation of a circle of believers, though experience is constantly demonstrating their fallacy. Mountain flax, prickly-ash, bark, bitter root, Cayenne pepper, laudanum, raw eggs, strong coffee, wormwood, hop tea,—but I might fill a page with the names of nauseous bitters, narcotics and stimulants which we are solicited to try, rather than subject ourselves to the terrific array of evils which are supposed to follow in the wake of the only true elixir. These are, dimness of sight, palpitation of the heart, obscurity of intellect, and general debility, even to the entire loss of the use of the limbs.

Now, it so happens that some or all of these are, in different degrees, the natural consequence of the agues themselves, and we have never seen them so severely experienced as in a case where not a particle of quinine had been used. But all this is as nothing in refutation of popular prejudice; and one of our neighbors has been twice *in articulo mortis* under his own prescriptions, when his friends have taken advantage of his nearly insensible state to send for a physician who administered quinine every hour or so for some time, to the evident saving of life in both cases.

But what is, in fact, the result of a class of diseases which requires the frequent exhibition of this powerful agent? Disastrous, undoubtedly; and it seems really marvellous that any who have experienced the disorder can suppose otherwise. The effect of an ordinary course of agues—say from six weeks to three months if no quinine be used,—is of a most discouraging character. The sight is usually a good deal affected, at least for the time, and, I almost fear, for life. There is a constant sense of feebleness, as well of mind as of body;—a confusion of ideas and a sombre view of ordinary circumstances. The limbs are prone to stiffness and inability, and the shrinking or quivering sensation about the heart is, as I can avouch, most depressing.

Why then is it that this condition, which I have described with all care and accuracy according to general as well as personal experience,—why is it that such a train of ills does not drive away the population in despair? What an inconsistency does it seem for such as can at any sacrifice strike the tent and remove to more fortunate regions, to remain a month in such an atmosphere? This has occurred to me a thousand times, yet I, like the rest, am content to live on, with the aid of that which supports all the world under every variety of difficulty and misfortune—hope. Everybody hopes this particular fit is to be positively the last visit of the foul fiend. If we can only get through to-day—if the shake does not dislocate the neckbone, or the fever set the house on fire,—we feel sure that we have had it so long, or we have had it so hard, or we have been so little subject to it—that it is not likely to return. This is certainly the most violent shake or the most delirious fever;—there is more perspiration, or less headache; or in some respect this attack differs from all that have preceded it; so that we feel confident there has been a change in the system, and any change must be for the better. And many times these prognostics at a venture prove quite true as if by miracle. An ague will quit one as suddenly and as inexplicably as it came on, without the use of remedies, whether of diet or medicine, and one may feel nothing of it for a year, perhaps for life. The consequences wear away, and we forget them. We look around us, through a translucent atmosphere, at a stout and even ruddy population; we see on every side a fertile and smiling country, abounding in natural resources and improving with unsurpassed rapidity,—a country where population is wealth;—and we ask ourselves, Is it really best to fly—to leave behind so many advantages,—and to lessen, even by our mite, the comforts of those who remain? Can we elude disease? And, since disease and death are everywhere, are the hopeless pulmonary ills of the seaboard less to be dreaded than these curable intermittents? All old people who have weathered the storm tell us that these troubles are concomitants only of new settlements, and that we shall see them diminish year by year,—to be replaced, however, by the less frequent but more fatal diseases of older countries.

Thus we live on, content to bear the ills we have, perhaps from a sense that there are ills everywhere; and that after all there may be worse things even than agues. Nine out of ten ague patients (as I suppose) are able to eat with good appetite as soon as the fit is over, and many continue about their ordinary business during all the time, save that absolutely occupied in shaking and burning. Those who have the complaint in this form generally keep up their spirits, and can, of course, be the more readily cured. Others see the matter in a different light, because they suffer agonies of pain, and perhaps rave during the long hours of fever. But there are few cases so desperate that they cannot be cured, at least temporarily, although again it must be confessed that it takes but a breath to call back the tormentor. The quivering of an aspen leaf will set one shaking from sympathy.

Among the rather novel remedies may be reckoned a cold shower-bath once or twice a day, which one may well believe would frighten away ague or anything else; and among those sanctioned by the learned, bleeding in the cold stage, which has been found successful in many cases. But neither of these modes is popular with us. We stick to thoroughwort,—balmony,—soot tea,—"number six,"—and the like; and avoid, as if for the life all "pothecary medicines." Yet if a petticoated professor of the healing art— a female physician so called—should prescribe the most deadly drugs, (purchased at the nearest druggist's,) or tell a man that his liver was grown fast to his side, and that he must release it by reaching upward while leaning on his elbow in bed,—or if she should pronounce oracularly that a dose of centipedes procured from beneath a fallen tree whose head should lie toward the east would cure "the spinevantosey that comes in the breast,"—she will find supporters who would not employ an educated physician on any account. I have been assured, with all seriousness, that the hepatic experiment alluded to had been tried with signal success; the patient having had the satisfaction of "hearing it tear" very distinctly. Happily this order of practitioners is not numerous, and from the general intelligence of the people, may be expected rather to diminish than to increase.

Of all the prominent curative theories of the day, that of the disciples of Hahnemann is, I think, the only one which we have not tried in some shape. It may be thought from what has been said, that we must be an imaginative community, and ought therefore to be good homœopathic subjects; but we have an instinctive disrespect for everything weak—except indeed coffee, which we take only in the "decillionth potence." And besides, it would never do to cure the ague by medicines which might be rendered destructive by much shaking. It would be safer indeed, upon the principle *similia similibus curantur,* to shake the patient soundly, without exhibiting a single globule or pellet of medicine, since we should thus avoid all danger of "drug-sickness" from over-dosing.

After all, though I believe homœopathy to be in advance of our present degree of Western civilization, I wish all my countrymen were converts to the doctrine that "it is impossible to give (or take) doses too small." They are terribly apt to err on the other side.

36

A TOUR IN THE FOREST

. . . A journey through the wilds, if performed by steam or post chaise, is just like a journey anywhere else, except a lack of some of the more refined accommodations for travelling. To find a spice of novelty,—to reap an advantage from position which shall in some degree counterbalance the deficiency necessarily observable in public conveyance so far from the great thoroughfares, we have devised a new mode of travel, or rather, we have adopted one which is new to us, although highly popular in these tramontane regions.

This resembles in no small degree that of the tinker in the story-book, whose equipage was a gigantic tea-kettle, the spout of which served for a chimney and the *tout ensemble* both for professional sign and family domicile; while its owner jogged along cosily, hammering as he went, chatting with the good wife within, and occasionally encouraging by a cherup the praiseworthy donkey that drew the entire establishment.

A pedlar of genius—a Yankee of course—has added yet one improvement to this ingenious plan. His *cow* serves a double purpose as a beast of *draught,* for she goes well in the harness, and he has only to stop and milk her when he is thirsty.

The nearest approach we have yet made to this compression of comforts took place recently, when after a most justifying course of agues we set out in the great waggon for a rambling tour of discovery, with everything we should be likely to want—including a large basket of provisions—embraced within its ample verge. Umbrellas good store—books and blankets—trunks and *sacs de nuit,*—besides some oats for the dear old ponies, and a pail wherefrom to give them drink, in case they should be athirst where water is more plenty than buckets,—all these made some ingenuity requisite in bestowing ourselves and our conveniences within the compass of even a regular backwoods waggon —the most capacious of vehicles;—and it took from early breakfast time until fully ten o'clock to "load up."

It may be that my dear reader being as I well surmise a dweller in cities, shall suppose this same farm waggon, which is so often referred to as a regular family vehicle, to be a sort of exaggerated britska—an able-bodied barouche, capable of containing, on crowded occasions, six ladies in bishop's sleeves: and that when we take a *fantaisie* for a week's ramble, it is only to send John to drive round at the appointed hour. Illusions all! The waggon consists of an oblong box of rough boards, mounted on the clumsiest of all possible wheels, and for springs we have two long slender tamarack poles placed within iron hooks appended to the sides. On these springs are board seats, with cushions or not, as the case may be, but always with buffalo skins by way of drapery. In the harness, all that is not leather is iron chain, except that there are generally weak points which are to be frequently fortified with twine or, alas! with the strings from your husband's vest if you forget to carry twine. Then your John, if you are so lucky as to have one, requires goodly notice of your errant intentions. Shoes are to be reset—harness to go to the *shoe-maker's* for repairs—white paint to be bottled for Quicksilver's shoulder, galled in ploughing. To secure a happy issue for your expedition requires only less deliberate preparation than Napoleon ought to have made for his jaunt to Moscow. It is awkward to discover important omissions when you are miles from efficient aid.

But everybody is waiting while I discuss these particulars. It was a cloudy day in July; a cloudy day after heavy showers,—showers which we felt confident had exhausted the watery reservoirs for the present, so that we congratulated ourselves upon the tempering clouds, and thought of leaving the umbrellas at home. However, it was not long before the sun shone in such force as to call forth the *parapluies* as parasols, and we were almost fainting under that particularly oppressive heat which belongs to such dropping weather in the midst of our summers. After we reached the boundaries of "the clearing" and plunged into the "timbered land," this heat was exchanged for a grotto-like coolness, and the horses trod leisurely as if to enjoy the damp, mossy soil and the grateful shade.

It was not long after noon when we began to think favorably of dinner, and we had not far to seek for a pleasant spot of green turf whereon to spread our couches of buffalo-skins and blankets. In the midst of a circle thus formed was the table-cloth with its accompaniments; and there in a *'café à mille colonnes'* which required no multiplying aid of mirrors, we took our first rustic repast,—all highly delighted with the novelty, but especially the young fry, who were allowed to go as often as they liked to a clear spring that welled from the hill-side, and dabble in the water which widened into a small, glassy pond below. They fed Prince with bread, which he took from their fingers with a care and delicacy worthy of his gentle blood, while poor Quicksilver showed his awkward rusticity by hanging his head or turning it sedulously aside when the same civility was offered him. But what they found most delightful of all was to see Leo's enthusiastic plunges in pursuit of the crackers which they sent skimming along the water as far as they could, trying his patience occasionally by the substitution of a flat stone by which he obligingly allowed himself to be deceived as often as they thought proper.

This said Leo is a particular friend of the family, not on account of his beauty, for he is an enormous creature with a ferocious bull-dog aspect—nor on the score of his services, for a more useless and chicken-hearted monster never

208

ate goslings—but just—because. This is the only assignable ground of Leo's popularity, and it is sufficient to secure his impunity in spite of many a misdemeanor, as well as to make him an inamissible member of the party whenever we go from home *en famille*. And indeed I have seen people admitted to society on slighter pretensions. . . .

Where was I? as the *causeurs impitoyables* always say. Oh! telling of our dinner in the woods.

When all was done, the cold beef and its attendant pickles,—the pies and the cake and the huge loaf were returned "each to the niche it was ordained to fill" in the champagne basket that served to hold our treasures. The little tin pail of butter which had been carefully placed in the water, was now re-wrapped in its shroud of fresh leaves, and we set forth again, but under a threatening aspect of the heavens. We had been so amused watching Leo's gambols in the still transparent water, that we had not noticed the gathering clouds, which now grew apace thicker and heavier than we could have desired. Nevertheless on we went, and at a good pace, for our steeds had been as well refreshed as ourselves, and seemed to understand beside that there might be a reasonable ground for haste. Not a house was to be descried, for in the back route we had chosen, settlers are few and scattered, and much of the road lay through tracts of untouched timber, where one was obliged sometimes to take good heed of the great H hacked on the trees by the surveyor's axe, to be sure that we were on the Highway.

And now the rain came down in earnest. No pattering drops,—no warning sprinkle,—but a sudden deluge, which wet everything through in half a minute. Onward, good Prince!—*en avant,* Quicksilver! (for thou art of French extraction;) shining and smoking as ye are, with torrents streaming down your innocent noses, adopt David Crockett's motto, so often quoted and acted upon by our compatriots,—"Go ahead!" If bonnets and veils,—if gingham and broadcloth or their wearers find any favor in your eyes, let not water extinguish your fire! Think of our soaking bread!

Think of your own swimming oats, and as ye love not "spoon-vittles," hasten.

The rain spatters up from the rail-fences so as to create a small fog on every rail. The puddles in the road look as if they were boiling, and the sky seems to grow more ponderous as it discharges its burden. We have emerged upon a clearing, and there is a liquid sheet between us and the distant woods.

But there is a roof! I see a stick chimney! and there is a drenched cow crowding in beneath a strawy barrack, and some forlorn fowls huddled under an old cart. We approach the habitations of men, and we may not doubt a good fire and a kind welcome,—so forward, good steeds!

The log-house proved a small one, and though its neat corn-crib and chicken-coop of slender poles bespoke a careful gudeman, we found no gate in front, but in its stead great awkward bars which were to be taken down or climbed over; and either of these is no pleasant process in a pouring rain. But by the aid of a little patience we made our way into the house, which had only a back door, as is very usual among the early settlers.

Within, marks of uncomfortable though strictly neat and decent poverty were but too evident. No well-stored dresser, —no snug curtains—no shining tins—no gorgeous piece-work bed-quilts, exhibiting stars of all magnitudes and moons in all quarters. Not even the usual display of Sunday habiliments graced the bare log walls. The good woman was of a shadowy thinness, and her husband, with a green shade over his eyes, wore a downcast and desponding air. One little girl with her yellow hair done up in many a papillote sat in a corner playing with a kitten. The mother put down her knitting as we entered, but the father seemed to have been sitting in listless idleness.

We were received with that free and hospitable welcome so general among the pioneers of the West. Our wet garments were carefully disposed for drying, and even the buffalo-robes and blankets found place on those slender poles which are usually observable above the ample fire-place of a regular log-hut; placed there for the purpose of drying—sometimes the week's wash, when the weather proves rainy,—sometimes whole rows of slender circlets of pumpkins for next spring's pies,—sometimes (when we can get them) festoons of sliced apples. The rain gave no sign of truce; the eaves poured incessantly, and we heard the rumbling of distant thunder. There was every prospect that we should be constrained to become unwilling intruders on the kindness of Mr. Gaston and his family, for the night at least.

When this was mentioned, the good woman, after expressing her willingness to do the very best she could for us, could not forbear telling us there *had been* a time when she could have entertained us decently under such circumstances. "But those days are gone by," she said with a sigh; "trouble has followed us so long that I don't look for anything else now. We left a good home in York state because my old man couldn't feel contented when he saw the neighbors selling out and coming to the West to get rich. And we bought so much land that we hadn't enough left to stock it, and improve it; but after a while we had got a few acres under improvement, and begun to have enough for our own consumption, although nothing to sell, and we had to part with some of our land to pay taxes on the rest—and then we took our pay in wild-cat money, that turned to waste paper before we got it off our hands. And my husband took on dreadful hard upon that,—and we all had the ague,—and then his eyes took sore,—and he is almost blind—too blind to see to work more than half the time. So we've been getting down, down, down! But I needn't cry," said the poor creature, wiping her eyes; "for I'm sure if tears could have bettered our condition, we'd have been well off long ago."

Here was an apology for poverty, indeed! How many complain of poverty, sitting in silks and laces, at tables covered with abundance! What groans over "hard times" have we not heard from jewelled bosoms within these two or three years! What rebuffs are always ready for those who take upon themselves the pleasant office of soliciting of the superfluity of the rich for the necessities of the poor. "Hard times!" say the unthinking children of luxury, as they sip their ice-cream, or hold up to the light the rosy wine!

This log-cabin with its civil and respectable inhabitants would furnish a lesson for such economists, if indeed they were willing to learn of the poor to appreciate the overabounding comforts of their lot.

Our hostess was a very active and tidy person, and she busied herself in all those little offices which evince a desire to make guests feel themselves welcome. She had small change of garments to offer, but she was unwearied in turning and drying before the fire such as we could dispense with for the time; for we hoped the storm would be but shortlived, and did not wish to open our trunks until we stopped for the night. The rain however slackened not, but on the contrary frequent flashes of lightning, and a muttering thunder which seemed momently to draw nearer, threatened still longer detention. The eaves poured merrily, and it was amusing to see our little hostess, with an old cloak over her head, fly out to place tubs, pails, jars, basins and milk-pans so as to intercept as much as possible of the falling treasure, intimating that as soap was pretty scarce she must try to catch rain-water, anyhow. A trough scooped from the portly trunk of a large whitewood-tree was so placed as to save all that fell from one side of the roof, but on the other almost all the utensils of the house were arranged by the careful dame, who made frequent trips for the purpose of exchanging the full for the empty—apologizing for not calling upon "th' old man" to assist her, because getting wet might increase the inflammation of his eyes.

Mrs. Gaston had carried out her last milk-pail and was returning to the door when the sound of wheels was heard above the rattling of the storm; and in another moment a loud "Hilloa!" told that other travellers beside ourselves were about to seek shelter.

"I'll tell 'em to drive on to Jericho," said Mrs. Gaston, "for we can't make them anyways comfortable here." "What! two mile further in this rain!" rejoined her husband; "no, no, that'll never do. The shower won't last long; let 'em come in." And he would take his great straw hat and go out to invite in this new windfall.

37

THE ELEGANT MARGOLDS

"HILLOA THERE! hilloa! where under the canopy *is* all the folks? be a joggin', can't ye?" shouted one of the newly arrived.

Mr. Gaston hurried as fast as his poor blind eyes would allow, and his wife threw fresh wood upon the fire, and swept the rough hearth anew, as well as she could with the remnant of a broom.

This was scarcely done when we heard voices approaching—at first mingled into a humming unison with the storm, then growing more distinguishable. A very shrill treble overtopped all the rest, giving utterance to all the approved forms of female exclamation.

"O dear!" "O mercy!" "O bless me!" "O Papa!" "O! I *shall* be drowned—smothered!" "O dear!" but we must not pretend to give more than a specimen.

A portly old gentleman now made his appearance, bearing, flung over his shoulder, what seemed at first view a bolster cased in silk, so limp and helpless was his burden. Behind him came as best she might, a tall and slender lady, who seemed his wife; and after scant salutation to the mistress of the cottage, the two old people were at once anxiously occupied in unrolling the said bolster, which proved, after the Champollion process was completed, to be a very delicate and rather pretty young lady, their daughter.

After, or rather with, this group entered a bluff, ruddy, well-made young man, who seemed to have been charioteer, and to whom it was not unreasonable to ascribe the adjuration mentioned at the head of our chapter. He brought in some cushions and a great-coat which he threw into a corner, establishing himself thereafter with his back to the fire, from which advantageous position he surveyed the company at his leisure.

"The luggage must be brought in," said the elderly gentleman.

"Yes! I should think it oughter," observed the young man in reply; "*I* should bring it in, if it was mine, anyhow!"

"Why don't you bring it in then?" asked the gentleman with rather an ominous frown.

"I! well, I don't know but what I could, upon a pinch. But look here, uncle! I want you to take notice of one thing —I didn't engage to wait upon ye. I a'n't nobody's nigger, mind that! I'll be up to my bargain. I came on for a teamster. If you took me for a servant, you've mistaken in the child, sir!"

"However," he continued, as if natural kindness was getting the better of cherished pride,—"I can always help a gentleman, if so be that he asks me *like* a gentleman; and, upon the hull, I guess I'm rather stubbeder than you be, so I'll go ahead."

And with this magnanimous resolution the youth departed, and with some help from our host soon filled up every spare corner, and some that could ill be spared, with a multifarious collection of conveniences very inconvenient under present circumstances. Three prodigious travelling-trunks of white leather formed the main body, but there were bags and cases without end, and to crown all, a Spanish guitar.

"That is all, I believe," said the old gentleman, addressing the ladies, as a load was set down.

"All!" exclaimed the teamster; "I should hope it was! and what anybody on earth can want with sich lots o' fixins, I'm sure's dark to me. If I was startin' for Texas I shouldn't want no more baggage that I could tie up in a handkercher. But what's curious to me is, where we're all

215

a-goin' to sleep tonight. This here rain don't talk o' stoppin', and here we've got to stay if we have to sleep, like pins in a pin-cushion, all up on end. It's my vote that we turn these contraptions, the whole bilin' on 'em, right out into the shed, and jist make up a good big shake-down, with the buffaloes and cushions."

The young lady, upon this, looked ineffable things at her mamma, and indeed disgust was very legible upon the countenances of all those unwilling guests. The house and its inhabitants, including our inoffensive and accidental selves, underwent an unmeasured stare, which resulted in no very respectful estimate of the whole and its particulars. Nor was this to be wondered at, for as to the house, it was, as we have said, one of the poorest and not one of the best of log-houses—there is a good deal of difference—and the people were much poorer than the average of our settlers.

The young lady at least, and probably her parents, had never seen the interior of these cabins before; indeed, the damsel, on her first unrolling, had said very naturally, "Why, Papa, is this a *house?*"

Then as to the appearance of our little party, it was of a truly Western plainness, rendered doubly plain, even in our own eyes, by contrast with the city array of the later comers. Theirs was in all the newest gloss of fashion, be-dimmed a little, it is true, by the uncourtly rain; but still handsome; and the young lady's travelling-dress displayed the taste so often exhibited by our young country-women on such occasions—it was a costume fit for a round of morning visits.

A rich green silk, now well draggled; a fine Tuscan-bonnet, a good deal trimmed within and without, and stained ruinously by its soaked veil; the thinnest kid shoes, and white silk stockings figured with mud, were the remains of the dress in which Miss Angelica Margold had chosen to travel through the woods. Her long ringlets hung far below her chin with scarce a remnant of curl, and her little pale face wore an air of vexation which her father and mother did their best most duteously to talk away.

216

"This is dreadful!" she exclaimed in no inaudible whisper, drawing her long damp locks through her jeweled fingers, with a most disconsolate air: "It is really dreadful! We can never pass the night here."

"But what else can we do, my love?" rejoined the mamma. "It would kill you to ride in the rain—and *you* shall have a comfortable bed at any rate."

This seemed somewhat consoling. And while Mrs. Margold and her daughter continued discussing these matters in an under tone, Mr. Margold set about discovering what the temporary retreat could be made to offer besides shelter.

"This wet makes one chilly," he said. "Haven't you a pair of bellows to help the fire a little?"

The good woman of the house tried her apron, and then the good man tried his straw hat—but the wood had been wet, and seemed not inclined to blaze.

"Bellowses!" exclaimed the young man, (whose name we found to be Butts;) "we can do our own blowin' in the woods. Here! let me try;" and with the old broom-stump he flirted up a fire in a minute, only scattering smoke and ashes on all sides.

The ladies retreated in dismay, a movement which seemed greatly to amuse Mr. Butts.

"Don't be scart!" he said; "ashes never pison'd anybody yet."

Mr. Margold was questioning Mrs. Gaston as to what could be had for tea,—forgetting, perhaps, that a farmer's house is not an inn, where chance comers may call for what they choose without offense.

"But I suppose you have tea—and bread and butter—and—"

"Dear!" exclaimed the poor woman, "I haven't seen any but sage tea these three months;—and as for bread, I could make you some johnny-cake if you like that; but we have had no wheat flour this summer, for my old man was so crowded to pay doctor bills and sich, that he had to sell his wheat. We've butter, and I believe I may say it's pretty good."

"Bless my soul! no bread!" said the old gentleman.

"No tea!" exclaimed his wife.

"O dear! what an awful place!" sighed Miss Angelica piteously.

"Well! I vote we have a johnny-cake," said the driver; "you make us a johnny-cake, aunty, and them that can't make a good supper off of johnny-cake and butter, deserves to go hungry, that's a fact!"

Mrs. Gaston, though evidently hurt by the rude manner of her guests, set herself silently at work in obedience to the hint of Mr. Butts, while that gentleman made himself completely at home, took the little girl in his lap with the loving title of "Sis," and cordially invited Mr. Margold to sit down on a board which he had placed on two blocks, to eke out the scanty number of seats.

"Come, uncle," said the facetious Mr. Butts, "jes' take it easy, and you'll live the longer. Come and set by me, and leave more room for the women-folks, and we'll do fust-rate for supper."

Mr. Butts had evidently discovered the true philosophy, but his way of inculcating it was so little attractive, that the Margolds seemed to regard him only with an accumulating horror.

Hitherto we had scarcely spoken, but, rather enjoying the scene, had bestowed ourselves and our possessions within as small a compass as possible, and waited the issue. But these people looked so thoroughly uncomfortable, so hopelessly out of their element, and seemed moreover, by decree of the ceaseless skies, so likely to be our companions for the night, that we could not help taking pity on them, and offering such aid as our more mature experience of forest life had provided. Our champagne basket was produced, and the various articles it contained gave promise of a considerable amendment of Mrs. Gaston's tea-table. A small canister of black tea and some sparkling sugar gave the crowning grace to the whole, and as these things successively made their appearance, it was marvellous to observe how the facial muscles of the fashionables gradually relaxed into the habitually bland expression of politer atmospheres. Mrs. Margold, who looked ten years younger when she smoothed the peevish wrinkles from her brow, now thought it worth while to bestow a quite gracious glance at our corner, and her husband actually turned his chair, which had for some time presented its back full to my face.

We got on wondrously after this. Mrs. Gaston, who was patience and civility personified, very soon prepared a table which was nearly large enough to serve all the grown people, and as she announced that all was ready, Mr. Butts, who had been for some time balancing a chair very critically on its hinder feet, wheeled round at once to the table, and politely invited the company to sit down. As there was no choice, the strangers took their seats, with prim faces enough, and Mrs. Gaston waited to be invited to make tea, while her poor half-blind husband quietly took his place with the children to await the second table.

Mr. Butts was now in his element. He took particular pains to press everybody to eat of everything, and observing that Miss Angelica persisted in her refusal of whatever he offered her, he cut with his own knife a bountiful piece of butter, and placed it on her plate with an air of friendly solicitude.

The damsel's stare would have infallibly have frozen any young man of ordinary sensibility, but Mr. Butts, strong in his conscious virtue, saw and felt nothing but his own importance; and moreover seemed to think gallantry required him to be specially attentive to the only young lady of the party. "Why, you don't eat nothing!" he exclaimed; "ridin' don't agree with you, I guess! now for my part it makes me as savage as a meat-axe! If you travel much after this fashion, you'll grow littler and littler; and you're little enough already, I should judge."

It was hardly in human nature to stand this, and Mr. Margold, provoked beyond the patience which he had evidently prescribed to himself, at last broke out very warmly upon Mr. Butts, telling him to mind his own business, and sundry other things not particularly pleasant to relate in detail.

"Oh! you're wrathy a'n't ye? Why, I didn't mean nothing but what was civil! We're plain-spoken folks in this new country."

Mr. Margold seemed a little ashamed of his sudden blaze when he found how meekly it was met, and he took no further notice of his republican friend, who on his part, though he managed to finish his supper with commendable *sang froid*, was evidently shorn of his beams for the time.

38

CITY PEOPLE AND FRONTIER WAYS

MOST LAMENTABLY amusing was the distress of Miss Angelica when it became necessary to concert measures for passing a night in a crowded log-cabin. The prospect was not a very comfortable one, but the view taken of its horrors by these city people was so ludicrously exaggerated that I am sure no spectator could help laughing. The philosophy that cannot stand one night's rough lodging should never travel west of Lake Erie. Not that lodging anywhere in these Western wilds is likely to be found more really uncomfortable than is often the lot of visitors at the Springs during crowded seasons; but fashionable sufferings are never quite intolerable.

The sleeping arrangements were of a more perplexing character than those which had been fortunately devised for the tea. There were two large beds and a trundle-bed, and these, with a scanty supply of bedding, comprised our available means; and besides our tea-party, two little boys had come dripping home from school to add to our numbers. After much consultation, many propositions, and not a few remarks calculated rather to wound the feelings of our civil entertainers, it was concluded to put the two large beds close together in order to enlarge their capabilities, and this extensive couch was to hold all the "women-folks" and some of the children. The trundle-bed by careful stowage took the little ones; and for the old gentleman, a couch of buffalo-robes and carriage-cushions was skilfully prepared by none other than the forgiving Mr. Butts, who seemed disposed to forget past rebuffs, and to exert himself very heartily in the public service. This disinterested individual was perfectly content to repose Indian fashion, with his feet to the fire, and anything he could get for a pillow; and the master of the house stretched himself out after the same manner.

When all was done, Mrs. Gaston made the ordinary cotton-sheet-partition for the benefit of those who chose to undress; and then began to prepare herself for the rest which I am sure she needed. All seemed well enough for weary travellers, and at any rate, these poor people had done their best. I hoped that all fault-finding would soon be hushed in sleep.

But it became evident ere long that Miss Margold did not intend to become a person of so small consequence. She had disturbed her father several times by requests for articles from different parts of the luggage, without which she declared she could not think of going to bed. She had received from her mother the attendance of a waiting maid without offering the slightest service in return, and now, when all her ingenuity seemed to be exhausted, she suddenly discovered that it would be in vain for her to think of sleeping in a bed where there were so many people, and she decided on sitting up all night.

A silence expressive of the deepest consternation held the assembly bound for some seconds. This was first broken by a long, low, expressive whistle from Mr. Butts, but the remembrance of past mischance bridled his tongue.

"Do you think you could sleep here, my dear?" inquired Mr. Margold from his snug nest in the corner.

The young lady almost screamed with horror. "Never mind, my darling," said the mamma, "I will sit in the rocking-chair by the fire, and you shall have plenty of room."

"Oh no, Ma! that will never do—why can't the woman sit up? I dare say she's used to it." This was said in a loud whisper which reached everybody's ears—but no reply was made.

Mrs. Margold and her daughter whispered together for some time further, and the result was that the lady drew one of the beds apart from the other, which movement caused Mrs. Gaston's little girl to roll out upon the floor with a sad resounding thump and a piteous cry.

This proved the drop too many. Outspoke at last the poor half-blind husband and father. His patience was, as Mr. Butts would say, "used up." "Neighbors," said he, "I don't know who you are nor where you come from, and I didn't ask, for you were driven into my house by a storm. My family were willing to accommodate you as far as they could; such as we had, you were welcome to, but we are poor, and have not much to do with. Now, you haven't seemed to be satisfied with anything, and your behavior has hurt my wife's feelings, and mine too. You think we are poor ignorant people, and so we are; but you think we haven't feelings like other folks, and there you are mistaken. Now the short and long of the matter is, that as the storm is over and the moon is up, it's my desire that you pick up your things and drive on to the next tavern, where you can call for what you like, and pay for what you get. I don't keep a tavern, though I'm always willin' to entertain a civil traveller as well as I can." "Hast thou not marked when o'er thy startled head Sudden and deep the thunder-cloud has rolled—" I do not know whether this unexpected display of spirit in poor Mr. Gaston was more like a thunderclap or a deluge from a fire engine. Like single-speech Hamilton, he was too wise to attempt to add anything to the effect it had produced. He waited in silence, but it was a very resolute silence.

The Margolds were in a very pitiable perplexity. Miss Angelica, knowing that none of the trouble would come upon herself, was for being very spirited upon the occasion; her papa, who had already begun to dream of Wall Street and Waverly Place, did hate to be recalled to the woods; and Mrs. Margold had no opinion of her own on this or any other occasion. Mr. Gaston, seeing no demonstrations of retreat, went to Butts, who was or pretended to be asleep, and, shaking him by the shoulder, told him he was wanted to get up his horses.

"Get up the poor critters at this time o' night!" said he, rubbing his eyes; "why! what upon the livin' earth's the matter! has the young woman got the high strikes?"

"Your folks is a-goin' to try to mend their lodgin', that's all," replied the host, whose temper was a good deal moved. "They a'n't satisfied with the best we could do for 'em, and it's my desire that they should try the tavern at Jericho. It is but two miles, and you'll soon drive it."

"I'll be tipp'd if I drive it to-night though, uncle," replied the imperturbable Mr. Butts; "I don't budge a foot. I sha'n't do no sich nonsense. As for their trying the tavern at Jericho, the tavern's a deuced sight more likely to try *them*, as you know very well. Anyhow, this child don't stir."

"But if we are turned out of doors," said Mr. Margold, who aroused himself most unwillingly to the consciousness of a new cause of disturbance, "you are bound to—"

"I a'n't bound to drive nobody in the middle of the night," said Mr. Butts, "so you don't try to suck me in there. But as to turning you out o' doors, this here chap a'n't the feller to turn any man out o' doors if he'll be civil. He's a little wrathy because your folks wa'n't contented with such as he had. I see he was a gettin' riled some, and I thought he'd bile over. You see that's the way with us Western folks. If folks is sassy we walk right into 'em, like a thousand o' brick. He'll cool down agin if you jist pat him a little. He's got some grit, but he a'n't ugly. You only make your women-folks keep quiet—get a curb-bridle upon their tongues, and we'll do well enough."

Poor Mr. Margold! here was a task! But sleep, though it makes us terribly cross when its own claims are interfered with, is a marvellous tranquillizer on all other subjects; and as Mr. and Mrs. Margold and Miss Angelica were all very, very weary—the latter of teasing her parents, the former of being teased—a truce was at length concluded by the intervention of Mr. Butts, who acted the part of a peacemaker, and gave sage advice to both parties.

The conduct of these city people, who were evidently of a very numerous class—that which possesses more money than intellect or cultivation—is not, after all, very surprising; for it is still fresh in our recollection that an English traveller of intelligence—one notorious for ultra-liberal principles too—made angry complaint because the mistress of a log-house somewhere on the Western prairies was not disposed to entertain a party of strangers, who found it convenient to enter her dwelling uninvited. It seems that this person, whoever she may have been, was insensible of the honor done her house by an Avatar of so much dignity. She thought, perhaps that travellers who had abundant means might have arranged their distances so as to make public-houses their stopping places. And if her dwelling had, by a chance which might not unnaturally occur in the wilds of the West, been the mansion of wealth and consequence, it may be doubted whether our "liberal" guests would have claimed hospitality at its gates. It was because the tenant of the log-cottage was supposed to be *poor,* that she was censured for her unwillingness to turn her humble lodge into a tavern.

Hospitality claimed as such is, I believe, *invariably* rendered among us, with a freedom worthy of Arcadia itself. It is only when there is evidently a supposition on the part of the guest that a poor man's house and family are necessarily at the service of anybody, for the sake of a few shillings, that our cherished independence is called into action. It is under such circumstances that those who are disposed to lord it in log-cabins discover that people who are not afraid to be poor can afford to be independent; and that uninvited guests must purchase civility by civility, or find themselves unwelcome in spite of money.

After much experience I can assert that I have never known or heard of an instance where those who have found it convenient to throw themselves on the kindness of a settler of any degree, have not been received with a frank welcome, which has appeared to me peculiarly admirable, because extended, in many cases, under circumstances of

225

the greatest inconvenience. Nor have I ever known compensation demanded, whatever may have been the trouble given; and where it has been accepted at all, it has been only sufficient to repay actual cost, and that usually upon urgency.

Less than this I could not say in fairness to the justly praised hospitality of the West; and I believe every reader will scarcely think our friend Gaston's apparent departure from the practice of the land needed this apology. It suggested itself unbidden, under the recollection of many a kindness received from strangers in the course of our numerous peregrinations.

39

A MORNING'S RIDE

WE HAD AGREED to make a twelve-mile stage before break-fast in company with the city people, whose way lay with ours so far. When the morning came and our mutual arrangements were to be made, the Margolds were so prodigiously sulky under the consciousness of last night's disagreeables, that I felt rather ashamed of the companion-ship, and would have preferred waiting to breakfast on sage-tea with poor Mrs. Gaston, who was evidently very uncomfortable between the recollection of the affronts put upon herself, and the fear that her husband had gone too far in resenting them. The die was cast however, and we were obliged to seem to belong to the offending side, who carried their wounded dignity very high at parting. Mr. Margold asked for Mr. Gaston's *"bill"*; our host declined making any charge. Mr. Margold insisted on his receiving payment, and finished by placing a bank-note on the table as he left the house without saying farewell, in which latter civility he was closely imitated by Mrs. Margold and Miss Angelica.

"*You* didn't think I was *on*civil did ye?" said Gaston, somewhat anxiously, as we prepared to follow.

"Not in the least! You were quite right," was the very sincere reply, for we thought the poor blind man had borne more than enough.

"Well! you've had a pretty mean time, I reckon!" said Mr. Butts, who stepped in to bid good-bye, just as we were departing; and I heard him add, "You larnt 'em a good lesson anyhow! I wouldn't ha' missed of it for a cow!"

Mr. Margold was to be my husband's companion as far as Wellington, where we were to take our coffee, and I was exalted to the back seat of the jingling barouche, which I shared with Mrs. Margold, leaving the front for Miss Angelica and her guitar.

The morning was a charming one, and a strong breeze from the west came as if on purpose to refresh the spirits and cool the temper of the party after the *contretemps* of the night. But this breeze, bearing on its fresh pinions some of the balmy moisture of last night's shower, blew Miss Angelica's long ringlets about most intolerably, and her little forehead became quite quilted with very unbecoming wrinkles, when, as we drove through a narrow way where the bushes almost met above our heads, a provoking puff sent down a copious shower from the leaves, demolishing the small remnant of curl and the smaller remnant of patience, and the young lady scolded outright.

"I never *did* see such an odious country as this is!" she exclaimed; "it is impossible to look decent for an hour!"

"Well! one comfort is," said Mr. Butts consolingly, "that there a'n't many folks to see how bad you look, here in the woods! We a'n't used to seein' folks look dreadful slick nother—so it don't matter."

Double-distilled scorn curled Miss Margold's lip, and she maintained an indignant silence, as the only shield against the impertinence of the driver, who found consolation in an unceasing whistle. They had picked up this youth at a neighboring village, supposing from his pleasant countenance and obliging manner, that they had gained a treasure of civility. It had been at Miss Angelica's especial instance that the party had quitted the usual road and taken to the woods. She wished to be a little romantic, but she had not counted the cost. Butts was indeed all they had supposed from his address, smart, good-tempered and kind-hearted, yet, as we have seen, he was not the less lacking in the kind of knowledge which was requisite for the part he had undertaken. He had never lived with any but those who considered him quite equal to themselves. He was the son of a respectable farmer, whose ample lands would cut up well among his heirs; and when our friend Dan engaged to "drive team" for Mr. Margold, he had no idea but that he was to be, to all intents and purposes, one of the party, saving and excepting his duty towards the horses, which he performed with scrupulous fidelity and no small skill. All this seemed so evident, that I almost wondered that Miss Margold could not have passed over his intrusiveness more good-humoredly, setting it to the account of sheer ignorance, and not evil intention. But unfortunately the young lady seemed to fear that her dignity would be irrevocably compromised if she did not resent each and every instance of impertinence, and as Butts was one of those who cannot take the broadest hint—even an Irish one—he only talked the more, thinking he had not yet hit upon the right way to make himself agreeable.

By and by, finding it impossible to extort a reply from the thready lips of the fair Angelica, he hailed a young man whom we overtook on the road.

"Hilloa! Steve! where are you a stavin' to? If you're for Wellington, scale up here and I'll give ye a ride. I swan! I'm as lonesome as a catamount! You won't have no objection, I suppose?" turning slightly to Mrs. Margold. The lady did not forbid, and the traveller was soon on the box, much to Mr. Butts's relief, as he now had an interlocutor.

"How do you stan' it nowadays?" was the salutation of Mr. Butts to his friend.

"O, so as to be a crawlin' most of the time. Be you pretty hearty this summer?"

"Why, I'm middlin' tough. I manage to make pork ache when I get hold on't."

"Are you hired with anyone now, or do you go on your own hook?"

"I've been teamin' on't some for old Pendleton that built

them mills at Wellington. I come on to drive a spell for this here old feller," (jerking his thumb backward,) "but I guess he sha'n't hitch long."

"Why not? Don't he pay?"

"Pay! O, no danger o' that! money's the thing he's got most of. But he wanted a *servant*, and that, you know, Steve, is a berry that don't grow on these bushes."

"So he hired you for a servant, eh?" and at the thought "Steve" laughed loud and long.

"Why! a body would think you had found a haw-haw's nest with a te-he's eggs in't!" said Mr. Butts, who seemed a little nettled by his friend's ridicule.

"Well, but it's too funny, anyhow," was the rejoinder; and the two friends branched off into various discussions, and regaled each other with sundry pieces of intelligence referring to the fortunes and characters of the Toms, Dicks and Harries of their acquaintance; leaving my attention at liberty to profit by many parallel passages from the lips of Mrs. Margold, who was well acquainted with the latest improvements in the choice and quality of refreshments at parties, the newest style of French embroidery, and the shape and trimmings of the bonnets by the last packet. I had become quite absorbed in these matters, and had fallen into a sort of doze, such as I suppose to be the only sleep needed by a French milliner, when I was aroused by a clear, manly voice, with just enough of a nasal twang to make me remember that I was still in the woods, singing an air that recalled "young Lochinvar," and which had doubtless originally been intended for none other. The words were those of a Western song which refers to that interesting period in our local history—the admission of Michigan into the Union,—on which occasion our General Government decided that between the States at least, "might makes right;"—the era of the Toledo war, which cost us so much inkshed, and the unfortunate borderers such numbers of water-melons and pumpkins. This song is *not*, I believe, the one written by Mrs. Sigourney on the occasion.

230

I

Oh! dashing young Mick is the pride of the West!
Of all its bold hunters the boldest and best,
He has town-house and villa, and water-craft fair,
And parks full of red-deer, enough and to spare.
He has meadow and woodland, lake, river, and lick,
And prairie-land plenty, has dashing young Mick.

II

Now Mick, while a minor, was under control
Of his loving mamma, a good careful old soul.
And to all her long lectures, so prudent and sage,
His pithy response was—"But, ma'am, I'm of age!"
Says she, "You must share with poor Philo and Dick."
"But a'n't I of age, ma'am?" cried dashing young Mick.

III

One time, when a party of gentlemen came
To prose with his mother, Mick sent in his claim:
Says he, "Here's the record—my nonage is o'er;
In this year thirty-five I've exceeded my score;
Make o'er my estate, ma'am, and please to be quick!
I can shear my own wolves, now!" quoth dashing young Mick.

IV

"But, my dear, there's your brothers—they worry my life—
And you know 'tis my duty to smother all strife!
They *will* have *that* farm—and—we'll pay on demand
Ten miles of good ice for an acre of land;
Of the pine-barrens north you the choicest may pick."
"I'll be blam'd if I do, ma'am!" growled dashing young Mick.

V

The dame, with a sigh, put her spectacles on;
"Now tell me, grave counsellers, what's to be done!"
"Oh! let it lie by till we taste your good cheer;
A twelvemonth's discussion will make it more clear.

You know what stout fellows are Philo and Dick,
And they'll nibble, if we don't, from dashing young Mick.

VI

Poor Mick! he talked big, and most roundly he swore
He'd at least have his own, if he couldn't get more:
But his ma' kept the farm and the money to stock it,
And quietly buttoned her purse in her pocket,
While the gentlemen argued through thin and through thick—
"Oh! I'll share and be thankful!" quoth dashing young Mick.

The ditty might have extended to the length of Chevy
Chase for aught I can tell, in spite of many signs of indignation on the part of Mrs. Margold and her daughter, if we
had not at that moment come in sight of the tavern at Wellington, which caused Mr. Butts to interrupt his vocal efforts, and give a rousing touch to his horses to insure "a
trot for the avenue."

40

THE BEAUTIES OF MICHIGAN

WE FOUND a decent inn and a tolerable breakfast, but the place itself was the image of desolation. It was one of those which had started into sudden life in speculating times, and the great mill, the great tavern and various other abortions had never known the luxury of a pane of glass or a paint-brush, nor did they bear marks of having at any time been occupied. A "variety store," offering for sale every possible article of merchandise, from lace gloves to goose-yokes,—ox-chains, tea-cups, boots and bonnets inclusive,—displayed its tempting sign; but the clerk sat smoking on the steps, and a few loungers around him looked like whiskey-customers only. There was a banking-house, of course; and (also of course) it was closed, though the sign still stared impudently at the cheated passenger. And this was "Wellington!" Hollow honor for "le vainqueur du vainqueur du monde!"

After breakfast—at which, bye the bye, Mr. Butts and his friend filled high places,—we bade adieu to the Margolds, who were to regain the great road after a few miles of further travel, while we took to the woods again. Before we parted, however, Mr. Butts sought occasion to call us to witness that he returned to Mr. Margold the bank-note which that gentleman had deposited on Mr. Gaston's table.

"You see, he a'n't no hand to make a fuss, Gaston a'n't; so he jist told me to give it to ye after you got away. And he said," added the agreeable youth with a smile, "that he'd rather you'd buy manners with it, if you could."

How Mr. Margold and his driver got on after we parted, I cannot pretend to say, but I must confess I did not find it difficult, on review of what had passed during our short acquaintance, to decide which party had been most deficient in propriety and good feeling.

Our way lay northward, through a broken and uneven tract, and the road wound round the base of high woody hills in many an intricate curve. This road is only one of Nature's laying. When it is what is technically called "laid," by the united wisdom of the district,—at present the owl and the fox are the only *savans* in the neighborhood,—it will go most determinedly straight up and straight down the hills, and in a "bee line," as we say, through the broadest marshes, if marshes lie in the way. We scorn to be turned aside when we are laying roads. Not that we run them in a direct line between the places we wish to connect. Nothing is further from our plan. We follow section lines most religiously, and consequently,—the sections being squares,—we shall in time have the pleasure of travelling zigzag at right angles, from one corner of the state to another. We do not submit to have notches and slices cut off our farms for the accommodation of the public. If fifty cents' worth of land would save digging down a hill or bridging a wide marsh at the expense of hundreds of dollars, no farmer would be found who would vote for so tyrannical a proceeding. Truly says Mons. De Tocqueville that ours is a most expensive mode of transacting public business.—But as I was saying, our road was not "laid." so it was a very even and pleasant one, although it led through a rough country.

We had not yet lost the fresh breeze of the early morning, but the sun had become so powerful as to make the flickering shade of these scattered woods very delightful to us all. The children were never tired of watching the vagaries of the little chipmunk as he glanced from branch to branch with almost the swiftness of light, but they screamed with pleasure when the noise of our wheels started three young fawns that were quietly nestled at the foot of a great oak, and now pursued their graceful flight over hill and hollow, lost to the sight at one moment, then reappearing on another eminence, and standing still to watch us, belling all the while. It was a pretty sight, and I was as much disappointed as the little folks when I found our fairy company had indeed left us, as the children said, "for good and all." On the whole, that morning ride was one of the pleasant trifles which one remembers for a long time.

Our scenery has been called tame. What is tame scenery? Is every landscape tame which cannot boast of mountains or cataracts? Save these I know of no feature of rural beauty in which our green peninsula is found wanting. If the richest meadow-land shut in by gently swelling hills and fringed with every variety of foliage—if streams innumerable, not wild and dashing it is true, but rapid enough to insure purity—if lakes in unparalleled variety of size and figure, studded with islands and tenanted by multitudes of wild fowl—if these be elements of beauty, we may justly boast of our fair domain, and invoke the eye of the painter and the pen of the poet. No spot on earth possesses a more transparent atmosphere. If it be true of any region that "the glorious sun enriches so the bosom of the earth that trees and flowers appear but like so much enamel upon gold—" we may claim the description as our own. The heavenly bodies seem to smile upon us without an intervening medium. The lustre of the stars and the white glittering moonlight seem more pure and perfect here than elsewhere.

"That's a little sun, Papa!" said wee Willie, pointing with rapt admiration at the evening star; and it is not long since I uttered an exclamation at seeing what I supposed to be a crimson flame bursting over the roof of a house at a little distance, but which proved to be Mars just risen above the horizon, and showing an aspect which in warlike times could be considered nothing less than portentous.

This peculiar transparency in the atmosphere is strikingly

evident in the appearance of the Aurora Borealis, which often looks to be so near us that one can almost fancy that the tall pines pierce its silvery depths and enjoy perpetual daylight.

Perhaps it is this that gives a charm to scenery which it has been the fashion to call tame. The waters are more like molten diamonds, and the herbage like living emeralds, because the lustrous sky brings out their hues in undimmed intensity, adding depth to shadow, and keeping back nothing of brilliancy. Philosophers might tell of refraction,— and painters of *chiar oscuro*—I have but one word—Beauty! and this expresses all that I know about that which fills me with delight.

We can at least boast some features unique and peculiar in our landscape—our "openings" and our wide savannahs are not to be found in Switzerland, I am sure. These—as to the picturesque which we are all wild about—bear something like the same proportion to the Alps that the fair, blue-eyed, rosy-cheeked and tidy daughter of one of our good farmers, does to the Italian improvisatrice with her wild black eyes and her soul of fire. There are many chances in favor of the farmer's daughter being the most comfortable person to live with, though she will attract no tourists to her *soirées*.

It is well understood that a large proportion of the *new* new world was found but scantily clothed with timber. Immense tracts are covered but thinly with scattered trees, and these are almost exclusively of the different kinds of oak. By contrast with the heavily timbered land these tracts seem almost bare, and they have received the appropriate name of "oak-openings." Innumerable are the hypotheses by which the learned and the ingenious have attempted to account for this peculiarity of the country. Many have ascribed it to the annual fires which the Indians are known to have sent through the forest with the intention of clearing away the almost impervious under-brush which hindered their hunting. But the fact that the soil of the openings is ordinarily quite different in its characteristics from that of the timbered land seems to oblige us to seek further for a reason for so striking a difference in outward appearance. Much of our soil is said to be diluvial,—the wash of the great ocean lakes as they overflowed toward the south. This soil, which varies in depth from one foot to one hundred, (say the explorers,) is light and friable, but it is based upon something emphatically called "hard pan," which is supposed to prevent the roots of large trees from striking to a proper depth. Whether oak-openings are found only where the soil is one foot in thickness, or equally where it extends to one hundred, we are not informed, I believe; but in all cases the hard pan gets the blame, from one class of theorists at least, of the want of large timber in these park-like tracts of our pleasant land.

The other "feature" to which I alluded—a very wide and flat one—the prodigious amount of wet prairie or "marsh" —the produce of millions of springs which percolate in every direction this diluvial mass—it is said to promise magnificent resources of wealth for—our great-grandchildren. At present it yields, in the first place, agues of the first quality, and, secondly, very tolerable wild grass for the cattle of the emigrant; which latter advantage is supposed very much to have aided in the rapid settlement of the country. People make their transit now as in the time of the patriarchs, with their flocks and their herds, certain of finding abundant though coarse food for the sustenance of all kinds of stock until they shall have had time to provide better.

As to future days, inexhaustible beds of peat and marl— the former to use as fuel when we shall have burned all the oaks, the latter to restore the exhausted soil to its pristine fertility—are to compensate to our descendants for the loss of energy and enterprise which we ancestors shall undoubtedly suffer through agues. So things will in time be equalized. We reap the advantages of the rich virgin soil; our hereafter is to find boundless wealth beneath its surface.

Not fewer than three thousand lakes—every one a mirror set in verdant velvet and bordered with the richest fringe

—with a proportionate number of streams—the very threadiest capable of being dammed into a respectable duckpond —supply moisture to our fields. What wonder then that those fields "stand dressed in living green!" One acre of water to less than forty of land! Small need, one would think, for artificial irrigation! Yet we have seen much suffering from drought, even in this land of water. For eighteen months, at one time, we of the interior had not a heavy shower, nor even a soft rain long enough continued to wet more than the surface of the ground. This lack of the ordinary supply of falling water is supposed to have effected materially the decrease of depth in the great lakes. Their periodical subsidence (a knotty subject, by the bye) went on much more rapidly than usual during that time. A smaller, though not unimportant, concomitant of the parching process was the thirsty condition of the poor cattle, who had to be driven, in some cases, miles for each day's drink. They do not like their champaign without water, so that they really suffered. At such times, one is almost disposed to wish, in defiance of the picturesque, that the state was laid out like a checkerboard—a lake in every other quarter-section. I suppose however that no country—except Holland perhaps—is more thoroughly soaked than ours; so that, notwithstanding this one arid period, we need scarcely fear that our history will be a dry one.

The quietly beautiful aspect of Michigan, tame though it be, is not without its consolations. Have not the learned agreed that people's characteristics usually bear some mysterious *rapport* to those of their native land? Few of our "natives" have as yet had time to show much character, but we as are bound to believe in the pretty notion that "lands gentle-featured, calm and softly fair, produce such men as should be dwellers there—" what of mildness, kindness and all the gentler virtues may we not augur for the rising race? It is true there may never be a William Tell among them, but the mountain hero was the bright creation of circumstances that will never arise in this sunny land of lakes. We can do without such, for we shall have no Gesslers.

41

A MILL RAISING

Wilder and rougher grew our winding way after we lost sight of the fawns, and I began to think Constantinople must be farther off than we had supposed, when our wheel plumped suddenly into a great dry hole so deep that it brought our steeds to a stand still. They, like ourselves, had been unprepared for anything of the sort, for the track had been as smooth, if not as level, as a bowling-green. It was green too, for it had not been enough travelled to destroy the original sward. What could be the meaning of this pitfall?

It was vain to question the trees or the chipmunks, and our own wits offered no satisfactory solution; so we drove on. A few yards more, and we came to a similar trap, and from this time onward they became more and more frequent. They were the oddest thing that could be, in this out of the way place, seeming freshly dug and without conceivable aim or purpose. We discussed the point without arriving at any satisfactory conclusion, till we became sensible of a new wonder—a distant sound of "Yo heave!" recurring at regular intervals, and transporting one's mind at once to the borders of the well-beloved sea, whose various music was far more familiar to our youthful ears than the murmur of the forest.

"Yo heave! Yo heave!" the mingled sound of many voices, became more and more distinctly audible as we ascended a high bank broken everywhere by the holes I have mentioned. When we reached its summit, from which the road descended suddenly into a deep, woody dell, a scene of strange beauty met our eyes, and explained all. Over a small stream in the bottom of the dell—a mere brooklet as it seemed from that distance—some eighty or perhaps a hundred men were erecting the frame-work of a large mill —an object which seemed almost as much out of place in this primal solitude as would the apparition of a three-decker upon the stocks, which indeed it much resembled. Nothing could be more striking than the contrast between this intricate specimen of human skill, and the majestic simplicity of nature around it. The trees which had been felled to make room for it, lay in their yet unfaded green on every side, and so scanty allowance had been made for the gigantic intruder, that the still living forest hung over its symmetrical spars. An immense *beat* was about to be raised, (borrowed learning this,) and as many men as could find hands-breadths on its edge were applying their united energies to the task, bringing to mind inevitably the sleeping Gulliver under the efforts of his Lilliputians. As the huge mass left the ground, poles and handspikes assisted its ascent, and the "Yo heave!" was repeated as a signal for every fresh effort, as on shipboard. When it had reached its place high in air, it made one's heart stand still to see men perched upon it, and leaning over to drive its corners home with heavy mallets; those below tossing up the requisite pins, which were caught with unerring precision.

When we could withdraw our attention from this part of the scene, we found much to attract it below. The spectacle of a "raising," though so commonplace an affair elsewhere, is something worth seeing in the woods; and accordingly there were almost as many boys and idlers as efficient hands present on this occasion. These were making the most of their time in various games of skill or strength—wrestling, running, leaping;—and shouts of merry laughter mingled with the cheering song of the workmen. Not a few lounged around the door of a temporary building or "shanty," as

240

we say—erected for the refreshment of the guests; for be it known that on these occasions neighbors one and all leave their own business, if possible, and lend their aid for love, and not for money—expecting only some good cheer, and in case of need a reciprocation of the kindness.

Where the country is settled but little, the assembling of so many able-bodied men is no small undertaking. I have no doubt the company before us cost several days' hard riding. And there were probably many there who would not have been hired to quit their own affairs to work for anybody. It is considered very churlish to refuse in such cases, and nothing would make a man more unpopular than the habit of excusing himself from raisings. Indeed few are disposed to offend in this way, for these are considered in the light of friendly visits, and constitute almost the sole attempt at merry-making in which the men of the country take part.

The work went on rapidly and well. Everything fitted, and the complicated structure grew as if by magic aid. When one thinks of such undertakings, it seems wonderful that terrible accidents do not often occur—but when we see the operation, it is more natural to ask how it is that they every occur, so great is the amount of skill, care and accuracy employed. The master mind, clear-headed and keen-eyed, stands by, calmly directing the minutest movement; and so complete is the confidence reposed in him that his commands are implicitly obeyed where the least mistake might cost many lives. This person took upon himself very properly the right of repressing, with some sternness, the jokes and laughter of the younger portion of his assistants; who, preferring of course the highest and most perilous parts of the work, yielded to the excitement of the moment, greatly increasing their own risk as well as that of all concerned.

"Ta'n't play-spell, boys!" said the "boss."

"Law! I tho't 'twas! I seen the master out o' doors," replied one of the pickles.

"Well, now you know it a'n't, you'd better keep your teeth warm," shouted the master in return; "put your tongue in your elbow, and then may-be you'll work!"

And under such auspices it was not long before the last rafter found its appropriate place, and nothing was lacking, from the huge foundation stones which had left such yawning cavities in the wood, through which we approached the scene, to the apex of the airy pile, which showed its outline with beautiful distinctness on the heavy foliage around it. This was the moment of triumph. The men, who had been scattered in every direction throughout the frame, giving it the appearance of an enormous bird-cage, rather aviary, now ranged themselves along the beams, and gave three thrilling cheers, presenting the most perfect image of the beautiful manoeuvre of "manning the yards" on board a vessel of war, that can possibly be conceived. With me the illusion was complete for the moment, and I found my eyes filled with tears—the tears of ancient and well-preserved memories,—in spite of the great old trees and the deep lonely dell.

Nothing now remained but to name the structure according to the formula invariably used on such occasions, let the terms suit as they may.

> "Upon this plain
> Stands a fair frame—
> Who'll give it a name?"

To which a voice from a distant corner responded, "we'll call it 'the miller's delight,'—To take toll all day and count the cash at night." This again reminded me of the ceremony of naming at a launch, but if there were libations on this occasion they were not poured upon the ground.

The whole company now adjourned to the shanty, where abundant refreshments were provided. We were very politely invited to partake, but the day was waning, and the scene had already beguiled us of so much time, that we declined anything beyond a glass of excellent spruce beer,

242

—a luxury which we of the woods know how to appreciate.

Sir Walter Scott observes that he always found "something fearful, or at least melancholy, about a mill." He had never seen one "raised," I am sure. Perhaps he owned one when wheat, having stood at twelve shillings, fell to six—and after some fluctuation settled at four. This would account for his impression.

42

INSECT LIFE

THE DAY had been sultry, and, spite of the woods, our horses began to look fagged and weary before we reached the place where we intended to pass the night. The sun was in mighty power, as if he had forgotten it was four hours after noon, but certain attendant clouds had already begun to "lay their golden cushions down" in preparation for his *coucher*. The land now lay low and level, much intersected by small streams, and covered with the long grass of our rich savannahs. On these wide, grassy plains, great herds of cattle were feeding, or lying stretched in luxurious idleness under the scattered trees. We might have been surprised, such was the solitariness of the region, to find such numbers of these domestic animals; but we have not lived so long in the wilds without having discovered that a herd of cattle, with its tinkling bells, is not to be considered as a sign of close vicinity to the abodes of men. When cattle feed in wild and unfenced pastures, they soon exhaust or spoil those nearest home; and even without this excuse, they will often wander at their "own sweet will," till the chase after them at milking-time becomes no small part of the day's business.

"Hunting cattle *is* a dreadful chore!" remarked one of our neighbors, with piteous emphasis, after threading the country for three weeks in search of his best ox.

This is one of the characteristic troubles of new-country life. In vain is the far-sounding bell strapped round the neck of the master ox or cow, (for we say *master*-cow by catachresis I suppose.) A good bell may be heard by practised ears four miles, if a valley or lake aid the transportation of sound; and a horse that has been accustomed to this species of coursing will prick up his ears and turn his head toward the sound of a well-known bell, thus serving as guide to the gudeman if he chance to be slow of hearing. Yet the herd will not always keep within bell sound. In vain too do we employ every ingenious artifice of temptation— supplying our *"salting-place"* with the great delicacy of the grazing people, and devoting the bran of each grist to the purpose of an extra feast, in the hope that the propensity to good feeding may overrule the national taste for unbounded liberty. "Home-bred memories" seem to have no place in the ruminations of the gregarious tribes. These expedients, which are resorted to only by the more provident, have indeed some efficacy, but they do not remedy the evil. It is sometimes mitigated by accidental causes.

When the flies become troublesome on the wide marshes, the whole herd, as if by previous agreement, will make for some well-known shade, near or distant, as the case may be, and there pass the sultry hours, only changing their positions gradually, as the sun throws the coveted shade eastward. And at the time of year when insects are most tormenting, the farmers make huge smokes in convenient spots near home, certain that to these all the cattle in the neighborhood will flock instinctively,—smoke being the best of all preventatives against flies and mosquitoes. So that, in the six weeks of mosquito-time, cattle-hunting becomes a less formidable "chore," and thus good comes out of evil. Evil! ay, the term is none too strong! I appeal to those who have travelled in the timbered land in July or August, I will not say to those who *live* in those regions, for I would fain hope their skin is hardened or armed in some way, as the fur of the ermine thickens and turns white in preparation for a Siberian winter.

One may observe, *en passant,* that ours is a rare region for the study of entomology. Those virtuosi who expend their amiable propensities in transfixing butterflies and impaling gnats would here find ample employment from May until November. Indeed they might at times encounter more specimens than they could manage comfortably and without undue precipitation. First, in early April, appear, few and far between, the huge blue-bottle flies, slow-motioned and buzzy, as if they felt the dignity of their position as ancestors. Next in order, if I forget not, come the most minute of midges, silent and stealthy, pretending insignificance in order that they may sting the more securely. These seem to be ephemera, and fortunately the race soon runs out, at least they trouble us but for a short time.

Flies proper—honest, sincere flies—come on so gradually that we can hardly date their advent; but it is when sultry weather first begins, when the loaded clouds and the lambent lightning foretell the warm shower, that twitchings are seen,—and quick slaps are heard,—and these, with the addition of something very like muttered anathemas, announce the much-dreaded mosquito. Then come evenings—fortunately not long ones,—passed in the dark, lest the light should encourage the intruders. Moonlight is praised; and even this must be admired through closed sashes, unless we can contrive by the aid of closely-fitted gauze blinds to turn the house into a great safety-lamp,— we burning within its sultry precincts. Then are white walls spotted with human blood, like the den of some horrible ogre. Then "smudges" are in vogue,—heaps of damp combustibles placed on the windward side of the house and partially ignited, that their inky steams may smother the mosquitoes while we take our chance. I have had a "smudge" made in a chafing-dish at my bedside, after a serious deliberation between choking and being devoured at small mouthfuls, and I conscientiously recommend choking, or running the risk of it, at least.

If one wished to make a collection for a museum, nothing more would be necessary than to light a few candles on any hot night in August, especially when the weather is

246

loud, and the open windows would be filled at once with a current of insect life, comprising all the varieties of *coleoptera* and their many-named kinsfolk; from the "shard-borne beetle with his drowsy wing," that goes knocking his back with unflinching pertinacity against every inch of the ceiling, to the "darning-needle," said to be an implement of Pluto himself, darting in all directions a body as long, and to all appearances as useless, as the sittings of our legislature.

We must not however claim preëminence for our dear Michigan in this particular point. The gallinippers of Florida are said to have aided the Seminoles in appalling our armies, and we have of late heard of a prodigious number of bites in all parts of the Union. And do we not know from unquestionable historic authority, namely, that of a British tourist in America, that a presumptious proboscis once dared to penetrate even General Washington's boots, as he rode through Newark marshes?

Our butterflies are nothing to boast of, and there are few of them with which one would be willing to change costumes, even to be "born in a bower." I have fancied that yellow predominates more than usual among them, and I have been tempted to believe they are bilious, like the rest of us. At any rate, the true ethereal and brilliant Psyche is but faintly represented by any specimen I have yet seen.

Mosquito-time, as before hinted, lasts, in its fury, but about six weeks, but flies are in season all summer. In the months of August and September particularly, black is the prevailing color of ceilings, looking-glasses and pictures, not to mention edibles of all classes. Much ingenuity is displayed in contriving what, in the paraphrastic tone of the day, we are bound to denominate destructive allurements for these intrusive and inconsiderate insects,—we used to call them fly-traps. These consist—in the more refined situations—of paper globes and draperies, delicately cut, so as to present externally an endless variety of cells and hiding-places, and these are well furnished within with poisoned sweets. Less fanciful people, frugal housewives and hard-hearted old bachelors,—place a large tumbler, partly filled with molasses, and covered with a piece of innocent-looking pasteboard having in the centre a hole large enough for a blue-bottle to enter *toute déployée,* but affording a poor chance for escape after he has clogged his feet and wings in the too eager pursuit of pleasure—a melancholy (and quite new) warning illustration of the *facilis descensus.* And again those of us who may by some chance have attended a course of chemistry, show our superior advantages by using a little water impregnated with cobalt, which carries swift destruction in every sip; and having at least the recommendation of not being sticky, answers a very good purpose, unless the children happen to drink it.

Yet this ingenious variety of deaths makes no perceptible diminution in the number of our tormentors, and I have heard a good old lady exclaim against such contrivances altogether, saying that if you kill one fly, ten will be sure to come to his funeral.

Yet we must not be persuaded to fancy ourselves worse off than other people in this particular either. I remember well—and perhaps you too, reader—the appearance of an elegant array of confectionary displayed in a verandah which hung over a lovely moonlit lake in a region where flies and midges had been for many years under the civilizing influences of good society. A blaze of light illumined the flower-wreathed pillars, and the gay crowd were ushered from the ball-room to the delicately furnished table, when lo! every article in sight appeared as if covered with black pepper; and the purest white and the most brilliant rainbow tints of creams and ices presented but one sad suit of iron gray. The very lights waxed dim in the saddened eyes of the gazers, for whole colonies of hapless gnats had found ruin in too warm a reception, and were revenging themselves by extinguishing their destroyers.

But return we to our herds feeding beside the still waters.

43

THE DEATH OF THE BEE-HUNTER

THE EVENING had fallen when we arrived at our lodging-place, and the stars were beginning to be visible, like specks of chaste silver in the dazzling but shaded gold of the western sky. We had left Constantinople several miles behind us, and the dwelling to which we had now come stood solitary in the centre of a wide clearing, with not a tree of the dense forest left to shade it from the burning sun. This was nothing new to us, for it is the prevailing taste of the country, but one can never get accustomed to so barbarous a fashion. The *new* feature on this occasion consisted in thirteen huge pillars, not supporting the low roof of the cottage, but standing in a semicircle, with nothing above them but the star-spangled arch of night. They were of Saxon proportions—almost as thick as they were high; and they bore not the outline of mere stumps, for they were of nearly even size throughout. Black-looking and ominous things were they, and in the dying light they gave the scene of Druid gloom. As we drew up at the bars the house-dogs barked, and with some aid from Leo, made abundance of noise, but no sign of humanity greeted our approach. One does not wait for invitation however in such cases, and we opened the door upon a sad scene.

The master of the family, a stout farmer of forty, whom we had met only a day or two before, lay extended on the bed, evidently beyond the help of man. His eyes had begun already to wear the cold glaze of death, and his countenance expressed an intensity of anxiety and distress which was fully reflected in the faces gathered around his bed. An awful silence, which we of course were most careful not to disturb, reigned in the room, broken only at long intervals by a faint moan from the dying man, echoed with heart-breaking emphasis by his poor wife, who wiped his forehead frequently, with a trembling hand. A large family of children, and two or three neighbors, made up the company, and one of the latter, stepping out of the door, beckoned my husband, and explained the dreadful casualty which had thus brought sorrow like a whirlwind.

The poor man had been crushed by a falling tree. He had been an adventurous and successful bee-hunter, and the pillars which had attracted our attention were the trophies of his triumphs in this line. He had by his very success been excited to still further effort, intending to surpass all his neighbors in his collections of bees, and in the quantity of honey which he should prepare for market. The thirteen monuments near his house had every one been procured at the risk of life or limb. They were the shafts of bee-trees, found in the forest at much expense of time and trouble, and cut down with so much skill as not to disturb the inhabitants, although this implies not only felling, but also cutting off all that part of the tree which grows above the hive.

The mode in which this is accomplished is this: another tree, or perhaps more than one, is first felled in such a direction as to form an elastic bed for the reception of the bee-tree, which thus falls without shattering itself to pieces, as from its hollowness it is sure to do when it falls on the ground. The upper portion is then to be removed, and when this is very heavy, as is generally the case, since the hives are almost always found in very large old trees, the greatest care and accuracy are requisite to prevent a tremendous and dangerous rebound of one or both parts.

After all his experience and all his triumphs, poor Mallory, perhaps grown less careful as he became more self-confident, had received the whole force of a huge limb across his neck and shoulders, and though no fracture could be discovered, it was evident from the first, that death was in the blow.

There was not only no medical aid in the neighborhood, but his son, who was his assistant on the occasion, was obliged to walk two miles before he could procure a yoke of oxen and a sled on which to bear him home. One scarcely dares to imagine what his wife must have suffered as she pursued her weary way over a thousand obstacles to the depth of the dense wood where she was to find him dying —perhaps dead. But it may be that our imaginations would not picture such scenes faithfully. He who "tempers the wind to the shorn lamb," does not, we may hope, give to those of his children, whose lot it is to dare the perils and trials of the unhewn wilderness, that cultivated sensitiveness which places new and keen weapons in the hand of sorrow. Their lives are occupied with stern realities—some of them sad and heavy ones; and the necessity for constant effort and for habitual fortitude, is a protection against the exaggerations of fancy.

The woodsman is continually subject to accidents of the most appalling kind. Added to the incredible toil of clearing heavily timbered land, the hardy settler goes to his work every morning with the consciousness that only the same Providence that could preserve him unharmed on the field of battle, can shield him from the perils of his daily labor. The ordinary operation of cutting down large trees, if performed where the timber is scattered, involves considerable risk; since a splinter, a limb heavier than was allowed for, or a heart more decayed than appeared outwardly, may thwart his nice calculations, and wound if not kill him. But it is in the dark and heavy wood, where the fathers of the forest stand in ranks almost as serried as those of the columns of Staffa, that peculiar dangers are found. If a tree, when felled, happen to lodge against another, it is almost a miracle if it is dislodged without an accident. This the best and most experienced woodsmen acknowledge, yet there are few of them who can resist the temptation to try.

In cutting down the supporting tree, the one first felled is almost certain either to slide or to rebound in a way which baffles all calculation, and accidents from this cause are frightfully frequent. The only safe course is to girdle the second tree, and let both stand until they decay, or until some heavy storm sweeps down the incumbrance. But this involves too great a vexation to the axeman, since his ambition is to see the piece of land he has undertaken to clear, bereft of every thing but the unsightly stumps which attest his skill and bravery.

Here the fatal consequences of too adventurous daring had brought wo unutterable, and we could read volumes of anguished thought in the darkening countenance of the sufferer, as he rolled his dim eye slowly round the circle of youthful countenances, and fixed it at last on the face of his wife.

"If you and they were provided for"—he said in a faint, husky voice,—and he tried to add—"God's will be done!"

The words were not fully audible, but the feeling was there, for the calm expression which belonged to it took gradual possession of the sunken features.

To stay to witness so heart-rending a scene would have been worse than useless, for what could we do or say? If a stranger "intermeddleth not with our joy," how much less with our sorrow!

A lad had been sent fifteen miles for the nearest physician, and at this moment a slight bustle at the door announced their arrival. As the medical man entered, we withdrew, and, setting out once more, drove on with over-burdened hearts to the next house, which was perhaps three miles off. There we explained our circumstances and asked for lodging, which was very hospitably accorded by the sole inmates, an old man and his wife. They had but one room, and much of one of its sides was occupied by a carpenter's bench and tools; but the space was still large, and they had plenty of bedding, so that it was not difficult to arrange resting-places for weary people.

After the children were in bed, I looked out for a while

at a low meadow which lay at no great distance from the house, now covered with a splendid show of fire-flies. The moon had not yet risen, and the evening being somewhat cloudy, the effect of this ever-changing expanse of green light was most brilliant. Yet all was saddened for the time by the impression of the scene we had just quitted. The busy flitting, the appearing and disappearing of these shining creatures, seemed to image only the efforts, the successes and the disappointments of human life; and I was glad at length to forget in sleep fatigue and heavy thoughts.

44

SETH MALLORY'S FUNERAL

So soon and so soundly did we rest after a weary day, that when we were awakened by a loud hammering, we supposed the night was gone, and the old carpenter arisen to his daily labor. He had a candle however, and I lay idly watching his movements, and noting the various operations of planing and shaping, till I became aware that his business was none other than the framing of a last receptacle for one of the tenants of the narrow house. I now remembered too, that it was Sunday morning.

"Are you really making a coffin?" I said, as if such a work could be strange anywhere.

"Surely I am," said the old man, "and for a good neighbor too."

"For whom, pray?"

"Seth Mallory, you know,—you saw him in the evening, —he was the man that got hurt yesterday."

"Mallory! he is dead then! and so soon—"

"No! I believe he wa'n't quite gone when they came and brought me the measure. You know they'll want to bury him pretty soon 'cause the weather's so warm."

The idea nearly curdled my blood. A coffin for the still living husband and father! My thoughts recurred to that agonized countenance, and its look of manly care and love for the dear one he was leaving.

"Is it possible his body was measured for the grave while he was yet alive?"

"Oh, he was past knowing anything, poor fellow, and they got his woman out of the room for a few minutes. You know, ma'am, such things must be done, and the sooner the better," said the old man as he stooped over his work.

He himself had nearly reached the limit of human life, and the few scattered hairs which remained on his temples shone like silver in the light of the one dim candle; yet he wrought away cheerily at the strong man's coffin, whistling occasionally to himself as the ghastly object assumed the proper shape. He might have personified Death as he fashioned this emblem of mortality, but it would have been Death in a mild and kind form. And is not this Death's usual form? and why do we ever picture him otherwise?

As much of the night was still to come, I tried to turn away and forget the scene and its associations, but it would not be. My eyes were fascinated to the spot, and I lost not a step of the process. A white lining was tacked to the sides, the cover was shaped, and smoothed, and fitted and screwed home; and to my excited mind, the body, still warm with scarce departed life, was pressed within these dark and narrow bounds. Why are we trained from infancy to such gloomy and terrifying views of all that belongs to this universal and inevitable change?

Day dawned before the work was finished, and the old man, carefully extinguishing his candle and setting open the door, put the last touches to it by the cold gray light of morning. He stained the whitewood with some reddish composition, and then, after turning it in every direction and surveying it with a look of professional complacency, set it up against the outside of the house to dry in the beams of the rising sun.

We were at breakfast when two young men came for the coffin.

"What time did he die?" asked the old man.

"He breathed till about midnight, but he never spoke after dark."

"Ay!" said the old lady, "I thought he would die about the turn of the tide. When do they bury him?"

"This afternoon, after meeting."

This strange custom obtains here, almost universally. A dead body is seldom kept in the house more than one night, and sometimes not even one. More especially if an opportunity occurs to bury the dead on Sunday is the last rite hastened; since the presence of a minister of religion, and a day of leisure and of best clothes, are all convenient. Such haste seems more excusable under such circumstances, when we consider the condition and habits of the country, but there are cases where it looks like an indecent or superstitious haste to get rid of a painful object. The superstitious feeling is not, perhaps, very common; but there are some who are, as they say, "afraid" of the bodies of their nearest friends. This is generally found, if at all, in young people; and it arises probably from their having been bred in neighborhoods so far scattered that deaths are very infrequent, and so came seldom under their notice. I have seen a young woman who did not dare to approach the corpse of her husband unless somebody went with her and remained close at her side.

The meeting of that day was held in a large barn at some miles' distance. It was a quarterly meeting of one of the sects most numerous in this country, and great numbers attended from every direction. The central part or "bay" of the barn was filled with seats of rough boards, and a long seat for the preachers was enclosed after the same style. The place was crowded to such a degree, that even after many men and boys had perched themselves on beams and other out of the way places, there were still numbers who remained in their waggons, drawn up as near as might be, so as to be able to hear all that was said. And this was not difficult, for in most cases the speakers, who were seven in number, exerted their lungs to a degree that I had seldom heard equalled.

In spite of many unpleasant circumstances naturally inseparable from a gathering of this kind, the scene was a very impressive one. The greatest attention prevailed, and there was an air of reverence and devotion which is not

256

always the attendant on the long-drawn aisle and the solemn organ. The speakers adverted more than once to the circumstances of our Savior's birth; and indeed nothing could be more natural than the connexion which brought that humble yet glorious scene to mind. It was needless then to warn us against despising our place of meeting. The idea had already consecrated it to purposes of worship.

The preachers all spoke in turn, but of course each briefly. Prayer and singing came between these short sermons, the singing seeming spontaneous, as no hymns were given out. One of the ministers would begin singing without any previous notice, and as if taking it for granted that everybody would be able to join, as indeed many did, forming a choral swell of wild and solemn melody. The sacrament followed, and it was administered and received with much appearance of earnest devotion. Ere yet the holy rite was finished, the body of the unfortunate Mallory, and with it his weeping wife and her bereaved children, were all in the midst before we were aware. The coffin was placed on trestles before the preacher's desk, and after the communion, one of the ministers, one who had been long a neighbor of the deceased, pronounced a funeral sermon— unpremeditated of course,—but who could lack most touching topics of instruction on such an occasion as this?

Funeral hymns were now sung, and prayers offered for the afflicted family; and then the whole multitude followed the corpse in solemn procession to the burial-place. This was a sweet, lonely spot, enclosed, even in the heart of the wilderness, with pious care. There were many tall trees left standing, and beneath them a few graves marked only by a piece of wood at the head and feet. In silence was the dust committed to its kindred dust,—in silence, if we except many a sob,—and when all was done, a venerable old man, in the name of the family, thanked friends and neighbors for their aid and sympathy, and with a bow of his silvery head, dismissed the assembly.

45

A BACKWOODS POLITICAL RALLY

HALF A DAY'S easy driving transported us from this scene
of primitive simplicity and rudeness to a beautiful and
populous town, whose hotel, spacious and elegant, and
exceedingly well managed, offered some temptation to an
extended stay, after our homely lodging at the old carpenter's, and sundry others not much more desirable. These
contrasts are very striking in a new country. The settlement
has been sudden, and very unequal, and you emerge from
the untouched forest, through which you have been threading your way long enough almost to forget that there are
such things as dwellings and enclosures, upon highly-cul-
tivated farms and busy villages. These contrasts we may
find in travelling any new country, but they are more striking in these newly-settled regions because of the wild fresh-
ness of the aspect of Nature in the intervening tracts.
Immense trees give an air of solitary grandeur to the landscape, and the absence of everything like fence or dividing
line of any sort ,inspires ideas of immensity—of solitude
—which make the sudden apparition of man and the
traces of his busy hands produce a feeling akin to surprise.

After we left the woods we came out upon what had
been, a few years since, a small prairie, now covered with
loads of nodding grain, swayed by every passing breeze
into the semblance of golden-brown billows. There are few
more beautiful sights than a wheat-field full half a mile
square, perfectly level, and unbroken by anything save

perhaps here and there a fine old tree, promising a noontide shelter to the reapers. One does not wonder that such views suggested to the poets of old the images of laughter and singing.

The prairie-land passed, our road was log-causeway; a long straight track through a dead swamp,—and in this all horrors are expressed, all mud-holes, all thumps, all impossibility of turning out. This was a pretty place in which to meet a political convention! a new kind of locomotive of immeasurable power, not very easily managed except by adepts.

It was a formidable apparition certainly; and we were fain to shrink into infinitesimal nothingness, and to find a place for our outer wheels on the sloping ends of the corduroy, even at the risk of a souse into a sea of black mud; for there was a deep ditch on either side. The chance that even our sober steeds would endure the clatter of drums and fifes, cymbals and triangles,—noisy orators and still noisier singers,—was a small one; but there was no retreat, and we remained perched on our "bad eminence," until the whole procession had passed.

There were perhaps thirty vehicles, of which the smallest were large waggons, with four horses each. There were gaily painted barges—"canoes," I ought to say, in the spirit of the day,—mounted on wheels, and drawn by unnumbered if not innumerable steeds, and containing crowds of people; every man and every horse bearing a banner, inscribed either with high-sounding patriotism on a large scale, or with electioneering squibs on a very small one. There were rectangular countenances, drawn evidently with the aid of compass and square, and haloed round with snow-white fleece—accredited representatives of the much-disfigured father of our country; then again, faces where in a very long drooping nose was surmounted by a pair of eyes that seemed running into one—awful travesties of the popular candidate. There were golden eagles spreading their gorgeous wings amid the stars, on fields of silk as blue as their own heaven, and raccoons enough (in effigy) to have fed the whole national eyry, if golden eagles could eat.

A huge ball was rolled along, with great appearance of effort, by several men, and these actors, by their shouted watchwords and their various significant decorations, gave us to understand that the said ball typified the interests of their favorite. A miniature log-cabin, the very ditto of those by the road side, mounted on a platform spacious enough to carry much of the out-door arrangements of a settler's primitive establishment, was drawn by a long string of oxen, the tips of whose horns streamed with flags and knots of gay ribbon. The emblems which met the eye every moment embraced all degrees of ingenuity and absurdity, and the costume of those who exhibited them was almost equally various.

There was an Indian, in blue and red paint and a feather-petticoat, bearing a banner with the inscription, "Our best brave;" here an impersonation of Liberty, strait-laced and anxious, in pink ribbons and black prunello boots. Now a car from which an orator was setting forth in no inelegant terms the pretensions of the idol; and anon another bearing his image, in the act of presenting a horse to a minister. Under the influence of omnipotent corduroy, the minister, first tottering like Mr. Stiggins, abominably knocked down by his benefactor, and the horse sympathetically tumbled on them both and completed the pyramid.

Such trifling disasters passed unfelt and almost unnoticed in the enthusiasm of the hour. Beneath all the little oddities which are almost inseparable from the getting up of a popular show on so large a scale with rather incongruous materials, there was evidently an under current of warm feeling and genuine interest which makes everything respectable; and however one might feel disposed to laugh at some particulars of the exhibition, there was an impressiveness about the whole which made one sensible of "the majesty of the people." For my own part I confess that this immense moving mass of life, with its alternations of war-like music, animated declamation, and sweet chorus of female voices, caused the blood to tingle in my veins and my heart to overflow at my eyes. Sympathy has wondrous power, and after waiting till the whole grotesque train had passed, we drove to the end of the corduroy, and then turned about, and, with a host of other gazers, followed the multitude.

The place of destination was a grove whose sylvan beauty never could be surpassed, even in Michigan, which is all groves. It was at no great distance from the road, but it was in all the wildness of nature, and looked as if the axe had never yet profaned its hallowed aisles. Here, in the midst of primeval solitude and silence, a wide amphitheatre of rough benches,—the whole roofed in by noble oaks and maples, with "unpierced shade."

Rapidly, and with a silence and regularity which bespoke thorough drilling, did the immense assemblage dispose itself appropriately over the broad area,—the orators and officials taking their places upon the platform, where the banners were planted and arranged in very effective drapery,—the ladies on the front seats next to the music, and the common world on the remaining benches.

The Marseillois was now performed—with verses by a native poet of course,—and the entire company joined in the chorus which imparted a stentorian energy to their "most sweet voices." A marshal now announced that a clergyman presented would "make a prayer," and the multitude stood, with heads uncovered, and in a throbbing silence, till it was finished. Then the band played and the ladies sang "Hail, Columbia," and again the leafy canopy quivered to the excitement of the hour. Then came the speeches, blazing with patriotism, and touching, in their wide scope, on every disputed and disputable point in politics. And here I was much amused with the discreet timing of the cheers, which was performed by a young gentleman furnished with a flag which he waved most graciously, bowing at every shout, as if to thank the "good friends, kind friends, sweet friends," who took his hints in such good part.

The "sentiments" were drank at intervals, in very innocent liquids; so that if there was truth in the rapture of the hour, it was not wine that brought it out. Everybody *seemed* to feel, to the heart's core, all the privileges, advantages, rights, grievances, and hopes, on which the chosen orators harangued so warmly, and I doubt not that vows were made that day which told afterwards for good or evil, in opinion and action.

All this time the sun had been trying his best to look in upon the animated scene, and although his vertical rays scarce succeeded in checkering here, and there a portion of the well-trodden green sward, yet the atmosphere confessed his power so unreservedly, that some of the ladies began to be very restless, and some even threatened an interlude of fainting-fits. One who sat near the stage with a child in her lap, insisted upon having the glass of water which had been placed on a table for the speaker handed down for the use of her baby, returning the remnant very coolly,—a mixed crystal, to say the least.

So it was judged best to adjourn for refreshment; and on the announcement, all was renewed animation in a moment. The band played, the ladies fluttered,—and the result of all was a very long procession on foot, in which "woman," as the toasts have it, bore a conspicuous part;—each fair hand carrying a bough, which our imaginations were bound to convert into palm or laurel, (I spare thee "Birnam wood," O reader!) and every swanlike throat trilling with most patriotic sentiments, married to popular airs, and stirring every heart as with the sound of a trumpet.

The long array passed over an open glade where the sun's rays were of the strongest, but this served only to enhance the delicious coolness of the shade which soon enveloped us—a shade, to form which, even the dense woods had been aided by great awnings, and bowers within bowers formed of immense branches and thick-leaved vines.

These varied and far-reaching canopies, adorned with wreaths of wild flowers and gay flags with emblematic devices, formed a splendid dining-hall, within whose circuit all the rural luxuries that most laborious search could procure had been displayed with a taste which, though it might not shine in more cultivated regions, certainly did honor to the Western wilderness. Huge venison pasties, such as (if we may believe veracious chroniclers) kings have ere now revelled in; wild turkeys prodigious as any tame ones to be found at the Sublime Porte; roast pigs delicate and crisp as those which run about the land of Cokaigne, crying, "Who'll eat me?" chickens in all attitudes, and pork under all disguises;—these were among the more solid and noticeable items of good cheer. But to give even a passing glance at the feminine contributions belonging to the department of the dessert, and in the preparation of which all the female skill of the county had been, as it were, brought to a focus,—this was a hopeless task, and especially to one who could not even guess at the names of half the recondite compositions that adorned the "lily lawn."

Here and there might be observed something in contrast to the general good taste; such as an unfortunate stag, roasted (or half roasted) whole, and standing, antlers and all, as if alive; only, alas! "upon another footing now!" propped in his erect posture by flower-wreathed sticks, and, in this position, sliced and eaten, after a fashion which ought to have sickened any but Abyssinians.

The immortal johnny-cake figured under every conceivable form,—round and square, rhomboid and parallelopipedon,—stuck with roses, or basted with gravy,—johnny-cake was everywhere—she was the universe." Hard cider there was none,—an inevitable omission; for either it had been all consumed at previous conventions, or the apple-trees of the neighborhood belonged to the opposite party, and there was none to be had. The song of "Drink to me only with thine eyes" might have been appropriate as suggesting some consolation in this emergency, but I believe the devotees pledged each other in the pure element—indeed I should judge it must have been so, from the exceeding order and good-humor of the day.

263

The zest with which the people, individually and collectively, attacked the goodly array, would have silenced the veriest croaker on the subject of Western agues.

Talk of city feasts! Your true alderman never earns an all-sanctifying appetite by rising three hours before day, and walking ten or twenty miles without tasting food beyond a crust of bread. He can never know the true gusto of roast pig, far less of johnny-cake. When he sits down at six to his turtle he may indeed have eaten "nothing to signify," since lunch; but that very lunch and its unconsidered sequence have stolen away all the piquancy from his dinner, and he might rationally, in his character of *gourmet*, envy the hardy backwoodsman his simplest cheer, with the accompaniment of his ordinary and sometimes rather importunate appetite. On this special occasion, there was not only the well-earned relish, but the choicest opportunity for its gratification, and the result must be left to the imagination of the reader.

❊   ❊   ❊   ❊   ❊

What changes may be wrought in one little hour! Where be now the shining roast—the delicate boiled—the *patés* —the pyramids—the temples—the universal johnny-cake?

The "banquet hall deserted,"—the theatre with its latest lamp expiring—the once trim deck after a sharply contested action,—these are sad images; but such a table after all are satisfied save a few voracious stragglers!

❊   ❊   ❊   ❊   ❊

We waited not to hear the concluding address. It may have been a good one,—I dare say it was,—but I fear it fell upon dull ears. We hastened onward, passed the log-causeway again, and reached the fine hotel at ——, two hours before the procession reëntered the town. We retired early after the fatigues of the day, forgetting that there might be such a thing as a ball-room at —— House. Fatal error! Those who had marched, and shouted, and sung, and eaten, in honor of their far-distant favorite, thought not

264

the rites complete until they had expended the remainder of their energies in dancing. Violins squeaked without stint or mercy, and till gray dawn did the house quiver in unison with the superhuman efforts of patriotic heels and elbows.

46

THE DONATION PARTY

WE HAVE ALL HEARD of a man who went through the ceremony of combing only once a year, and who always, when
the dread moment came, pitied those poor creatures who
endured the operation every day. Even so, after one day of
dissipation, did we, dwellers in the voiceless woods, where
it is a task to remember the days of the week—one being
so much like another,—pity those unfortunates whose lot
it is to "go a pleasuring" all the time. The fatigue of eye and
ear,—the heat, the dust, the din of yesterday, and after all,
the sleepless night,—made repose really necessary; and we
lounged away the morning, visiting several friends, and
surveying, under their guidance, what was best worth
notice in the village and its neighborhood. The place
stands on rising ground, and commands a fine view of the
surrounding country, then smiling in soft summer loveliness, and diversified everywhere with wood and water,
though destitute of any striking features, if we except the
one deep dell, whose full and rapid stream forms the wealth
of the village.

"Hard times" had made no impression on the sweet face
of Nature. Not a frown reproved the ungrateful grumbler,
man; who, if he cannot find the superfluity which is required by an insatiable thirst for distinction, overlooks and
contemns the kind care that richly provides for all his real
wants. All was peace, industry and abundance, and the
heart could not but dilate with pleasure at the sight of a

multitude of objects all typical of the overflowing goodness of God, and calling upon his rational creatures for "the honor due his name."

We were most hospitably treated—for the spirit of hospitality is not confined to the cottages of the West—and our kind entertainers proposed several plans for a pleasant evening; but the one which proved most attractive was a visit at the house of a clergyman with whom we had some acquaintance, and who was to receive all the world within five miles of ——, in the form of that relic of primitive Puritanism known among us as a "donation party." We had heard of this custom—a general visit to the clergyman, each guest bringing something by way of offering,—and we were delighted with the opportunity of assisting at one—assisting à *la Francaise,* I mean. We presented ourselves, by special request, at an early hour; but, early as it was, dozens of good plain folks from the country had preceded us. Some indeed, we were told, had been on the ground since breakfast-time. We always do things in earnest here. When we say, "Come and spend the day,"—we should stare to see the invited guest come at two o'clock, just as we had put away the dinner dishes, and taken out our knittingwork or our patchwork for the afternoon. *Avis au lecteur,* in case he ventures to invite a Western friend without specifying the hour.

But, as we were saying, some good ladies had taken time by the forelock, and here they were, beginning already to yawn (covertly), and to long for their tea. Two great baskets in the hall were already pretty well filled with bundles of yarns, woollen stockings of all sizes, (sure to fit, in a clergyman's family,) rolls of home-made flannel, mysterious parcels enveloped in paper, and bags which looked as if they might contain a great many precious things. Flocks of company were arriving, and no one empty handed, so that the "removal of the deposits" became a measure of necessity, and the contents of the two baskets were transferred to some reservoir above stairs. Before the baskets had been restored to their places, there was some embarrassment among the new comers as to the proper bestowment of their contributions, etiquette requiring that an air of mysterious reserve should be observed. But the difficulty was obviated by the arrival of a handsome tea-table, borne by two young men as the representatives of a little knot who had hit upon this pretty thought of a present for the minister's lady. Upon this the tasteful class of offerings were displayed to good advantage, and I observed among the rest a study-lamp, a richly-bound Shakspere, and a bronze inkstand with proper appurtenances. Among the more magnificent were a standing fire screen elegantly wrought; and a pair of foot-stools on which the skill of the cabinet-maker had done its utmost in displaying to advantage very delicate embroidery. The variety as well as the beauty of the gifts was very ingenious, and nobody could find fault with a handsome purse, filled with gold, bearing, in minute letters wrought into its beadwork, the inscription, "To the Reverend Mr. ——, from the young men of his church."

Where so many people, young and old, were collected with a kind purpose, and under circumstances which levelled, for a time, all distinctions, conversation was not likely to flag. In truth, the general complacency evinced itself in a ceaseless stream of talk,—with only a moderate infusion of scandal, for everybody was present. The old ladies chatted soberly among themselves, and their husbands talked politics in corners. The young ladies fluttered about busily, as in duty bound; for on them devolves, by inviolable usage, all the ministering necessary on the occasion—all the reception of the company and bestowing of their offerings—all care of tea affairs and distribution of refreshments in order due. Such a dodging of pretty heads—such dancing of ringlets,—such gleaming of white teeth as there was among them! I scarcely wondered that the young men became a little bewildered, and forgot where they ought to stand, and had to be ordered about or turned out into the hall to make room for the more dignified or bulky part of the assembly, only to slip back again upon the first opportunity. So much youthful beauty is not collected everyday, and especially beauty endowed with such a pretty little coquettish station of command. I cannot doubt that much execution was done, and, in truth, there were some very obvious symptoms—but I shall not betray.

The clergyman's lady occupies rather an equivocal station on these occasions. She is not exactly in the position of hostess, for every article set before the company is furnished by themselves; and all the ordinary attentions are rendered by the young stewardesses of the hour; so the domine's wife has only to smile and look happy, and to show by her manner that she is gratified by the interest evinced, and if to this she superadds good talking powers, and can entertain those of her guests who are not particularly easy to entertain, she has accomplished all that is expected of her. And all this the fair and lady-like heroine of the present occasion did very sweetly.

The tea hour drew on, and now the *mêlée* began to assume a business-like air. The scampering reminded me of "Puss in the Corner," such was the sudden chase for seats. The old ladies put away their knitting, and their spouses began to spread their handkerchiefs on their knees, at the first rattle of the tea-spoons. Those who were not so fortunate as to secure seats, insinuated themselves as near as possible to tables and mantel-pieces, which might serve to hold the anticipated good cheer.

The younger gentlemen officiated as footmen, and they had an arduous task. Over and above the bearing of great trays of tea and coffee, and bounteous salvers of cake, biscuits, sandwiches, cheese, tongue, and all that belongs to the city and country tea-table, they had, in addition, to attend to the contradictory directions of a host of capricious mistresses of the ceremonies, who delighted in perplexing them, and who gave orders and counter-orders for the very purpose of seeing them go on bootless errands and get laughed at for their pains. But they bore all very good-humoredly, and managed to render something like a return to their fair tyrants by persuading the old ladies to drink as much tea as possible, and commending and urging the excellence of the coffee to the gentlemen in such sort that an extra supply was required, and the damsels' elbows were fain to sue for quarter. After all were served, the attendants were at liberty to provide for themselves, and whatever may have been left for them to eat and drink, I can testify that they had abundance of talking and laughing.

I ought sooner to have mentioned that the pastor in whose behalf such general interest was shown, was a person accustomed to society, and an adept in the best power of hospitality—that of making everyone feel welcome and at ease. Mr. —— was everywhere, and in everybody's thoughts. Grave with the old, gay with the young, and cheerful with all, he was in every respect the life and soul of the occasion, and each felt the time spent in conversation with him to have been "the sweet of the night." An enviable power! and one possessed in its perfection only by those whose hearts are full of kindly sympathies,—who *are* what others only try to appear.

After the bustle attendant upon serving the tea had subsided, the conversation gradually, and as if spontaneously, took a more serious turn, and, before we were aware, the sweet and solemn notes of a hymn, well supported in all its parts, stole upon the ear, and hushed all lighter sounds. When several stanzas had been sung, the clergyman, after a short address, invited all present to unite in prayer and thanksgiving to the bounteous Giver of all good. And thus seriously closed a very cheerful evening, without any violent transition or unpleasant contrast.

This custom of donation parties certainly seems to belong to a very primitive and simple state of society, yet its observance is by no means limited to these newly-settled regions. Wherever New Englanders have given a tone, these little gatherings have been introduced, and though there are various opinions as to the general question whether this is the best or a good way of contributing to the support of a clergyman, people generally unite in them very heartily, which affords at least a presumption in their favor. This

very union is something. As far as I have been able to observe, they certainly have the one good effect of creating a
nearer personal interest in the pastor and his family; and
whatever tends to draw closer and nearer the ties which
bind minister and people, may not be lightly discouraged;
for in this calculating and utilitarian age the dangers lie
on the opposite side—the side of proud indifference and
chilling neglect, the most discouraging and impracticable
of all atmospheres for a minister of religion.

47

THE ENGLISH SPORTSMAN

HOMEWARD once more. Skies and bowers of fairy-land, but most earthly corduroy; and some few mud-holes that would have suited well with a still grosser sphere. Endless wheat-fields—Indian corn glittering in the sunbeams as the morning wind dashed the dew from its broad leaves; rich pastures, where a few maples, kindly left alive, formed shady lounges for the cattle; quiet streams, in which the cows were very sensibly standing half-leg deep, browsing occasionally upon the over-hanging boughs;—such were the commonplace objects that served to give an interest to our journey homewards. The road by which we were returning was a closely-settled one, crossed however here and there by a tract of deep shade, in which the solitude of creation seemed never to have been disturbed, and in one part passing through a strip of unbroken prairie, scarcely tenanted except by wild-fowl and other pensioners of nature.

Jogging along slowly under a blistering sun across this shelterless tract, we saw far in the prairie a moving object, which we took at first for some wild animal, whose outline the dazzling nature of the light prevented our tracing distinctly. But presently, when the strange figure moved towards us, which it did rapidly enough when we came within its range, it proved to be no prairie wolf, but a human being, oddly accoutred and exhibiting considerable complexity. He would walk a few steps forward, and then, shading his eyes with his hand, gaze earnestly around him.

Then turning his eyes to our side, he would seem resolved to reach the road, yet after a few moments turn and gaze wistfully as before. At length we came within speaking distance, and our wild beast turned out an English gentleman who seemed to have been gunning on the prairie. The capacious pockets of a very curious-looking jacket were stuffed with prairie-hens, and instead of a hat a silk pocket-handkerchief was tied about the dissolving head of the sportsman.

We could do no less than stop and inquire the cause of his evident perplexity.

"Pray—I beg your pardon—but can you observe anything on the prairie?" he said, pulling the kerchief from his head, and wiping his brow with a half-distracted air.

We tried faithfully, standing on tiptoe in the waggon, but there was nothing visible but the tall, waving grass, and the long straight road. Not an object broke the line of the horizon except some far distant trees.

"Well now," said our new acquaintance, "d'ye know, this is so very awkward! these prairies of yours—one might as well be on the ocean in a cock-boat. I have been shooting on this very ground for four successive days, and bagged so many birds everyday—grouse too—that I couldn't make up my mind to quit. But this morning I had determined should be the last, you know; and I was enticed further and further; and after I was so loaded that I could scarcely walk, I still saw so much sport that I made a pile of game on a convenient spot, and put my cap upon the heap by way of landmark, so that I should be quite sure, you know, to find it again. But upon my word, I had not brought down three birds after this, before I came to the end of my powder, and then I set out to find my cap and my game. And here I am, wandering about these two hours, you know, and can see nothing but grass every where. It is really excessively awkward"—and again he wiped his forehead, as well he might.

He was a gentleman by no means well fitted for searching the prairies under the fervors of a summer noon, for he was short and very fat, and his head was pink and shining as if it had never known the "excrescence of a moist brain." But he tried to laugh off his vexation like a wise man, saying that he supposed a wolf he had shot at early in the morning had devoured cap and game too, by way of revenge for his evil intentions.

We were so fortunate as to have a spare straw hat—no unusual provision for a summer journey hereabouts,—and this the stranger gladly adopted, his crimsoned countenance looming out from beneath its wide brim like the rising harvest moon encountering a stray bank of clouds. He accepted also a seat in our rough vehicle as far as the next village, and before we had reached the place of destination, we had set him down as a very pleasant Englishman indeed. He was full of animation, interested in everything connected with this new world, and much more desirous of gaining information than of impressing the "Yenkees" with an overwhelming idea of his own born and bred superiority. Such an Englishman being almost a wonder in America, we cultivated Mr. Sibthorpe accordingly, and an acquaintance of some duration, since that chance encounter on the prairie, has given us no reason to regret having yielded to first impressions.

We reached Mr. Sibthorpe's lodging-place—the little village of Temperance—a knot of log-houses clustering about a blacksmith's shop, and a "Variety-Store," (I quote the sign,)—just as the world was going to dinner; and Mr. Sibthorpe had so many good things to say of his landlady that we were induced to apply to her for our dinner, instead of making a pic-nic meal in the woods, as we had intended.

The good woman was the picture of neatness, and she was most appropriately framed, for a trimmer cottage sun never shone upon. Everything shone with cleanliness, and the gown and shawl of the poor soul herself had been washed and starched until they were of a gauzy thinness. Poverty was everywhere, but it was cheerful, industrious, and most tidy poverty, and the manners of the hostess and

274

er children were such as would have appeared well in far better circumstances. Her husband was at his work, she said, and had taken his noon-meal with him, but she had prepared dinner for Mr. Sibthorpe, and could soon add to it for our accommodation.

There were not plates and knives enough to allow the children to eat at the same time with us, so that it took a good while to despatch the dinner. Meanwhile our newly-found acquaintance was getting his "traps" together, (an expression picked up on this side of the water, I *guess*,) and by the time the little folks were repacked and ready, he too had mounted his shaggy pony, and with well-stuffed saddle-bags, and blanket and boot-hose, stood prepared to ride on with us.

The road grew bad enough as we plunged into the "timbered land," so bad that fast driving was out of the question. The late heavy rains, falling upon land that was never shone upon except at noonday, had soaked the clayey soil so completely that in many places we made our way with difficulty; and in this drawling way we travelled several miles. And here our prairie hunter's cheerful and intelligent conversation served as a most agreeable relief to the tedious dulness naturally attendant upon ruts and mudholes. Mr. Sibthorpe had travelled a good deal, and always with his eyes open, and he had beside a fund of enthusiasm, and a genuine love for fresh, free and unpolished nature, which was absolutely romantic. His information was extensive, and his manner of communicating it natural and easy, excluding every idea of ostentation or arrogance.

After all, the charm of his conversation (to me at least) was the tinge of romance which pervaded his views, and which unconsciously to himself, probably, gave a poetical cast to every sentiment and opinion. It is the fashion of the day to laugh at romance, yet who is not fascinated by it when it is evidently genuine? People who dare to be romantic are becoming every day more rare. The spirit of the age, analytical and disenchanting as it is, is fast eradicating the few romantic notions that have survived till this time; and

275

if any country bids fair to be preëminent in the tearing away of all illusion from the dull realities of life—in the systematic exaltation of the material above the ideal, I fear it is our own.

We sometimes encounter a foreigner who has brought with him the fruit of the seed sown by the lore of his in fancy, and who will charm us, in spite of ourselves, into something like sympathy with his passionate estimate of the light which imagination can shed on the trials and vexations of the world; but where is the American who would not blush to be suspected of such childish, such unfashionable views?

Mons. De Tocqueville, who has of all others written of us in the kindliest as well as most profound and discriminating spirit, has not failed to perceive and to warn us of this tendency to materialism. He should perfect the good work by pointing out some great practical remedy—some counteracting power or principle by the aid of which we may apply ourselves to the cultivation of the poetical rather than the prosaic estimate of things; learn to crave the intellectual before the physical,—the beautiful *with* the true,—and, above all, the "believing spirit,"—lately so eloquently commended by a countryman of our own,— in preference to the skeptical, into which so many of our thinkers seem to be relapsing.

But what has all this digression to do with Mr. Sibthorpe? More than appears, perhaps; for the reminiscence of that pleasant afternoon in the muddy "timbered land" brought with it a floating idea of some of the many themes upon which our discursive talk touched; lightly enough, but so amusingly, that we could scarce believe the sun had set, when the woody way became suddenly embrowned, and the cold dew began to fall perceptibly, while we were still at some distance from our purposed resting-place.

48

DEMOCRATIC VISTAS

WE HASTENED onward at the expense of some terrible thumps, and half an hour or so brought us within hearing, at least, if not within sight, of the village where we had agreed to pass the night. We were made aware of our approach to the abodes of men, by a clatter and howling, a clash of tin pans and a beating of drums, which made together a din sufficiently startling after the long dark drive through the forest, where nothing was heard beyond the screech of the owl or the occasional bark of a fox. So loud and angry were these warlike sounds, that Mr. Sibthorpe concluded at once that they must be occasioned by some great popular commotion.

"What do you suppose it can be?" he inquired; "d'ye know I've the greatest curiosity to see an American mob! Do you think it can be anything of that sort?"

Our replies dampened his hopes. We thought anything else more likely. And very soon we reached the inn, where all was quiet as one could wish, although the crowd from which the noise proceeded was visible by the light of its own restless lanterns, at the further end of the street.

"It's only a parcel of fellers gone to serenade an old widower that's been a marrying of a young girl, and didn't ask the neighbors to the wedding—that's all!" said the landlord. "If he'd come out and treat 'em, they'd go off peaceable; but he's so spunky he won't do that, and I'll warrant ye they'll keep up that hullabaloo all night."

277

"A *charivari* in the woods!" exclaimed our companion; "an old French custom transplanted into these Western wilds! You observe the New-year with the Dutch, and 'Thanksgiving' with the Yankees; and I have noticed that you fail not to eat mince-pies religiously with the English at Christmas, and cod-fish and potatoes with Paddy on his saint's day."

We responded by a wish that the naturalization of holidays had been carried still further, as we have so few of our own; and we might have been inclined to enlarge a little upon this point, (it being a favorite one,) but our host had no idea of awaiting the conclusion of an untimely discussion.

"Well!" said he somewhat testily, "if you're a comin' in, come along! if not, it a'n't of no use for me to be a standin' here. I've got sacks of things to do."

Mr. Sibthorpe laughed, as an Englishman well might, and very good-humoredly responded to this crusty speech of our landlord by asking whether he did not consider it a part of his business to wait upon his customers?

"Why, if a man wants a meal's victuals for himself, or his folks, or his dumb critters," responded Mr. Hotchkins, "I am willing to furnish it; but I don't calc'late to wait upon nobody. D'ye want your horses put up? Here, Zack! take these men's horses and put 'em in the stable." Then to the guests —"You can tell him how many oats you want 'em to have."

And with this the innkeeper went into the house, to consult the "women-folks," I suppose.

Zack was kind enough to take off our luggage, which he placed in the entry; and we seated ourselves in a forlorn parlor, with a funereal row of chairs, and one table, on which stood a sepulchral lamp that looked as if it had been intended to burn on for ages, making darkness visible, so minute was the quantity of flame that glimmered on its little wick.

The evening was very chilly, as is often the case after a day of intense heat, and we felt the need of fire to dry our dewy garments, as well as to cheer the dark dismal parlor.

The landlord, who was forthcoming upon a call, said there was a fire in the bar-room, and that the "men-folks" could go there, and the women and children could sit in the kitchen.

"But couldn't we have a fire here?"

"Why—the fact is—no, not very well. You see my woman has slicked up her stove, and got her posy-pot in't and all— and she wouldn't like to have it nastied up jist for one night. I guess you'd better fix it t'other fashion."

And to the kitchen we went, and a very nice kitchen it was, with a somewhat prim but kindly dame at the head of affairs, who made the rosy-cheeked damsels under her sway fly about so nimbly that our tea was soon ready. How they managed to do anything was marvellous, for the kitchen was full of newly-ironed sheets, spread on clothes-frames and the backs of chairs, and steaming in the hot air.

The eating-room felt like a cellar, but there was a fire just kindled in a close stove, which, by the time we had finished, began to make it tolerably warm—a not unusual arrangement in taverns. Whether the incipient stages of freezing are induced with a view of benumbing the appetite with the other powers, or whether the air is kept cool for the convenience of the waiters, who might find much exercise uncomfortable in a well-warmed atmosphere, I never was able to guess.

When the children were prepared for bed, one must have been very good-natured indeed not to observe that the sheets were not of the number of those which had just passed beneath the smoothing-iron.

"How is this!" I exclaimed to the maiden in attendance; "these sheets have been used?"

"Oh, yes, ma'am," simpered the girl. "We ha'n't no new sheets."

"But I must have *clean* sheets," I said, in plain English,— "sheets that have not been slept in since they were washed."

"Oh!" exclaimed the young lady, as if light had suddenly broken in upon her understanding;—"yes—I dare say!— but, you see, ma'am, we've had sich lots of company—

279

there was the Dimocratic Wig convention—they slept here two nights—and then there was this here Log-Cabin celebration—and so all of our sheets but these is a drying in the kitchen—and we thought you'd like these better, 'cause they're so much healthier! you know damp sheets is dreadful unwholesome—and there ha'n't nobody slept in these but some *very* nice gentlemen!"

But all this eloquence was wasted upon my prejudices, and the chamber-maid, with a toss of her head, went to hasten the airing of the sheets, while we returned to wait by the dining-room stove.

Here we found our gentlemen in conversation with the landlord, who was, with all his odd roughness, a very civil sort of man, and very fond of hearing himself talk, although he had shown so little patience with our prolixity.

He seemed to be warmly engaged in arguing with Mr. Sibthorpe some point connected with the vexed question of distinctions in society.

"Respect!" he exclaimed; "why should I show more respect to any man than he does to me? Because he wears a finer coat? His coat don't do me any good. Does he pay his taxes any better than I do? Is he kinder to his family? Does he act more honestly by his neighbors? Will he have a higher place in heaven than I shall? Show me the man that's a *better* man than I am, and you'll see if I don't treat him with respect! But to fawn and cringe before a fellow-critter because he's got more money than I have, is agin my principles. I sha'n't help to blow up nobody's pride."

"But," persisted Mr. Sibthorpe, waiving, however, the main question, *as one must always do in similar cases,* "are you sure that it is not your own pride that makes the difficulty? otherwise, what could be easier than to recognize those different grades in society which have always been marked since the beginning of time, and in all probability will continue to be so as long as earth endures, in spite of the resistance of those who are unwilling to foster anybody's pride but their own?"

"Ah! stop a little!" rejoined the landlord; "there's where

280

you go too far! You think these ranks and distinctions will go on always, because you wish they should go on. *I* believe they are coming to an end as fast as the earth rolls round. In my opinion this etarnal Yankee nation has set the example to all the rest of the world, and before many years is gone by, there won't be a man in England that'll take off his hat to the queen unless she makes her manners first. All men—and women too—was born not only free but equal; and equal they've got to be, on earth as well as in heaven."

"Well!" said Mr. Sibthorpe, with his usual good humor, "I am glad to have met at last with *one* consistent American. You believe in the equal rights of all human beings. You are not for exalting one class of men at the expense of another, or depressing any class that another may live in pride and luxury at their expense—"

"No, indeed!" said our host, with a virtuous severity depicted on his countenance. "Give every man a fair chance, that's what I say; and then we can see what stuff he's made of. Outside a'n't nothing."

"You are not one of those," continued Mr. Sibthorpe, "who would shut a man out from all the privileges of society because God has given him a black skin. You would look only at his worth, his abilities, or his piety; you would be willing to associate with him, and assist him in maintaining his just natural rights in spite of a cruel prejudice. You would—"

"What upon airth *are* you talking about?" exclaimed our host, quite aghast at this sweeping conclusion. "I should ra'ally be glad to know if you mean to insult me! Are you talking of niggers? Do you suppose I look upon a nigger as I do upon a white man? Do you think I am sich a fool as not to know who the Africans is? Should I put myself upon an equality with the seed of Cain, that was done over black to show that they was to be sarvants and the sarvants of sarvants? I'm no abolitionist, thank God! and if you're one, the sooner you get back to your own country the better."

"I have not been long enough in your *land of liberty,*"

said Mr. Sibthorpe, with a quiet smile, "to have enrolled myself under any of your party banners; I only wished to ascertain how far you carried your creed of equality; and I find you draw the line, like most of your countrymen, just where your interest or your inclination indicates. I can see very plainly why you think there ought to be no distinction of ranks in the world." And without waiting for the angry reply which seemed laboring in the mind of the landlord, Mr. Sibthorpe bade good night, and desired to be shown to his room.

"What prejudiced critters these English are!" said our host as he left the room.

We thought the observation true enough in the main, but not particularly applicable to our friend of the prairie, who had evidently seen the world with too philosophic an eye to be a *mere* Englishman. To those who have been so happy as to meet with an English gentleman of this character, one for whom nature, education and travel have all done much, I need hardly say how very delightful is such companionship. Agreeable Englishmen are much more like each other than agreeable Americans. Whether their nationality of feeling is so strong as to give always a predominating tone to the character, whatever be its distinctive points, or whether they derive a more obvious national resemblance from the possession of fixed standards of taste, education and manners, I have not had an opportunity of judging. The fact has struck me frequently.

Mr. Sibthorpe continued to be our companion for the rest of our homeward journey, and we were much pleased to learn from him that he had actually purchased a farm about twenty miles from our cottage, and intended proving to his own satisfaction the delights of American forest life.

"Why do you smile?" said he.

"*Did* I smile?" was the reply, *faute de mieux*.

"Yes indeed, but you have not seen Mrs. Sibthorpe. She is more romantic, if so you call it, more indifferent to outward appliances, even than I. To rove in the summer woods

282

and read or gather wild flowers makes a paradise for her."

"But we have long—very long winters—"

"More charming still, if possible! fine bracing air for exercise during the day, and long quiet evenings for your favorite pursuits—no wheels thundering on the pavement to break in upon the dreams of fancy—no well-dressed bore coming in to rob you of your time and patience."

There was nothing in this view of country pleasures to be disputed, and it was not necessary to draw a *counter* picture. This was better left for a *photogenic* impression. So we parted with Mr. Sibthorpe with the willing promise of an early visit, twenty miles being but dining distance when the roads are good.

49

A BACKWOODS POLITICIAN

Mr. Simeon Jenkins entered at an early stage of his career upon the arena of public life, having been employed by his honored mother to dispose of a basket full of hard-boiled eggs, on election day, before he was eight years old. He often dwells with much unction upon this his debût; and declares that even at that dawning period, he had cut his eye-teeth.

"There wasn't a feller there," Mr. Jenkins often says, "that could find out which side I was on, for all they tried hard enough. They thought I was soft, but I let 'em know I was as much baked as any of 'em. 'Be you a dimocrat?' says one. Buy some eggs and I'll tell ye, says I; and by the time he'd bought his eggs, I could tell well enough which side *he* belonged to, and I'd hand him out a ticket according, for I had blue ones in one end o' my basket, and white ones in the other, and when night come, and I got off the stump to go home, I had eighteen shillin' and four pence in my pocket."

From this auspicious commencement may be dated Mr. Jenkins' glowing desire to serve the public. Each successive election day saw him at his post. From eggs he advanced to pies, from pies to almanacs, whiskey, powder and shot, foot-balls, playing-cards, and at length, for ambition ever "did grow with what it fed on," he brought into the field a large turkey, which was tied to a post and stoned to death at twenty-five cents a throw. By this time the still youthful aspirant had become quite the man of the world; could smoke twenty four cigars per diem, if anybody else would pay for them; play cards, in old Hurler's shop, from noon till day-break, and rise winner; and all this with suitable trimmings of gin and hard words. But he never lost sight of the main chance. He had made up his mind to serve his country, and he was all this time convincing his fellow-citizens of the disinterested purity of his sentiments.

"Patriotism," he would say, "patriotism is the thing! any man that's too proud to serve his country aint fit to live. Some thinks so much o' themselves, that if they can have jist what they think they're fit for, they wont take nothing; but for my part, *I* call myself an American citizen; and any office that's in the gift o' the people will suit *me*. I'm up to anything. And as there aint no other man above here,—no suitable man, I mean—that's got a horse, why I'd be willing to be constable, if the people's a mind to, though it would be a dead loss to me in my business, to be sure; but I could do anything for my country. Hurra for patriotism! them's my sentiments."

It can scarcely be doubted that Mr. Jenkins became a very popular citizen, or that he usually played a conspicuous part at the polls. Offices began to fall to his share, and though they were generally such as brought more honor than profit, office is office, and Mr. Jenkins did not grumble. Things were going admirably. "The spoils of office glitter in his eyes, He climbs, he pants, he grasps them—" Or thought he was just going to grasp them, when, presto! he found himself in the minority; the wheel of fortune turned, and Mr. Jenkins and his party were left undermost. Here was a dilemma! His zeal in the public service was as ardent as ever, but how could he get a chance to show it unless his party was in power? His resolution was soon taken. He called his friends together, mounted a stump, which had fortunately been left standing not far from the front of his shop, and then and there gave "reasons for my ratting" in terms sublime enough for any meridian.

"My friends and feller-citizens," said this self-sacrificing patriot, "I find myself conglomerated in sich a way, that my feelin's suffers severely. I'm sitivated in a peculiar sitivation. O' one side, I see my dear friends, pussonal friends— friends, that's stuck to me like wax, through thick and thin, never shinnyin' off and on, but up to the scratch, and no mistake. O' t'other side I behold my country, my bleedin' country, the land that fetch'd me into this world o' trouble. Now, since things be as they be, and can't be no otherways as I see, I feel kind o' screwed into an auger-hole to know what to do. If I hunt over the history of the universal world from the creation of man to the present day, I see that men has always had difficulties; and that some has took one way to get shut of 'em, and some another. My candid and unrefragable opinion is, that rather than remain useless, buckled down to the shop, and indulging in selfishness, it is my solemn dooty to change my ticket. It is severe, my friends, but dooty is dooty. And now, if any man calls me a turncoat," continued the orator, gently spitting in his hands, rubbing them together, and rolling his eyes round the assembly, "all I can say is, let him say it so that I can hear him."

The last argument was irresistible, if even the others might have brooked discussion, for Mr. Jenkins stands six feet two in his stockings, when he wears any, and gesticulates with a pair of arms as long and muscular as Rob Roy's. So though the audience did not cheer him, they contented themselves with dropping off one by one, without calling in question the patriotism of the rising statesman.

The very next election saw Mr. Jenkins justice of the peace, and it was in this honorable capacity that I have made most of my acquaintance with him, though we began with threatenings of a storm. He called to take the acknowledgement of a deed, and I, anxious for my country's honor, for I too am something of a patriot in my own way, took the liberty of pointing out to his notice a trifling slip of the pen;

videlicet, "Justas of Piece," which manner of writing those words I informed him had gone out of fashion.

He reddened, looked at me very sharp for a moment, and then said he thanked me; but subjoined.

"Book-learning is a good thing enough where there aint too much of it. For my part, I've seen a good many that know'd books that didn't know much else. The proper cultivation and edication of the human intellect, has been the comprehen*sive* study of the human understanding from the original creation of the universal world to the present day, and there has been a good many ways tried besides book-learning. Not but what that's very well in its place."

And the justice took his leave with something of a swelling air. But we are excellent friends, notwithstanding this hard rub; and Mr. Jenkins favors me now and then with half an hour's conversation, when he has had leisure to read up for the occasion in an odd volume of the Cyclopedia, which holds an honored place in a corner of his shop. He ought, in fairness, to give me previous notice, that I might study the dictionary a little, for the hard words with which he arms himself for these "keen encounters," often push me to the very limits of my English.

I ought to add, that Mr. Jenkins has long since left off gambling, drinking, and all other vices of that class, except smoking; in this point he professes to be incorrigible. But as his wife, who is one of the nicest women in the world, and manages him admirably, pretends to like the smell of tobacco, and takes care never to look at him when he disfigures her well-scoured floor, I am not without hopes of his thorough reformation.

50

THE SUIT FOR SLANDER

I<small>T</small> <small>WAS</small> "an honor that I dreamed not of," to be called before this same Squire Jenkins in his dignified capacity of "Justas." I had not even heard a murmur of the coming storm, when I was served with a *subpoena,* and learned at the same time the astounding fact, that at least half the Montacute Female Beneficent Society were about to receive a shilling's worth of law on the same occasion. A justice court? "My flesh did creep, and each particular hair did stand on end—" but there was no remedy.

The court was to be held at the Squire's, and as Mrs. Jenkins was a particular friend of mine, I went early, intending to make her a call before the awful hour should approach, and hoping that in the interval I might be able to learn something of the case in which I was expected to play the important part of witness.

But good Mrs. Jenkins, who was in her Sunday gown and looked very solemn, considered herself bound to maintain an official mysteriousness of deportment, and she therefore declined entering upon the subject which was so soon to come under the cognizance of "the good people of this state." All she would be persuaded to say was, that it was a slander suit, and that she believed "women-folks" were at the bottom of it.

But ere long the more prominent characters of the drama began to drop in. Mrs. Flyter and her "old man," and two babies were among the first, and the lady looked so prodigiously sulky, that I knew *she* was concerned in the fray at least. Then entered Squire Jenkins himself, clean shaved for once, and arrayed in his meetin' coat. He asked his wife where the pen and ink was, and said he should want some paper to write down the "dispositions."

And the next comer was the plaintiff, the Schneider of our village, no Robin Starveling he, but a magnificent Hector-looking fellow, tall enough to have commanded Frederick of Prussia's crack regiment; and so elegantly made, that one finds it hard to believe his legs have ever been crossed on a shop-board. The beetle-brows of this stitching hero were puckered like the seams of his newest 'prentice, and he cast magnanimous glances round the assembly, as who should say—"Come one, come all! this rock shall fly from its firm base as soon as I!" Though the rock was but slenderly represented by Mrs. Jenkins's bureau, against which he leaned.

The world now began to flock in. The chairs were soon filled, and then the outer edges of the two beds. Three young pickles occupied the summit of the bureau to the imminent jeopardy of the mirrored clock which shone above it. Boards were laid to eke out the chairs, and when the room was packed so that not a chink remained, a sensation was created by the appearance of Mrs. Nippers and Miss Clinch. Much turning out and tumbling over was now to be done, although those active ladies appeared less than usually desirous of attracting attention.

All was at length ready, and the Squire opened the court by blowing his nose without calling upon his pocket handkerchief.

What was my surprise when I learned that our "most magnanimous mouse," Mr. Shafton, the tailor, had been set down a thief; and that Mr. Flyter had been called on, by the majesty of law, to answer for the calumny; not that *he* had ever thought of bringing such a charge against his neighbor, for he was a silent man, who always had his mouth too full of tobacco to utter slander, or anything else; but that his lady, on a certain occasion where women had convened in aid of one of the afflicted sisterhood, had, most "*un*prudently," as she said herself, given vent to certain angry feelings towards Mr. Shafton, "in manner as aforesaid." To think of bringing a woman into trouble for what she happened to say after tea! I began to consider Mr. Shafton as no more than the ninth part of a man, after all.

Things went on very quietly for a while. The "dispositions" occupied a good deal of time, and a vast amount of paper; the scribe finding the pen less germane to his fingers than the plough, and making his lines bear no small resemblance to the furrows made by a "breaking-up team." But when the ladies began to figure on the stage, the aspect of affairs was altered. Each wished to tell "the truth, the whole truth, and nothing but the truth;" and to ask one question, elicited never less than a dozen answers; the said answers covering a much larger ground than the suit itself, and bringing forward the private affairs and opinions of half the village. In vain did Mr. Jenkins roar "silence!" his injunctions only made the ladies angry, and of course gave their tongues a fresh impetus.

"Cabbage! yes, you said he took a quarter of a yard of satinett, and that that was as bad as stealing!" "Yes! and then Miss Flyter said he *did* steal cloth, and thread and buttons too!" "Well, Miss Nippers told me so, and she said she see a chair-cushion at Miss Shafton's, that was made all out of great pieces of fulled cloth!" "Who? I? oh, mercy! I don't believe I ever said such a word!" "Oh you did, you did! I'm willin' to take my afferdavy of it!" "Silence!" vociferated Squire Jenkins. "Ladies," began Mr. Phlatt, the plaintiff's counsel, "if you *would* wait a minute"—"In vain—alas! in vain, ye gallant few!" In vain do ye assay to control "The force of female lungs, sighs, sobs and passions, and the war of tongues." And Mr. Phlatt sat down in despair, looked out of the window, and drummed on the table with his fingers, as if to pass away the time till he could be heard.

Squire Jenkins, who was but newly dignified, and did not like to proceed to extremities, now adjourned the court for one hour, a recess much needed by the exhausted state of some of the witnesses. During this interval, and while the wordy war was waxing stronger and stronger, Mr. Flyter and Mr. Shafton very wisely withdrew, and in less than five minutes returned, and informed the company that they had "settled it." Mr. Flyter was to pay Mr. Shafton three dollars and fifty cents worth of lumber for his character, with costs of suit; and Mrs. Flyter was to unsay all she had said, and confess that three yards of satinett for a pair of pantaloons, would leave the tailor no more than his regular cabbage.

So here was four hours' time of something like thirty people spent to good purpose in chasing a Will-o'-the-wisp. And Montacute sees equally important suits at law every few weeks; expensive enough, if "settled" midway as they often are, between the parties themselves; still more so if left to pursue the regular course, and be decided by the Justice.

The intelligence of the "settlement" was received with various aspects by the persons concerned. The counsel on both sides were of course disappointed, for they had calculated largely upon the *spunk* of the splendid-looking son of the shears, and had counted on a jury-trial at least, if not an appeal. Mrs. Flyter was evidently much relieved to find that she had come off so easily; and sundry other ladies, who had been trembling under the consciousness of conversational "sins unwhipped of justice," shawled and India-rubbered with more than usual alacrity, and I doubt not, made vows, sincere, whether well-kept or not, to let their neighbors' business alone for some time.

Mr. Jenkins was evidently disappointed at the tame result of so much glorious preparation. He had made up his own mind on the first statement of the case, and had prepared his decision, with the addition of a concise view of the universe from chaos to the present day. But that will do for the next time, and he will not be obliged to reserve it long. Bartholine Saddletree himself would weary of the "never-ending, still-beginning" law-pleas of Montacute.

Bad fences, missing dogs, unruly cattle, pigs' ears, and women's tongues, are among the most prolific sources of litigation; to say nothing of the satisfactory amount of business which is created by the collection of debts, a matter of "glorious uncertainty" in Michigan. These suits are so frequent, that they pass as part and parcel of the regular course of things; and you would find it impossible to persuade a thorough-bred Wolverine, that there was anything unfriendly in suing his next door neighbor for a debt of however a trifling amount.

Actions for trespass and for slander are rather more enjoyed, as being somewhat less frequent; but anything like a trial, will always be enough to keep half a dozen unconcerned people idle for a day or more.

Mr. Shafton's spirited defence of his fair fame will, I see plainly, prove a lasting benefit to the talking sex of Montacute. It is perfectly incredible how much was done and how little said at the last week's meeting of the Female Beneficent Society. Mrs. Nippers to be sure had the ague, and did her chattering at home, and Miss Clinch staid to take care of her, as in duty bound. But I think that alone would not account for the difference. We shall see next week.

51

THE SCHOOLMASTER'S DILEMMA

I HAVE DEPARTED from all rule and precedent in these wandering sketches of mine. I believe I set out, a great many pages ago, to tell of the interesting changes, the progressive improvements in this model of a village of ours. My intention, as far as I had any, was to convey to the patient reader some general idea of our way of life in these remote and forgotten corners of creation. But I think I have discovered that the bent of my genius is altogether towards digression. Association leads me like a Will-o'-the-wisp. I can no more resist following a new train of thought, than a coquette the encouraging of a new lover, at the expense of all the old ones, though often equally conscious that the old are most valuable. This attempt to write one long coherent letter about Montacute, has at least been useful in convincing me that History is not my forte. I give up the attempt in despair, and lower my ambition to the collection of scattered materials for the use of the future compiler of Montacutian annals.

Yet it seems strange, even to my desultory self, how I could have passed in silence the establishment of a weekly mail, that sweetener of our long delicious winter evenings —that rich atonement for all that we lack of fresh scandal and new news. Since this treasure was ours, I have learned to pity most sincerely those who get their letters and papers at all sorts of unexpected and irregular times; a shower of scattering fire, feeble and ineffectual—a dropping in at all hours, seasonable and unseasonable, like some classes of visitors; coming often when one's mood is anything but congenial; and sure to stay away when one longs for company—gay ones intruding when we had determined to be blue and miserable, and sad ones casting their long shadows on our few sunny hours.

But a weekly mail! a budget that one waits and gets ready for; a regularly-recurring delight, an unfailing pleasure, (how few such have we!) hours, nay days, of delicious anticipation—sure harvest of past care and toil, an inundation of happiness! Let no one think he has exhausted all the sources of enjoyment till he has lived in the back-woods and learned to expect a weekly mail with its lap-full of letters and its tumulous of papers; a feast enjoyed by anticipation for a whole week previous, and affording ample materials for *resumées* for that which succeeds.

This pleasure has become so sacred in my eyes, that nothing vexes me so intolerably as seeing our lanky mail-bags dangling over the bony sides of Major Bean's lame Canadian, and bestridden and over-shadowed by the portly form of the one-eyed Major himself, trotting or rather hobbling down Main-street on some intermediate and unpremeditated day. Men of business are so disagreeable and inconsiderate! To think of anybody's sending fourteen interminable miles over bush and bog to B——, up hill both ways, as everyone knows, just to learn the price of flour or salt three days sooner, and thereby spoiling the rest of the week, leaving an objectless blank where was before a delicious chaos of hopes; substituting dull certainty for the exquisite flutterings of that sort of doubt which leaves us after all quite sure of a happy result. I have often thought I would not open up the treasures which reached me in this unauthorized, over-the-wall sort of way. I have declared that I would not have Saturday morning spoiled and the next week made ten days long. But this proper and becoming spirit has never proved quite strong enough to bear me through so keen a trial of all feminine qualities. One must be more or less than woman to endure the sight of unopened letters, longer than it takes to find the scissors. I doubt whether Griselidis herself would not have blenched at such a requisition, especially if she had been transplanted to the wilderness, and left behind hosts of friends, as well as many other very comfortable things.

Another subject of the last interest which I have as yet wholly neglected, is the new school-house, a gigantic step in the march of improvement. This, in truth, I should have mentioned long ago, if I could have found anything to say about it. It has caused an infinity of feuds, made mortal enemies of two brothers, and separated at least one pair of partners. But the subject has been exhausted, worn to shreds in my hearing; and whenever I have thought of searching for an end of the tangled clew, in order to open its mazes for the benefit of all future school-committees and their constituency, I have felt that every possible view of the case has been appropriated, and therefore must be borrowed or stolen for the occasion. I might indeed have given a description of the building as it now smiles upon me from the opposite side of the public square. But the reader may imagine St. Paul's, St. Peter's, the Parthenon, the mosque of St. Sophia, or any edifice of that character, and then think of the Montacute school-house as something inexpressibly different, and he will have as good an idea of it as I could give him in half a page. I think it resembles the Temple of the Winds more nearly than any other ancient structure I have read of; at least, I have often thought so in cold weather, when I have beguiled the hours of a long sermon by peeping through the cracks at the drifting snow; but it is built of unplaned oak-boards, and has no under-pinning; and the stove-pipe, sticking out of one window, looks rather modern; so the likeness might not strike everybody.

The school-ma'am, Miss Cleora Jenkins, I have elsewhere introduced to the reader. From April till October, she sways "the rod of empire;" and truly may it be said, "there through the summer day green boughs are waving," though I believe she picks the leaves off, as tending to defeat the ends of justice. Even the noon-spell shines no holiday for the luckless subjects of her domination, for she carries her bread and pickles rolled up in her pocket-handkerchief, and lunches where she rules, reading the while "The Children of the Abbey,"—which took her all summer, —and making one of the large girls comb her hair by the hour.

During the snowy, blowy, wheezy, and freezy months, the chair has been taken—not filled—by Mr. Cyrus Whicher —not Switcher,—a dignitary who had "boarded round" till there was very little of him left. I have been told, that when he first bore the birch,—in his own hand I mean,— he was of a portly and rather stolid exterior; had good teeth and flowing locks; but he was, when I knew him, a mere cuticle—a "skellinton," as Mr. Weller would say—shaped like a starved grey-hound in the collapsed stage, his very eyes faded to the color of the skim-milk which had doubtless constituted his richest potation, since he obtained the empty honors of a district school.

When he came under my care, in the course of his unhappy gyrations, I did my best to fatten him; and to do him justice, his efforts were not lacking: but one cannot make much progress in one week, even in cramming a turkey poult, and he went as ethereal as he came.

One additional reason for his "lean and hungry" looks I thought I discovered in his gnawing curiosity of soul—I suppose it would be more polite to say, his burning thirst for knowledge. When he first glided into my one only parlor, I asked him to sit down, expecting to hear his bones rattle as he did so. To my astonishment he noticed not my civility, but, gazing on the wall as who should say—"look you, how pale he glares!" he stood as one transfixed.

At length—"Whose profile is that?" he exclaimed, pointing to a portrait of my dear, cheerful-looking grand-mamma —a half-length, by Waldo.

I told him all about it, as I thought, but left room for a dozen questions at least, as to her relationship—whether by father or mother's side—her age when the picture was

296

taken, &c., &c., &c.; and Mr. Whicher's concluding remark, as he doubled up to sit down, was—

"Well! she's a dreadful sober-lookin' old critter, ain't she now!" But ere he touched the chair, he opened again like a folded rule out of a case of instruments, and stood erect save head and shoulders.

"Is that a pi-anner?" he asked with a sort of chuckle of delight. "Well! I heard you had one, but I didn't hardly believe it. And what's this thing?" twirling the music-stool with all his might, and getting down on his poor knees to look underneath both these curiosities.

"Jist play on it, will you?"

"Dinner is ready, Mr. Whicher: I will play afterwards."

He balanced for one moment between inanition and curiosity; then, "with his head over his shoulder turn'd," he concluded to defer pleasure to business. He finished his meal by the time others had fairly begun; and then, throwing himself back in his chair, said, "I'm ready whenever you be."

I could not do less than make all possible speed, and Mr. Whicher sat entranced until he was late for school: not so much listening to the tinkling magic, as prying into the nature and construction of the instrument, which he thought must have taken "a good bunch o' cypherin'."

That week's sojourn added a good deal to the schoolmaster's stores of knowledge. He scraped a little of the chrystallized green off my inkstand to find out how it was put on; pulled up a corner of the parlor-carpet, to see whether it was "wove like a bed-spread;" whether it was "over-shot or under-shot;" and not content with ascertaining by personal inspection the construction of every article which was new to him, he pumped dry every member of the household, as to their past mode of life, future prospects, opinion of the country, religious views, and thoughts on every imaginable subject. I began to feel croupish before he left us, from having talked myself quite out.

One of his habits struck me as rather peculiar. He never saw a letter or a sealed paper of any kind that he did not deliberately try every possible method, by peeping, squeezing, and poking, to get at its contents. I at first set this down as something which denoted a more than usually mean and dishonest curiosity; but after I had seen the same operation performed in my presence without the least hesitation or apology, by a reverend gentleman of high reputation, I concluded that the poor schoolmaster had at least some excuse for his ill-breeding.

Mr. Whicher had his own troubles last winter. A scholar of very equivocal, or rather unequivocal character, claimed admission to the school, and, of all concerned, not one had courage or firmness to object to her reception. She was the daughter of a fierce, quarrelsome man, who had already injured, either by personal abuse, or by vexatious litigation, half the people in the place; and though all detested her, and dreaded contamination for their daughters, not a voice was raised—not a girl removed from the school. This cowardly submission to open and public wrong seems hardly credible; but I have observed it in many other instances, and it has, in most cases, appeared to arise from a distrust in the protecting power of the law, which has certainly been hitherto most imperfectly and irregularly administered in Michigan. People suppress their just indignation at many abuses, from a fear that they may "get into trouble;" i.e. be haled before an ignorant justice of the peace, who will be quite as likely to favor the wrong as the right, as interest or prejudice may chance to incline him. Thus a bad man, if he have only the requisite boldness, may trample on the feelings, and disturb the peace of a whole community.

When Hannah Parsons applied for admission to the district school, Mr. Whicher made such objections as he dared in his timidity. He thought she was too old—her mother said she was not nineteen, though she had a son of two years and upwards. And she did not wish to study anything but arithmetic and writing; so that there could be no objection as to classes. And the wretched girl forced herself into the

298

ranks of the young and innocent, for what purpose or end I never could divine.

From this hour the unfortunate Whicher was her victim. She began by showing him the most deferential attention, watching his looks, and asking his aid in the most trivial matters; wanting her pen mended twenty times in the course of one copy, and insisting upon the schoolmaster's showing her again and again exactly how it should be held. She never went to school without carrying a tribute of some sort, a custard, or an apple,—apples are something with us, —or a geranium leaf at least. Now these offerings are so common among school-children, that the wretched master, though writhing with disgust, knew not how to refuse them, and his life wore away under the anguish inflicted by his tormentor.

At length it was whispered that Hannah Parsons would again bring to the eye of day a living evidence of her shame; and the unfortunate schoolmaster saw himself the victim of a conspiracy.

It needed but this to complete his distraction. He fled in imbecile despair; and after the wonder had died away, and the scandal had settled on the right head, we heard no word of the innocent pedagogue for a long time. But after that came news, that Cyrus Whicher, in the wretchedness of his poverty, had joined a gang of idlers and desperadoes, who had made a vow against honest industry; and it is not now very long since we learned that he had the honor of being hanged in Toronto as a "Patriot."

52

LA FRATERNITÉ OU LA MORT!

ONE MUST COME quite away from the conveniences and refined indulgences of civilized life to know anything about them. To be always inundated with comforts, is but too apt to make us proud, selfish, and ungrateful. The mind's health, as well as the body's, is promoted by occasional privation or abstinence. Many a sour-faced grumbler I wot of, would be marvellously transformed by a year's residence in the woods, or even in a Michigan village of as high pretensions as Montacute. If it were not for casting a sort of dishonor on a country life, turning into a magnificent "beterinhaus" these "haunts of deer, and lanes in which the primrose ere her time peeps through the moss," I should be disposed to recommend a course in Michigan to the Sybarites, the puny exquisites, the world-worn and sated Epicureans of our cities. If I mistake not, they would make surprising advances in philosophy in the course of a few months' training. I should not be severe either. I should not require them to come in their strictly natural condition as featherless bipeds. I would allow them to bring many a comfort—nay, even some real luxuries; books, for instance, and a reasonable supply of New-York Safety-Fund notes, the most tempting form which "world's gear" can possibly assume for our western, wild-cat wearied eyes. I would grant to each Neophyte a ready-made loggery, a garden fenced with tamarack poles, and every facility and convenience which is now enjoyed by the better class of our settlers, yet I think I might after all hope to send home a reasonable proportion of my subjects completely cured, sane of life.

I have in the course of these detached and desultory chapters, hinted at various deficiencies and peculiarities, which strike, with rather unpleasant force, the new resident in the back-woods; but it would require volumes to enumerate all the cases in which the fastidiousness, the taste, the pride, the self-esteem of the refined child of civilization, must be wounded by a familiar intercourse with the persons among whom he will find himself thrown, in the ordinary course of rural life. He is continually reminded in how great a variety of particulars his necessities, his materials for comfort, and his sources of pain, are precisely those of the humblest of his neighbors. The humblest, did I say? He will find that he has no humble neighbors. He will very soon discover, that in his new sphere, no act of kindness, no offer of aid, will be considered as anything short of insult, if the least suspicion of *condescension* peep out. Equality, perfect and practical, is the *sine qua non;* and any appearance of a desire to avoid this rather trying fraternization, is invariably met by a fierce and indignant resistance. The spirit in which was conceived the motto of the French revolution, "La fraternité ou la mort," exists in full force among us, though modified as to results. In cities we bestow charity—in the country we can only exchange kind offices, nominally at least. If you are perfectly well aware that your nearest neighbor has not tasted meat in a month, nor found in his pocket the semblance of a shilling to purchase it, you must not be surprised, when you have sent him a piece, to receive for reply,

"Oh! your pa wants to *change,* does he? Well, you may put it down." And this without the remotest idea that the time for repayment ever will arrive, but merely to avoid saying, "I thank you," a phrase especially eschewed, so far as I have had opportunity to observe.

This same republican spirit is evinced rather amusingly, in the reluctance to admire, or even to approve, anything like luxury or convenience which is not in common use among the settlers. Your carpets are spoken of as "*one* way to hide dirt;" your mahogany tables, as "dreadful plaguy to scour;" your kitchen conveniences, as "lumberin' up the house for nothin';" and so on to the end of the chapter. One lady informed me, that if she had such a pantry full of "dishes," under which term is included every variety of china, glass and earthenware, she should set up store, and "sell them off pretty quick," for she would not "be plagued with them." Another, giving a slighting glance at a French mirror of rather unusual dimensions, larger by two-thirds, I verily believe, than she had ever seen, remarked, "that would be quite a nice glass, if the frame was done over."

Others take up the matter reprovingly. They "don't think it right to spend money so;" they think too, that "pride never did nobody no good;" and some will go so far as to suggest modes of disposing of your superfluities.

"Anybody that's got so many dresses, might afford to give away half on 'em;" or, "I should think you'd got so much land, you might give a poor man a lot, and never miss it." A store of anything, however simple or necessary, is, as I have elsewhere observed, a subject of reproach, if you decline supplying whomsoever may be deficient.

This simplification of life, this bringing down the transactions of daily intercourse to the original principles of society, is neither very eagerly adopted, nor very keenly relished, by those who have been accustomed to the politer atmospheres. They rebel most determinedly, at first. They perceive that the operation of the golden rule, in circumstances where it is all *give* on one side, and all *take* on the other, must necessarily be rather severe; and they declare manfully against all impertinent intrusiveness. But, sooth to say, there are in the country so many ways of being made uncomfortable by one's most insignificant enemy, that it is soon discovered that warfare is even more costly than submissiveness.

And all this forms part of the schooling which I propose for my spoiled child of refined civilization. And although

302

many of these remarks and requisitions of our unpolished neighbors are unreasonable and absurd enough, yet some of them commend themselves to our better feelings in such a sort, that we find ourselves ashamed to refuse what it seemed at first impertinent to ask; and after the barriers of pride and prejudice are once broken, we discover a certain satisfaction in this homely fellowship with our kind, which goes far towards repaying whatever sacrifices or concessions we may have been induced to make. This has its limits of course; and one cannot help observing that "levelling upwards" is much more congenial to "human natur'," than levelling downwards. The man who thinks you ought to spare him a piece of ground for a garden, because you have more than he thinks you need, would be far from sharing with his poorer neighbor the superior advantages of his lot. He would tell him to work for them as *he* had done.

But then there are, in the one case, some absolute and evident superfluities, according to the primitive estimate of these regions; in the other, none. The doll of Fortune, who may cast a languid eye on this homely page, from the luxurious depths of a velvet-cushioned library-chair, can scarce be expected to conceive how natural it may be, for those who possess nothing beyond the absolute requisites of existence, to look with a certain degree of envy on the extra comforts which seem to cluster round the path of another; and to feel as if a little might be spared, where so much would still be left. To the tenant of a log-cabin whose family, whatever be its numbers, must burrow in a single room, while a bed or two, a chest, a table, and a wretched handful of cooking utensils, form the chief materials of comfort, an ordinary house, small and plain it may be, yet amply supplied, looks like the very home of luxury. The woman who owns but a suit a-piece for herself and her children, considers the possession of an abundant though simple and inexpensive wardrobe, as needless extravagance; and we must scarcely blame her too severely, if she should be disposed to condemn as penurious, any reluc-

303

tance to supply her pressing need, though she may have no shadow of claim on us beyond that which arises from her being a daughter of Eve. We look at the matter from opposite points of view. *Her* light shows her very plainly, as she thinks, what is *our* Christian duty; we must take care that ours does not exhibit too exclusively her envy and her impertinence.

The inequalities in the distribution of the gifts of fortune are not greater in the country than in town, but the contrary; yet circumstances render them more offensive to the less-favored class. The denizens of the crowded alleys and swarming lofts of our great cities see, it is true, the lofty mansions, the splendid equipages of the wealthy—but they are seldom or never brought into contact or collision with the owners of these glittering advantages. And the extreme width of the great gulf between, is almost a barrier, even to all-reaching envy. But in the ruder stages of society, where no one has yet begun to expend anything for show, the difference lies chiefly in the ordinary requisites of comfort; and this comes home at once "to men's business and bosoms." The keenness of their appreciation, and the strength of their envy, bear a direct proportion to the *real* value of the objects of their desire; and when they are in habits of entire equality and daily familiarity with those who own ten or twenty times as much of the *materiel* of earthly enjoyment as themselves, it is surely natural, however provoking, that they should not be studious to veil their longings after a share of the good, which has been so bounteously showered upon their neighbors.

I am only making a sort of apology for the foibles of my rustic friends. I cannot say that I feel much respect for anything which looks like a willingness to live at others' cost, save as a matter of the last necessity.

I was adverting to a certain unreservedness of communication on these points, as often bringing wholesome and much-needed instruction home to those whom prosperity and indulgence may have rendered unsympathizing, or neglectful of the kindly feelings which are among the best ornaments of our nature.

But I am aware that I have already been adventurous far beyond the bounds of prudence. To hint that it may be better not to cultivate *too* far that haughty spirit of exclusiveness which is the glory of the fashionable world, is, I know, hazardous in the extreme. I have not so far forgotten the rules of the sublime *clique* as not to realize, that in acknowledging even a leaning toward the "vulgar" side, I place myself forever beyond its pale. But I am now a denizen of the wild woods—in my view, "no mean city" to own as one's home; and I feel no ambition to aid in the formation of a Montacute aristocracy, for which an ample field is now open, and all the proper materials are at hand. What lack we? Several of us have as many as three cows; some few, carpets and shanty-kitchens; and one or two, piano-fortes and silver tea-sets. I myself, as *dame de la seigneurie*, have had secret thoughts of an astral lamp! but even if I should go so far, I am resolved not to be either vain-glorious or over-bearing, although this kind of superiority forms the usual ground for exclusiveness. I shall visit my neighbors just as usual, and take care not to say a single word about dipped candles, if I can possibly help it.

53

A FOND FAREWELL

THE GROWTH of our little secluded village has been so gradual, its prosperity so moderate, and its attempts so unambitious, that during the whole three years which have flown since it knew "the magic of a name," not a single event has occurred which would have been deemed worthy of record by anyone but a midge-fancier like myself. Our brief annals boast not yet one page, enlivened by those attractive words, "prodigious undertaking!" "brilliant success!" "splendid fortune!" "race of enterprise!" "march of improvement!" "cultivation of taste!" "triumph of art!" "designed by Vitruvius!" "unequalled dome!" "pinnacle of glory!" Alas! the mere enumeration of these magnificent expressions, makes our insignificance seem doubly insignificant like the joke of our school-days—"soared aloft on eagles' wings—then fell flat down, on father's wood-pile." Irredeemably little are we; unless, which Heaven forefend! a rail-road stray our way. We must content ourselves with grinding the grists, trimming the bonnets, mending the ploughs, and schooling the children, of a goodly expanse of wheat-fields, with such other jobs as may come within the abilities of our various Jacks-of-all-trades. We cannot be metropolitan, even in our dreams; for Turnipdale has secured the County honors. We cannot hope to be literary; for all the colleges which are to be tolerated in Michigan, are already located. The State-Prison favors Jacksonburg; the Salt-works some undistinguished place at the north-east; what is left for Montacute?

Alas for Tinkerville! less happy under the cruel blight of her towering hopes, than we in our humble notelessness. She rose like a rocket, only to fall like its stick; and baleful were the stars that signalized her explosion. Mournful indeed are the closed windows of her porticoed edifices. The only pleasurable thought which arises in my mind is that connected with her whilome president. Mrs. Rivers is coming to spend the summer with Mrs. Daker, while Mr. Rivers departs for Texas with two or three *semblables*, to attempt the carving out of a new home, where he need not "work." I shall have my gentle friend again; and her life will not lack interest, for she brings with her a drooping, delicate baby, to borrow health from the sunny skies and soft breezes of Michigan.

The Female Beneficent Society grows, by dire experience, chary of news. The only novel idea broached at our last meeting, was that of a nascent *tendresse* between Mrs. Nippers and Mr. Phlatt, a young lawyer, whose resplendent "tin," graces, within the month, the side-post of Squire Jenkins' door. I have my doubts. This is one of the cases wherein much may be said on both sides. Mr. Phlatt is certainly a constant visitor at Mrs. Nippers', but the knowing widow does not live alone. He praises with great fervor, Mrs. Nippers' tea and biscuits, but then who could do less? they are so unequivocally perfect—and besides, Mr. Phlatt has not access to many such comfortable tea-tables—and moreover, when he praises he gazes, but not invariably on Mrs. Nippers. I am not convinced yet. Miss Clinch has a new French calico, *coleur de rose*, and a pink lining to her Tuscan. And she is young and rather pretty. But then, she has no money! and Mrs. Nippers has quite a pretty little income—the half-pay of her deceased Mr. Nippers, who died of a fever at Sackett's Harbor—and Mrs. Nippers has been getting a new dress, just the color of blue-pill, Dr. Teeny says. I waver, but time will bring all things to light.

Many new buildings are springing up in Montacute. Mr. Doubleday has ensconced himself and his wife and baby, in a white and green tenement, neat enough even for that queen of housewives; and Betsey, having grown stout, scours the new white-wood floors, *à merveille*. Loggeries are becoming scarce within our limits, and many of our ladies wear silk dresses on Sunday. We have two physicians, and two lawyers, or rather one and a half. Squire Jenkins being only an adopted son of Themis. He thought it a pity his gift in the talking line should not be duly useful to the public, so he acts as advocate, whenever he is not on duty as judge, and thereby ekes out his bread and butter, as well as adds to his reputation. And in addition to all the improvements which I have recorded, I may mention that we are building a new meeting-house, and are soon to have a settled minister.

And now, why do I linger? As some rustic damsel who has, in her simplicity, accepted the hurried "Do call when you come to town," of a fine city guest, finds that she has already outstaid the fashionable limit, yet hesitates in her awkwardness, when and how to take leave; so I— conscious that I have said forth my little say, yet scarce knowing in what style best to make my parting reverence, have prolonged this closing chapter—a "conclusion wherein nothing is concluded." But such simple and sauntering stories are like Scotch reels, which have no natural ending, save the fatigue of those engaged. So I may as well cut short my mazy dance and resume at once my proper position as a "wall-flower," with an unceremonious adieu to the kind and courteous reader.